OPEN ARCHITECTURE
AS
COMMUNICATIONS POLICY

OPEN ARCHITECTURE
AS
COMMUNICATIONS POLICY

PRESERVING INTERNET FREEDOM
IN THE BROADBAND ERA

MARK N. COOPER
EDITOR

CENTER FOR INTERNET AND SOCIETY
STANFORD LAW SCHOOL

Editorial Note: The papers collected in this volume were published in different Journals that use different footnoting conventions. The original footnotes are preserved. Because there are many citations common to the articles, however, one bibliography was compiled. The Bibliography accepts the shortened law review style that predominated in the articles. To ensure ease of identification and location of sources, the bibliography uses an alphabetical rule -- Author's last name, then first name followed by the Title. Occasionally, a single article was cited using different footnoting conventions. Each citation is included in the bibliography.

2004

ISBN 0-9727460-8-0

Acknowledgments

The following publications have graciously granted permission to reprint excerpts from previously published works:

Earl W. Comstock and John W. Butler, *Access Denied: The FCC's Failure to Implement Open Access as Required by the Communications Act,* 8 JOURNAL OF COMMUNICATIONS LAW AND POLICY, Winter: 2000.

Mark N. Cooper, *Open Communications Platforms: Cornerstone Of Innovation And Democratic Discourse In The Internet Age,* 2 JOURNAL OF TELECOMMUNICATIONS AND HIGH TECHNOLOGY LAW, 1: 2003.

Mark A. Lemley and Lawrence Lessig, *The End of End-to-End: Preserving the Architecture of the Internet in the Broadband Era,* 48 UCLA LAW. REVIEW, April: 2001.

Timothy Wu, *Network Neutrality, Broadband Discrimination,* 2 JOURNAL OF TELECOMMUNICATIONS AND HIGH TECHNOLOGY LAW, 1: 2003.

Timothy Wu, *Broadband Policy: A User's Guide,* JOURNAL OF TELECOMMUNICATIONS AND HIGH TECHNOLOGY LAW, forthcoming.

Contents

PART I:
THE INTERACTION BETWEEN TECHNOLOGY AND POLICY IN THE CREATION OF THE INTERNET

PART II:
EMPIRICAL STUDIES, THE ROLE OF OPEN ARCHITECTURE IN STIMULATING INNOVATION

I. INTRODUCTION

THE FUTURE OF THE INTERNET IN THE BROADBAND AGE

The papers in this volume are collected from speakers at a forum held on Capitol Hill entitled *Broadband Technology Forum: The Future Of The Internet In The Broadband Age.*[1] All of the speakers are active in the public policy debates, regulatory proceedings and court cases that have been defining the contours of the next generation of the Internet. The purpose of the forum was to engage staffers from Congressional offices and federal agencies in a dialogue over the importance of preserving the vibrant nature of the Internet.

With that purpose in mind, this volume blends new papers and comments with several that are half a decade old (ancient by Internet standards). Taken together they seek to provide a comprehensive basis for understanding the interaction of technology and public policy in the development of the Internet. Written at different times and for different purposes over the past five years, the papers are powerful testimony to the proposition that open architecture is critical to the success of the Internet. The end-to-end principle of the Internet and the open communications networks in which it was incubated are critical building blocks of a dynamic, innovative information economy.

The papers address three aspects of the environment in which the Internet was created and flourished – technology, economy and law – three of the critical modalities of regulation, as Lawrence Lessig called them in CODE AND OTHER LAWS OF CYBERSPACE.[2]

PART I: TECHNOLOGY AND POLICY IN THE CREATION OF THE INTERNET

Chapter II is a paper by Robert E. Kahn and Vinton G. Cerf, *What Is the Internet (and What Makes It Work)?*, INTERNET POLICY INSTITUTE (1999, revised 2004). It provides a brief discussion of the architecture of the Internet through the chronology of the development of its fundamental technologies. Both of the authors were at the center of the creation of the seminal technologies. They are keenly aware of the role of institutions and public policies in the creation of the Internet.

Chapter III is a paper by Mark A. Lemley and Lawrence Lessig, *The End of End-to-End: Preserving the Architecture of the Internet in the Broadband Era,* 48 UCLA LAW REVIEW (April: 2001). The paper presents a discussion of the design principle of the Internet. Not only does it explain how the design principle operates to promote innovation, but it directly refutes many of the economic arguments made by those who would abandon, or allow the network facility owners to abandon, the end-to-end principle and open communications networks.

PART II: EMPIRICAL STUDIES: THE ROLE OF OPEN ARCHITECTURE IN STIMULATING INNOVATION

Part II presents empirical studies of the dynamic environment created by open architecture in digital networks and the negative impact on innovation of closure and discrimination in communications networks.

Chapter IV presents a paper prepared for the forum by Mark N. Cooper that takes a broad view of the impact of the Internet. It attempts to use network theory and recent analyses of technological change to reinforce the long-standing claim that the open architecture of the Internet represents a fundamental change and improvement in the innovation environment. It concludes with an examination of the role of Internet Service Providers in the spread of the Internet.

Chapter V is excerpted from a paper by Mark N. Cooper, *Open Communications Platforms: Cornerstone Of Innovation And Democratic Discourse In The Internet Age,"* 2 JOURNAL OF TELECOMMUNICATIONS AND HIGH TECHNOLOGY LAW (1: 2003). It demonstrates the increased possibility of anticompetitive practices by firms that dominate key points of the digital communications platform. It links the potential harm back to the network theory by presenting a case study of the elimination of Internet Service Providers.

Chapter VI is excerpted from a paper by Timothy Wu, *Network Neutrality, Broadband Discrimination,"* 2 JOURNAL OF TELECOMMUNICATIONS AND HIGH TECHNOLOGY LAW (1: 2003). It attempts to precisely define the characteristics of the Internet that should be preserved. In contrast to chapters IV and V, which emphasize the commercial relationships between network owners and Internet Service Providers (ISPs), Wu provides a detailed study of the customer contract provisions that threaten or infringe on the freedom for consumers to use the Internet and applications.

PART III: POLICY AND LEGAL FRAMEWORK FOR PRESERVING OPEN ARCHITECTURE

Part III maps out the current terrain of law and regulatory policy. The papers share the objective of preserving open architecture. They would travel somewhat different routes to achieve that goal.

Chapter VII is composed of two papers. It opens with a paper by Timothy Wu, *Broadband Policy: A User's Guide, Journal* OF TELECOMMUNICATIONS AND HIGH TECHNOLOGY LAW, forthcoming. It reviews several aspects of the current policy debate and offers a recommendation of nondiscrimination. The chapter then presents a formal proposal for network neutrality that was presented to the Federal Communications Commission (FCC) in an *ex parte* filed at the FCC by Wu and Lawrence Lessig.

Chapter VIII combines two documents by Earl W. Comstock and John W. Butler, *Access Denied: The FCC's Failure to Implement Open Access as Required by the Communications Act,"* 8 JOURNAL OF COMMUNICATIONS LAW AND POLICY, (Winter: 2000), and the legal brief filed on behalf of Earthlink in the second case heard by the Ninth Circuit involving broadband (*Brand X v. FCC,* 345 F. 3d 1120 9 9th Cir. 2003*).* Comstock and Butler show why the FCC has had so much trouble convincing the Ninth Circuit Court of Appeals that its approach to deregulating advanced telecommunications networks fits under the statute. Twice the Court found that the obligations of nondiscrimination and interconnection of Title II of the Communications Act apply to cable modem service. The detailed recounting of the history and purpose of the Computer Inquiries that runs through the legal arguments is a strong reminder that the FCC adopted the correct policy over 35 years ago when it recognized the fundamental importance of nondiscriminatory access to the essential telecommunications function of the network on which applications and services ride.

Chapter IX begins with a letter from Vinton G. Cerf to the head of the Secretary of Commerce and the Chairman of the Federal Communications Commission raising concerns about the apparent public policy shift away from open communications networks. The chapter then moves to a paper by Richard Whitt of MCI that formed the basis for Vinton Cerf's comments to the forum. The paper picks up and develops the distinction between transmission and applications as it is being discussed in regard to contemporary digital networks. Whitt attempts to synthesize the emerging thinking about reforming regulation of communications by moving from the old vertical view, in which industries are regulated because of their underlying technologies or the services they provide, to a horizontal view, in which similar functionalities are treated similarly across networks, regardless of which technology is used.

The remainder of this chapter is composed of the opening remarks at the forum. FCC Commissioner Michael Copps established the policy context for the forum by summarizing a speech he had made in October 2003 that asked a critical question "The Beginning of the End of the Internet?"[3] His subtitle identified the critical issues as "Discrimination, Closed Networks and the Future of Cyberspace."

OPENING REMARKS OF COMMISSIONER
MICHAEL J.COPPS

Good morning. Thank you for having me here, thank you all for coming. I've got to say that I feel more than a little intimidated being on the same program with Vint Cerf and Larry Lessig. They are the digital revolution's dream team, pioneer thinkers and doers whose fame and contributions will long outlive what some little regulatory agency does over in Greater Southwest. Let me also thank my friend Mark Cooper for his unflagging efforts on behalf of the public interest, his leadership at the Consumer Federation of America, his work for the Center for Internet and Society at Stanford Law School, and for organizing this very timely forum today.

We all take pride in the dynamic forum that the Internet has become. From right to left, Republicans and Democrats, rural and urban, we view the Internet as a place of freedom where technology and business innovation flourish. End-to-end openness has always been at the heart of what the Internet community and its creators celebrate. The Internet has become a fountain of innovation; a well of opportunity for consumers and entrepreneurs. It may just be the most democratic public forum that has ever existed.

But this Internet may not be the one we know in the future. There are threats to it out there and I think we had better begin to understand them *before* they derail the promise of this technology, not *after* the damage has been inflicted. Entrenched interests are already jockeying to constrain the openness that has been the Internet's defining hallmark and they are lobbying the FCC to aid and abet them. They claim all they are advocating is a "deregulated" environment where the "market can reign supreme." But in reality they are seeking government help to allow a few companies to turn the Internet from a place of competition and innovation into an oligopoly. Power over the Internet would then reside with the network owners, who could use chokepoint power to constrain consumer choices, limit sources of news, information and entertainment, undermine competitors and quash disruptive new technologies. They may talk in terms of Schumpeter and creative destruction, but in reality what they are asking is for the Commission to pick winners and to choose existing technologies and businesses over new technologies and entrepreneurs. They can talk "competition" all they want, but the race to combine distribution and content spells economic constraint here as clearly as it did when John D. Rockefeller married distribution to his product.

We cannot afford to buy into this vision. If we do, we'll wind up looking back, shaking our heads and wondering whatever happened to that open, dynamic and liberating Internet that we once knew. "What promise it held," we'll say. If that happens, history won't forgive us. Nor should it.

So it's time to take stock. What is the future of the broadband Internet? What regulation, deregulation, unregulation, whatever, made it so that this dynamic and open platform developed as it did? And as the Internet matures from its dial-up infancy to its broadband adolescence— how do we keep it this way?

These are the questions that should be our starting point. To answer them, begin with a little history. Not so long ago, one company ran the whole show in the wireline world. When innovators showed up with new ideas and technologies, Ma Bell just shooed them away. And the FCC was totally complicit in this! Keeping those new and novel ideas at bay would keep the network stable, keep economies of scale in place and ensure quality service. Or so they thought. But this kind of government protectionism only ensured that the network was closed to new innovation and consumer benefits.

Thankfully the FCC changed course. More than thirty-five years ago, the Commission decided to let consumers attach devices like the Carterfone to the end of the network. And you know what? The doomsday loss of quality and control didn't come to pass. Instead, a right to attachment came into being. It brought consumers the basic freedom to attach any device to the network as long as it causes no network harm. And look at its benefits—fax machines and computer modems are direct descendants of this principle.

In the years after the Carterfone decision the FCC reaffirmed its policy of openness and competition in the Computer Inquiry cases. And Internet pioneers like Vint Cerf built the network on the now famous end-to-end principle. This combination of policy and principle charged the nation's entrepreneurial batteries. It has empowered consumers to go where they want and do what they want on the Internet. We must not allow these core tenets of non-discrimination to wither and die.

Consider what might happen if your broadband Internet provider could discriminate. It might, for example, choose to prevent you from using a spam-jamming service that blocks its own spam, or a filtering technology to keep your kids from cruising the back alleys of the Internet. Maybe it's not weird fantasy that someday somebody might want to decide which news sources or political sites you could visit. We ought to at least be thinking about this now and maybe even taking steps to ensure that it doesn't happen. Where *are* the boundaries between legitimate bandwidth management and denial of access? The lines are blurry.

I was pleased to read a recent speech by Chairman Powell setting out some key principles of Internet freedom—the freedom to access content, use applications, attach personal devices and obtain service plan information.[4] It is, I hope, a sign that a deeper discussion may finally be starting and that we may be developing consensus around the idea that there just may be some problems here after all. I saw his comments as a call to action for the broadband industry. Perhaps this will serve a good purpose, but with so much at stake we have to ask ourselves if this is action enough to get the job done. People like Vint Cerf and Larry Lessig have devoted too much time and talent to maximizing this paradigm-busting technology to see it subordinated to some empty and outdated debate about regulation versus deregulation. Let's get serious! And the reason to get serious now is because consumers and innovators have precious little recourse once discrimination occurs—if they even know it is happening.

Until that happy day when we have a robust and competitive market for access, and when there are no longer any dangerous bottleneck facilities on a network, I believe the FCC needs to be on the job ensuring that conduits are accessible, neutral and open, just as they are in the dial-up world. We are not picking winners and losers when the government makes sure the roads of the Internet are open to all.

In the past, too few people outside of Washington have been able to tune into these issues. They have been classic, inside-the-Beltway games. But last spring in the media debate we woke a sleeping giant. The brazenness of what the FCC decided on media concentration and the stealth process it used to get there aroused the ire of millions of Americans. In previously unheard of numbers they made it known that they were not interested in surrendering content control over music, entertainment and information; gatekeeper control over the civil dialogue of our country; and veto power over the majority of what we watch, hear and read to an ever-smaller number of corporate giants. They got mad. They'll get mad again if we let their Internet go down the same road.

So let's not let the same regulatory tunnel vision drive Internet policy that has driven telecom and media policy in this Commission. The time is right for those of us who have concerns—be we businesses, innovators, technologists, content providers, regulators, legislators, consumers, citizens all—to seize the opportunity we have now to think and talk and maybe do something about the Internet in the broadband age. We need to make sure that it continues to foster freedom and innovation, that the openness that is its hallmark has a future every bit as bright as its past. I think we're going to learn a lot about all this today, and because I'd much rather listen and learn, I'm going to get out of the way now and turn the floor over to probably the two best people in all of America to help us sort through all of this—Vint Cerf and Larry Lessig. Thank you.

MODERATOR'S REMARKS

Chairman Michael Powell made it clear that his approach to preserving the freedom of the Internet is entirely a voluntary enterprise. He would impose no mandate on the network owners to ensure these freedoms. Are the four freedoms he mentioned enough and will a voluntary approach work to restore innovation to this information space? Those are a few of the critical questions and these are just the latest exchanges in a debate that stretches back several decades, a debate that was started in some sense by Vinton Cerf. Janet Abbate writes in her book entitled *Inventing the Internet*:

> In the course of trying to resolve some dilemmas they encountered in these other networking projects, researchers Robert Kahn and Vinton Cerf began to consider how to interconnect dissimilar networks. The Internet architecture that Cerf and Kahn proposed was eventually used not only to build the Internet itself but also as a model for other networks. According to Cerf in a 1990 interview "We wanted to have a common protocol and a common address space so that you couldn't tell, to first order, that you were actually talking through all different kinds of networks."[5]

If there is a message you should take away from Vint Cerf's history it is not only that architecture is the critically important characteristic of the Internet, but that architecture does not just happen, you have to fight for it. Cerf was not only one of the inventors of Internet architecture, he has remained one of its most dedicated and ardent defenders.

That is the lesson I took in the late 1980s when another challenge to the open architecture of the Internet was mounted. In January of 1990, I wrote a paper for the Consumer Federation of America and the American Association of Retired Persons in which we embraced the architecture of the Internet, stating "[t]he fact that a great deal of the necessary intelligence is currently located on the periphery of the information age network has led to a pragmatic, decentralized pattern of development."[6] Give individuals maximum flexibility in the choice of equipment and services, allowing them to develop applications at the periphery of the network, and the resulting decentralized decisions will select the most cost-effective technologies for specific applications.

A decade later at the end of the 1990s, yet another threat to the architecture of the Internet arose. Larry Lessig's first book, *Code and Other Laws of Cyberspace,* sounded a clarion call.

> We are enabling commerce in a way we did not before; we are contemplating the regulation of encryption; we are facilitating identity and content control. We are remaking the values of the Net. We can no more stand neutral on the question of whether the Net should enable centralized control of speech than Americans could stand neutral on the question of slavery in 1861.[7]

> Code is law; architecture is policy.

After a decade of phenomenal success, this policy debate involved a whole new sector of the economy. The practical implications were clear to Earl Comstock, representing Internet Service Providers and other clients engaged in the competitive provision of communications services. In a 2000 law review article entitled "Access Denied"[8] he and his co-author John Butler wrote

> The Commission is on the wrong course. It must return to a path within the authority of the Communications Act before its present "parallel universe" policy becomes so embedded in the Internet access marketplace that it causes irreparable harm to competition, consumers, thousands of independent ISPs and the structure of the global Internet itself.

He predicted that "the Commission's choice so far... cannot ultimately be upheld by the courts."[9] Thus far, he is correct on both counts. Denied access, the ranks of the ISPs have been devastated and the Ninth Circuit has twice ruled against the FCC. Earl Comstock is in that case. CFA is in that case. Even if Professor Lessig is not formally in the case, his spirit is in the Courtroom. The Ninth gets it. Listen to their words:

> Among its broad reforms, the Telecommunications Act of 1996 enacted a competitive principle embodied in the dual duties of nondiscrimination and interconnection... The Internet's protocols themselves manifest a related principle called "end-to-end": control lies at the ends of the network

where the users are, leaving a simple network that is neutral with respect to the data it transmits, like any common carrier. On this role of the Internet, the codes of the legislator and the programmer agree.[10]

Tim Wu has studied the actual terms written into contracts in a paper entitled "Network Neutrality: Broadband Discrimination."[11] Giving real world examples, he and Lessig proposed a network neutrality regime to the FCC based on the premise that

> [t]he question an innovator, or venture capitalist, asks when deciding whether to develop some new Internet applications is not just whether discrimination is occurring today, but whether restrictions might be imposed when the innovation is deployed. If the innovation is likely to excite an incentive to discriminate, and such discrimination could occur, then the mere potential *imposes a burden on innovation today.*"[12]

Andrew McLaughlin represents just such a young, innovative company – Google – that recognizes how important an open Internet is. We could have invited any of a dozen companies, but Google is unique in one sense. The application on which the company is built has a special role to play in the future of the Internet (you can always tell which applications are critical by observing which companies Microsoft decides to imitate).[13] Searchability and access are critical characteristics for the continuing success of the Internet.

As Commissioner Copps reminds us, and much to the consternation of the cable industry and the majority at the Federal Communications Commission , the public debate will not go away. The Ninth Circuit Appeals Court has twice rejected the view that the advanced telecommunications networks are not subject to the obligations of nondiscriminatory interconnection and carriage to which telecommunications services have been subject for almost a century, once in the case of *Portland v. AT&T* and once in the case of *Brand X v. FCC.*[14]

Although one of the concurrences in the Ninth Circuit decision worried that the ruling would end the policy debate, in fact, quite the opposite is the case.[15] A Declaratory Ruling by the FCC in the Cable Modem proceeding was a pre-emptive strike against the public policy that the Commission had embraced for 35 years and the Telecommunications Act of 1996 had adopted.[16]   The Declaratory Order that the Ninth Circuit overturned was an attempt to end the debate. But for the Court ruling, the FCC would have quickly eliminated all requirements for nondiscrimination and interconnection on the two dominant advanced telecommunications networks.[17] By emphatically turning down the FCC's request for rehearing – pointing out that not one judge supported a rehearing – the court ensures that the public policy discussion will be with us for some time to come.

Some argue that the Supreme Court will not take *Brand X v. FCC* because the statutory construction is so clear, the legal/administrative avenues for deciding the policy issue have not been exhausted (the FCC could conduct a forbearance proceeding under Section 10 of the Act), and there are no compelling constitutional questions (notwithstanding the cable operators' vacuous First Amendment claims). If the Supreme Court grants *cert*, it will hear a great deal about public policy, but it is likely to decide the issue on statutory grounds. If it upholds the Appeals Court decision, the issue will be thrown back to the agency, which has failed to resolve it in repeated tries over eight years.[18] If the Supreme Court reverses, the Congress is likely to become engaged.

Many in Washington are aware that there is a lot of talk about rewriting the Telecommunications Act of 1996. The Ninth Circuit may accelerate things, but whenever the rewrite comes, it is unthinkable and would be irresponsible for Congress to set the environment for the digital information age without addressing this issue.

Thus, a full appreciation of why the open architecture of the Internet and the communications network interacted to create a dynamic environment for innovation remains vital to the continuing public policy debate. Being trained as a historian, Commissioner Copps will appreciate the irony of the current situation. George Santayana's adage "**Those who do not** understand the past **are destined to repeat it**," is usually invoked as a caution not to repeat mistakes; but when it comes to the architecture of the Internet, our plea is to study its history in order to repeats its past success.

ENDNOTES

[1] Cosponsored by the Consumer Federation of America and the Center for Internet and Society, Stanford Law School, March 26, 2004.

[2] Lawrence Lessig, *Code and Other Laws of Cyberspace* (1999), at Chpater 7. See also, Mark Cooper, *Inequality in Digital Society: Why the Digital Divide Deserves All the Attention it Gets*, 20 CARDOZO ARTS & ENTERTAINMENT LAW J. (2002), which expands the modalities of regulation into realms of social order..

[3] Michael J. Copps, THE BEGINNING OF THE END OF THE INTERNET? DISCRIMINATION, CLOSED NETWORKS, AND THE FUTURE OF CYBERSPACE, New America Foundation, Washington, D.C., October 9, 2003.

[4] Michael Powell, *Preserving Internet Freedom: Guiding Principles for the Industry*, the DIGITAL BROADBAND MIGRATION: TOWARD A REGULATORY REGIME FOR THE INTERNET AGE, University of Colorado School of Law, February 8, 2004.

[5] Janet Abbate, INVENTING THE INTERNET (1999).

[6] Mark Cooper, EXPANDING THE INFORMATION AGE FOR THE 1990s: A PRAGMATIC CONSUMER VIEW (Washington, DC: American Association of Retired Persons and Consumer Federation of America, January 11, 1990).

[7] Lessig, *supra* note 2, at 205.

[8] Earl Comstock and John Butler, *Access Denied: The FCC's Failure to Implement Open Access as Required by the Communications Act,* J. OF COMM. L. & POL. (Winter 2000), at 6.

[9] *Id.,* at 21.

[10] *AT&T Corp. v. City of Portland*, 216 F.3d 871 (9th Cir. 2000).

[11] Tim Wu, *Network Neutrality & Broadband Discrimination*, 2 COL. J. TELECOMM. & HIGH TECH. L. 5 (2003).

[12] Tim Wu, and Lawrence Lessig, *Ex Parte Submission in CS Docket No. 02-52,* August 22, 2003, at 7-8.

[13] Cooper, Mark, *Antitrust as Consumer Protection in the New Economy: Lessons from the Microsoft Case*, 52 HASTINGS L.J. (2001).

[14] *Brand X v. FCC,* U.S. Court of Appeals for the Ninth Circuit, No. 02-70518, October 2003.

[15] *Id.* Concurrence of Judge O'Scannalin.

[16] Federal Communications Commission, *Declaratory Ruling and Notice of Proposed Rulemaking, IN* THE MATTER OF INQUIRY CONCERNING HIGH-SPEED ACCESS TO THE INTERNET OVER CABLE AND OTHER FACILITIES, INTERNET OVER CABLE DECLARATORY RULING, APPROPRIATE REGULATORY TREATMENT FOR BROADBAND ACCESS TO THE INTERN T OVER CABLE FACILITIES, GN Docket No. 00-185, CS Docket No. 02-52, March 15, 2002.

[17] Federal Communications Commission, *Notice of Proposed Rulemaking, IN* THE MATTER OF APPROPRIATE FRAMEWORK FOR BROADBAND ACCESS TO THE INTERNET OVER WIRELINE FACILITIES, UNIVERSAL SERVICE OBLIGATIONS OF BROADBAND PROVIDERS, COMPUTER III FURTHER REMAND PROCEEDING: BELL OPERATING COMPANY PROVISION OF ENHANCED SERVICES; 1998 BIENNIAL REGULATORY REVIEW – REVIEW OF COMPUTER III AND ONA SAFEGUARDS AND REQUIREMENTS, CC Docket No. 02-33; CC Docket Nos. 95-20, 98-10.

[18] These include the FEDERAL-STATE JOINT BOARD ON UNIVERSAL SERVICE, CC Docket No. 96-45, Report to Congress, 13 FCC Rcd 1105, 11516 (1998); *Inquiry Concerning the Deployment of Advanced Telecommunications Capability to* ALL AMERICANS IN A REASONABLE AND TIMELY FASHION, AND POSSIBLE STEPS TO ACCELERATE SUCH DEPLOYMENT PURSUANT TO SECTION 706 OF THE TELECOMMUNICATIONS ACT OF 1996, CC Docket No. 98-146, 15 FCC Rcd 20913, 20918 (2000); INQUIRY CONCERNING HIGH-SPEED ACCESS TO THE INTERNET OVER CABLE AND OTHER FACILITIES, GN Docket No. 00-185, Notice of Inquiry, 15 FCC Rcd 19287 (2000), the Declaratory Order, and the Notice of Proposed Rulemaking, *supra* note 16, IN RE APPROPRIATE FRAMEWORK FOR BROADBAND ACCESS TO THE INTERNET OVER WIRELINE FACILITIES, CC Docket Nos. 02-33, 95-20 and 98-10.

PART I:
THE INTERACTION BETWEEN TECHNOLOGY AND POLICY IN THE CREATION OF THE INTERNET

II. WHAT IS THE INTERNET (AND WHAT MAKES IT WORK)?

December, 1999
Revised May 2004

PREFACE

This paper was originally prepared by the authors at the request of the Internet Policy Institute (IPI), a non-profit organization based in Washington, D.C., for inclusion in their series of Internet related papers. It is a condensation of a longer paper in preparation by the authors on the same subject. Many topics of potential interest were not included in this condensed version because of size and subject matter constraints. Nevertheless, the reader should get a basic idea of the Internet, how it came to be, and perhaps even how to begin thinking about it from an architectural perspective. This will be especially important to policymakers who need to distinguish the Internet as a global information system apart from its underlying communications infrastructure.

INTRODUCTION

As we enter a new millennium, the Internet is revolutionizing our society, our economy and our technological systems. No one knows for certain how far, or in what direction, the Internet will evolve. But no one should underestimate its importance.

Over the past century and a half, important technological developments have created a global environment that is drawing the people of the world closer and closer together. During the industrial revolution, we learned to put motors to work to magnify human and animal muscle power. In the new Information Age, we are learning to magnify brainpower by putting the power of computation wherever we need it, and to provide information services on a global basis. Computer resources are infinitely flexible tools; networked together, they allow us to generate, exchange, share and manipulate information in an uncountable number of ways. The Internet, as an integrating force, has melded the technology of communications and computing to provide instant connectivity and global information services to all its users at very low cost.

Ten years ago, most of the world knew little or nothing about the Internet. It was the private enclave of computer scientists and researchers who used it to interact with colleagues in their respective disciplines. Today, the Internet's magnitude is thousands of times what it was only a decade ago. It is estimated that about 250 million host computers on the Internet today serve about 800 million users in over 200 countries and territories. Today's telephone system is much larger still: about 3 billion people around the world now talk on 2.3 billion telephones (about half of which are actually radio-based mobile phones). Although the Internet has grown rapidly, mobile telephony continues to outpace the spread of Internet access. Ironically, the rapid evolution of mobile telephone technology will likely meld the two systems as mobile phones become Internet-enabled. It might be reasonable to anticipate that by the end of the decade, many billions of devices will be interlinked through the Internet, including most mobile telephones and personal digital assistants.

THE EVOLUTION OF THE INTERNET

The underpinnings of the Internet are formed by the global interconnection of hundreds of millions of otherwise independent computers, communications entities and information systems. What makes this interconnection possible is the use of a set of communication standards, procedures and formats in common among the networks and the various devices and computational facilities connected to them. The procedures by which computers communicate with each other are called "protocols." While this infrastructure is steadily evolving to include new capabilities, the protocols initially used by the Internet are called the "TCP/IP" protocols, named after the two protocols that formed the principal basis for Internet operation.

On top of this infrastructure is an emerging set of architectural concepts and data structures for interconnecting heterogeneous information systems that renders the Internet a truly global information system. In essence, the Internet is an architecture, although many people confuse that with its implementation. When the Internet is looked at as an architecture, it manifests two different abstractions. One abstraction deals with communications connectivity, packet delivery and a variety of end-to-end communication services. The other abstraction deals with the Internet as an information system, independent of its underlying communications infrastructure, which allows creation, storage and access to a wide range of information resources, including digital objects and related services at various levels of abstraction.

Interconnecting computers is an inherently digital problem. Computers process and exchange digital information, meaning that they use a discrete mathematical "binary" or "two-valued" language of 1s and 0s. For communication purposes, such information is mapped into continuous electrical or optical waveforms. The use of digital signaling allows accurate regeneration and reliable recovery of the underlying bits. We use the terms computer, computer resources and computation to mean not only traditional computers, but also devices that can be controlled digitally over a network, information resources such as mobile programs, and other computational capabilities.

The telephone network started out with operators who manually connected telephones to each other through "patch panels" that accepted patch cords from each telephone line and electrically connected them to one another through the panel, which operated, in effect, like a switch. The result was called circuit switching, since at its conclusion, an electrical circuit was made between the calling telephone and the called telephone. Conventional circuit switching, which was developed to handle telephone calls, was inappropriate for connecting computers because it made limited use of the telecommunication facilities and took too long to set up connections. Although reliable enough for voice communication, the circuit-switched voice network had difficulty delivering digital information without errors.

For digital communications, packet switching is a better choice, because it is far better suited to the typically "bursty" communication style of computers. Computers that communicate typically send out brief but intense bursts of data, and then remain silent for a while before sending out the next burst. These bursts are communicated as packets, which are very much like electronic postcards. The "postcards" are relayed from computer to computer until they reach their destination. The special computers that perform this forwarding function are called variously "packet switches" or "routers" and form the equivalent of many bucket brigades spanning continents and oceans, moving buckets of electronic postcards from one computer to another. Together these routers and the communication links between them form the underpinnings of the Internet.

Without packet switching, the Internet would not exist as we now know it. Going back to the postcard analogy, postcards can get lost. They can be delivered out of order, and they can be delayed by varying amounts. The same is true of Internet packets, which, on the Internet, can even be duplicated. The Internet Protocol is the postcard layer of the Internet. The next higher layer of protocol, TCP, takes care of re-sending the "postcards" to recover packets that might have been lost, and putting packets back in order if they have become disordered in transit.

Of course, packet switching is about a billion times faster than the postal service or a bucket brigade would be. It also has to operate over many different communications systems, or substrata. The authors designed the basic architecture to be so simple and undemanding that it could work with most communication services. Many organizations, including commercial ones, carried out research using the TCP/IP protocols in the 1970s. Email was steadily used over the nascent Internet during that time and to the present. It was not until 1994 that the general public began to be aware of the Internet by way of the World Wide Web application, particularly after Netscape Communications was formed and released its browser and associated server software.

Thus, the evolution of the Internet was based on two technologies and a research dream. The technologies were packet switching and computer technology, which, in turn, drew upon the underlying technologies of digital communications and semiconductors. The research dream was to share information and computational resources. But that is simply the technical side of the story. Equally important were the other dimensions that enabled the Internet to come into existence and flourish. This aspect of the story starts with cooperation and far-sightedness in the U.S. government, which is often derided for lack of foresight but is a real hero in this story.

It leads on to the enthusiasm of private sector interests to build upon the government-funded efforts to expand the Internet and make it available to the general public. Perhaps most important, it is fueled by the development of the personal computer industry and significant changes in the telecommunications industry in the 1980s, not the least of which was the decision to open the long distance market to competition. The role of workstations, the Unix operating system and local area networking (especially the Ethernet) are themes contributing to the spread of Internet technology in the 1980s into the research and academic community from which the Internet industry eventually emerged.

Many individuals have been involved in the development and evolution of the Internet. Their work covers a span of almost four decades if one goes back to the early writings on the subject of computer networking by Leonard Kleinrock,[1] Joseph Licklider,[2] Paul Baran,[3] Larry Roberts,[4] and Donald Davies.[5] The ARPANET, described below, was the first wide-area computer network. The NSFNET, which followed more than a decade later under the leadership of Erich Bloch, Gordon Bell, Bill Wulf and Steve Wolff, brought computer networking into the mainstream of the research and education communities. It is not our intent here to attempt to attribute credit to all those whose contributions were central to this story, although we mention a few of the key players. A readable summary on the history of the Internet, written by many of the key players, may be found on the website of the Internet Society.[6]

FROM ONE NETWORK TO MANY: THE ROLE OF DARPA

Modern computer networking technologies emerged in the early 1970s. In 1969, The U.S. Department of Defense Advanced Research Projects Agency (variously called ARPA and DARPA), commissioned a wide-area computer network called the ARPANET. This network, initiated under the leadership of Charles Herzfeld, Robert Taylor and Larry Roberts at ARPA, made use of new "packet switching" concepts for interconnecting computers and linked computers at universities and other research institutions in the United States and in selected NATO countries. At that time, the ARPANET was essentially the only wide-area computer network in existence, with a base of several dozen organizations, perhaps twice that number of computers and numerous researchers at those sites. The program was led at DARPA by Larry Roberts. The packet switches were built by Bolt Beranek and Newman (BBN), a DARPA contractor. Others directly involved in the ARPANET activity included the authors, Len Kleinrock, Frank Heart, Howard Frank, Steve Crocker, Jon Postel and many, many others.

Back then, the methods of internetworking (that is interconnecting computer networks) were primitive or non-existent. Two organizations could interwork technically by agreeing to use common equipment, but not every organization was interested in this approach. Absent that, there was jury-rigging, special case development and not much else. Each of these networks stood on its own with essentially no interaction between them – a far cry from today's Internet.

In the early 1970s, ARPA began to explore two alternative applications of packet switching technology based on the use of synchronous satellites (SATNET) and ground-based packet radio (PRNET). The decision by Kahn to link these two networks and the ARPANET as separate and independent networks resulted in the creation of the Internet program and the subsequent collaboration with Cerf. These two systems differed in significant ways from the ARPANET so as to take advantage of the broadcast and wireless aspects of radio communications. The original SATNET strategy was to embed the SATNET software into an ARPANET packet switch and interwork the two networks through memory-to-memory transfers within the packet switch. This approach would make SATNET an "embedded" network within the ARPANET; users of the network would not even need to know of its existence. The technical team at BBN, having built the ARPANET switches and now building the SATNET software, could easily produce the necessary patches to glue the programs together in the same machine. Indeed, this is what they were under contract with DARPA to provide. By embedding each new network into the ARPANET, a seamless internetworked capability was possible, but with no realistic possibility of unleashing the entrepreneurial networking spirit that has manifest itself in modern day Internet developments. A new approach was in order.

The PRNET program had not yet gotten underway so there was ample opportunity to change the approach there. In addition, up until then, the SATNET program was only an equipment development activity. No commitments had been obtained for the use of actual satellites or ground stations to access them. Indeed, since there was not yet a domestic satellite industry in the U.S., the only two viable alternatives were the use of Intelsat or U.S. military satellites. The time for a change in strategy, if it was to be made, was then.

THE INTERNET ARCHITECTURE

The authors created an architecture for interconnecting independent networks that could be federated into a seamless whole without changing any of the underlying networks. This was the genesis of the Internet as we know it today.

In order to work properly, the architecture required a global addressing mechanism (or Internet address) to enable computers on any network to reference and communicate with computers on any other network in the federation. Internet addresses fill essentially the same role as telephone numbers did in early telephone networks.[7] The design of the Internet assumed first that the individual networks could not be changed to accommodate new architectural requirements; but this was largely a pragmatic assumption to facilitate progress. The networks also had varying degrees of reliability and speed. Host computers would have to be able to put disordered packets back into the correct order and discard duplicate packets that had been generated along the way. This was a major change from the virtual circuit-like service provided by ARPANET and by then contemporary commercial data networking services such as Tymnet and Telenet. In these networks, the underlying network took responsibility for keeping all information in order and for resending any data that might have been lost. The Internet design made the computers responsible for tending to these network problems.

A key architectural construct was the introduction of gateways (now called routers) between networks to handle disparities such as different data rates, packet sizes, error conditions, and interface specifications. The gateways would also check the Internet destination addresses of each packet to determine the gateway to which it should be forwarded. These functions would be combined with certain end-to-end functions to produce reliable communication from source to destination.[8]

DARPA contracted with Professor Cerf's group at Stanford to carry out the initial detailed design of the TCP software and, shortly thereafter, with BBN and University College London to build independent implementations of the TCP protocol (as it was then called – it was later split into TCP and IP) for different machines. BBN also had a contract to build a prototype version of the gateway. These three sites collaborated in the development and testing of the initial protocols on different machines. Cerf provided the day-to-day leadership in the initial TCP software design and testing. BBN deployed the gateways between the ARPANET and the PRNET and also with SATNET. Under Kahn's overall leadership at DARPA, the initial feasibility of the Internet Architecture was demonstrated during this period.

The TCP/IP protocol suite was developed and refined over a period of four more years and, in 1980, it was adopted as a standard by the U.S. Department of Defense. On January 1, 1983 the ARPANET converted to TCP/IP as its standard host protocol. Gateways (or routers) were used to pass packets to and from host computers on "local area networks." Refinement and extension of these protocols and many others associated with them continues to this day by way of the Internet Engineering Task Force.[9]

GOVERNMENT'S HISTORIC ROLE

Other political and social dimensions that enabled the Internet to come into existence and flourish are just as important as the technology upon which it is based. The federal government played a large role in creating the Internet, as did the private sector interests that made it available to the general public. The development of the personal computer industry and significant changes in the telecommunications industry also contributed to the Internet's growth in the 1980s. In particular, the development of workstations, the Unix operating system, and local area networking (especially the Ethernet) contributed to the spread of the Internet within the research community from which the Internet industry eventually emerged.

THE NATIONAL SCIENCE FOUNDATION AND OTHERS

In the late 1970s, the National Science Foundation (NSF) became interested in the impact of the ARPANET on computer science and engineering. NSF funded the Computer Science Network, a logical design for interconnecting universities that were already on the ARPANET and those that were not. Telenet was used for sites not connected directly to the ARPANET and a gateway was provided to link the two. Independent of NSF, another initiative called BITNET ("Because it's there" Net)[10] provided campus computers with email connections to the growing ARPANET. Finally, AT&T Bell Laboratories' development of the Unix operating system led to the creation of a grass-roots network called USENET,[11] which rapidly became home to thousands of "newsgroups" where Internet users discussed everything from aerobics to politics and zoology.

In the mid 1980s, NSF decided to build a network called NSFNET to provide better computer connections for the science and education communities. NSF made a critical decision to use TCP/IP for the NSFNET although in some government circles favoring the alternative OSI protocols, this decision was strongly criticized. NSF stuck to its decision. The NSFNET made possible the involvement of a large segment of the education and research community in the use of high-speed networks. A consortium consisting of MERIT (a University of Michigan non-profit network services organization), IBM and MCI Communications won a 1987 NSF competition for the contract to build the network. Within two years, the newly expanded NSFNET, operating at a backbone speed of over a million bits per second, had become the primary backbone component of the Internet, augmenting the ARPANET until ARPANET was decommissioned in 1990. At about the same time, other parts of the U.S. government had moved ahead to build and deploy networks of their own, including NASA and the Department of Energy. While these groups originally adopted independent approaches for their networks, they eventually decided to support the use of TCP/IP.

The developers of the NSFNET, led by Steve Wolff who had direct responsibility for the NSFNET program, also decided to create intermediate level networks to serve research and education institutions and, more importantly, to allow networks that were not commissioned by the U.S. government to connect to the NSFNET. Nearly a dozen intermediate level networks were created, most with NSF support. This strategy reduced the overall load on the backbone network operators and spawned a new industry: Internet Service Provision. Nearly a dozen intermediate level networks were created, most with NSF support,[12] some, such as UUNET, with private sector[13] and Defense support, and some without any government support. The NSF contribution to the evolution of the Internet was essential in two respects. It opened the Internet to many new users and, drawing on the properties of TCP/IP, structured it so as to allow many more network service providers to participate.

For a long time, the federal government did not allow organizations to connect to the Internet to carry out commercial activities. By 1988, it was becoming apparent, however, that the Internet's growth and use in the business sector might be seriously inhibited by this restriction. That year, the Corporation for National Research Initiatives (CNRI)[14] requested permission from the Federal Networking Council to interconnect the commercial MCI Mail electronic mail system to the Internet as part of a general electronic mail interconnection experiment. Permission was given and the interconnection was completed by CNRI, under Cerf's direction, in the summer of 1989. Shortly thereafter, two of the then non-profit Internet Service Providers (UUNET[15] and NYSERNET) produced new for-profit companies (UUNET and PSINET,[16] respectively). In 1991, they were interconnected with each other and CERFNET.[17] Commercial pressure to alleviate restrictions on interconnections with the NSFNET began to mount.

In response, Congress passed legislation allowing NSF to open the NSFNET to commercial usage. Shortly thereafter, NSF determined that its support for NSFNET might not be required in the longer term and, in April 1995, NSF ceased its support for the NSFNET. By that time, many commercial networks were in operation and provided alternatives to NSFNET for national level network services. The NSFNET was operated by the non-profit Advanced Networks and Services (ANS) under contract to NSF and it sold its networking assets to America OnLine (AOL).[18] Today, there are thousands of Internet Service Providers (ISPs) around the world.

A DEFINITION FOR THE INTERNET

The authors feel strongly that efforts should be made at top policy levels to define the Internet. It is tempting to view it merely as a collection of networks and computers. However, as indicated earlier, the authors designed the Internet as an architecture that provided for both communications capabilities and information services. Governments are passing legislation pertaining to the Internet without ever specifying to what the law applies and to what it does not apply. In U.S. telecommunications law, distinctions are made between cable, satellite broadcast and common carrier services. These and many other distinctions all blur in the backdrop of the Internet. Should broadcast stations be viewed as Internet Service Providers when their programming is made available in the Internet environment? Is use of cellular telephones considered part of the Internet and if so under what conditions? This area is badly in need of clarification.

The authors believe the best definition currently in existence is that approved by the Federal Networking Council (FNC) in 1995.

RESOLUTION:

The Federal Networking Council (FNC) agrees that the following language reflects our definition of the term "Internet."

"Internet" refers to the global information system that –

(i) is logically linked together by a globally unique address space based on the Internet Protocol (IP) or its subsequent extensions/follow-ons;

(ii) is able to support communications using the Transmission Control Protocol/Internet Protocol (TCP/IP) suite or its subsequent extensions/follow-ons, and/or other IP-compatible protocols; and

(iii) provides, uses or makes accessible, either publicly or privately, high level services layered on the communications and related infrastructure described herein.[19]

Of particular note is that it defines the Internet as a global information system, and included in the definition is not only the underlying communications technology, but also higher-level protocols and end-user applications, the associated data structures and the means by which the information may be processed, manifested, or otherwise used. In many ways, this definition supports the characterization of the Internet as an "information superhighway." Like the federal highway system, whose underpinnings include not only concrete lanes and on/off ramps, but also a supporting infrastructure both physical and informational, including signs, maps, regulations, and such related services and products as filling stations and gasoline, the Internet has its own layers of ingress and egress, and its own multi-tiered levels of service.

The FNC definition makes it clear that the Internet is a dynamic organism that can be looked at in myriad ways. It is a framework for numerous services and a medium for creativity and innovation. Most importantly, it can be expected to evolve.

WHO RUNS THE INTERNET

THE DOMAIN NAME SYSTEM

The Internet evolved as an experimental system during the 1970s and early 1980s. It then flourished after the TCP/IP protocols were made mandatory on the ARPANET in January 1983; these protocols thus became the standard for many other networks as well. Indeed, the Internet grew so rapidly that the existing mechanisms for associating the names of host computers (e.g. UCLA, USC-ISI) to Internet addresses (known as IP addresses) were about to be stretched beyond acceptable engineering limits. Most of the applications in the Internet referred to the target computers by name. These names had to be translated into Internet addresses before the lower level protocols could be activated to support the application. For a time, a group at SRI International in Menlo Park, California called the Network Information Center (NIC) maintained a simple, machine-readable list of names and associated Internet addresses which was made available on the net. Hosts on the Internet would simply copy this list, usually daily, so as to maintain a local copy of the table. This list was called the "host.txt" file (since it was simply a text file). The list served the function in the Internet that directory services (e.g. 411 or 703-555-1212) do in the U.S. telephone system - the translation of a name into an address.

As the Internet grew, it became harder and harder for the NIC to keep the list current. Anticipating that this problem would only get worse as the network expanded, researchers at USC Information Sciences Institute launched an effort to design a more distributed way of providing this same information. The end result was the Domain Name System (DNS)[20] which allowed hundreds of thousands of "name servers" to maintain small portions of a global database of information associating IP addresses with the names of computers on the Internet.

The naming structure was hierarchical in character. For example, all host computers associated with educational institutions would have names like "stanford.edu" or "ucla.edu". Specific hosts would have names like "cs.ucla.edu" to refer to a computer in the computer science department of UCLA, for example. A special set of computers called "root servers" maintained information about the names and addresses of other servers that contained more detailed name and address associations. The designers of the DNS developed seven generic "top level" domains, as follows:

Education - EDU

Government - GOV

Military - MIL

International - INT

Network - NET

(non-profit) Organization - ORG

Commercial - COM

Under this system, for example, the host name "UCLA" became "UCLA.EDU" because it was operated by an educational institution, while the host computer for "BBN" became "BBN.COM" because it was a commercial organization. Top level domain names also were adopted for every country.[21] United Kingdom names would end in ".UK" while the ending ".FR" was adopted for the names of France.

In addition to the top level domains listed above, .ARPA, originally created in the 1970s to map Arpanet names into "internet names," was used to hold infrastructure information. The so-called "inverse IP address" tables, IN-ADDR, are in .ARPA as are the inverse telephone number tables, E164.ARPA, used to map telephone numbers into Internet destinations, in accordance with the ENUM standard.

The Domain Name System was and continues to be a major element of the Internet architecture, which contributes to its scalability. It also contributes to controversy over trademarks and general rules for the creation and use of domain names, creation of new top-level domains and the like. At the same time, other resolution schemes exist as well. One of the authors (Kahn) has been involved in the development of a different kind of standard identification and resolution scheme[22] that, for example, is being used as the base technology in the publishing industry to identify digital objects on the Internet by adapting various identification schemes. For example, International Standard Book Numbers can be used as part of the identifiers. The identifiers then resolve to state information about the referenced books, such as location information (which can include multiple sites) on the

Internet that is used to access the books or to order them. These developments are taking place in parallel with the more traditional means of managing Internet resources. They offer an alternative to the existing Domain Name System with enhanced functionality.

To add to the list, Instant Messaging has become a popular application on the Internet and as each participant goes online, his or her instant messaging identifier is associated with the IP address through which the particular participant is connected to the Internet. Thus, these instant messaging identifiers are bound to IP addresses directly and not through the DNS.

The growth of Web servers and users of the Web has been remarkable, but some people are confused about the relationship between the World Wide Web and the Internet. The Internet is the global information system that includes communication capabilities and many high level applications. The Web is one such application. The existing connectivity of the Internet made it possible for users and servers all over the world to participate in this activity.

Electronic mail is another important application. As of today, an estimated 750 million personal computers are in use. It is estimated that on the order of 250 million servers are on the Internet. While it is not known exactly how much web content is online, estimates range from 750 to 7,500 terabytes. Much of the content is in databases and is not visible unless the database is queried and a web page is produced in real time in response. One of the popular web search services, Google, reports that it indexes 4.29 billion pages of material. The number of users online is estimated to be on the order of 700 million to as many as 1 billion. Virtually every user of the net has access to electronic mail and web browsing capability. Email remains a critically important application for most users of the Internet, and these two functions largely dominate the use of the Internet for most users.

THE INTERNET STANDARDS PROCESS

Internet standards were once the output of research activity sponsored by DARPA. The principal investigators on the internetting research effort essentially determined what technical features of the TCP/IP protocols would become common. The initial work in this area started with the joint effort of the two authors, continued in Cerf's group at Stanford, and soon thereafter was joined by engineers and scientists at BBN and University College London. This informal arrangement has changed with time and details can be found elsewhere.[23] At present, the standards efforts for the Internet are carried out under the auspices of several groups including the Internet Society, CNRI and ICANN. The Internet Engineering Task Force (IETF) operates under the leadership of its Internet Engineering Steering Group, which is populated by appointees approved by the Internet Architecture Board, which is, itself, now part of the Internet Society. Teh IETF Secretariat is run by CNRI and the IANA functions are primarily the responsibility of ICANN. The IETF comprises over one hundred working groups categorized and managed by Area Directors specializing in specific categories.

There are other bodies with considerable interest in Internet standards or in standards that must interwork with the Internet. Examples include the International Telecommunications Union Telecommunications standards group, the European Telecommunication Standards Institute, the International Institute of Electrical and Electronic Engineers (IEEE) local area network standards group, the Organization for International Standardization, the American National Standards Institute, the World Wide Web Consortium, and many others.

As Internet access and services are provided by existing media such as telephone, cable and broadcast, interactions with standards bodies and legal structures formed to deal with these media will become an increasingly complex matter. The intertwining of interests is simultaneously fascinating and complicated, and has increased the need for thoughtful cooperation among many interested parties.

MANAGING THE INTERNET

Perhaps the least understood aspect of the Internet is its management. In recent years, this subject has become the subject of intense commercial and international interest, involving multiple governments and commercial organizations, and, recently, congressional hearings. At issue is how the Internet will be managed in the future, and, in the process, what oversight mechanisms will insure that the public interest is adequately served.

In the 1970s, managing the Internet was easy. Since few people knew about the Internet, decisions about almost everything of real policy concern were made in the offices of DARPA. It became clear in the late 1970s, however, that more community involvement in the decision-making processes was essential. In 1979, DARPA formed the Internet Configuration Control Board (ICCB) to insure that knowledgeable members of the technical community discussed critical issues, educated people outside of DARPA about the issues, and helped others to implement the TCP/IP protocols and gateway functions. At the time, there were no companies that offered turnkey solutions to getting on the Internet. It would be another five years or so before companies like Cisco Systems were formed, and while there were no PCs yet, the only workstations available were specially built and their software was not generally configured for use with external networks; they were certainly considered expensive at the time.

In 1983, the small group of roughly twelve ICCB members was reconstituted (with some substitutions) as the Internet Activities Board and about ten "Task Forces" were established under it to address issues in specific technical areas. The attendees at Internet Working Group meetings were invited to become members of as many of the task forces as they wished.

The management of the Domain Name System offers a kind of microcosm of issues now frequently associated with overall management of the Internet's operation and evolution. Someone had to take responsibility for overseeing the system's general operation. In particular, top-level domain names had to be selected, along with persons or organizations to manage each of them. Rules for the allocation of Internet addresses had to be established. DARPA had previously asked the late Jon Postel of the USC Information Sciences Institute to take on numerous functions related to administration of names, addresses and protocol related matters. With time, Postel assumed further responsibilities in this general area on his own, and DARPA, which was supporting the effort, gave its tacit approval. This activity was generally referred to as the Internet Assigned Numbers Authority (IANA).[24] In time, Postel became the arbitrator of all controversial matters concerning names and addresses, which he remained until his untimely death in October 1998.

It is helpful to consider separately the problem of managing the domain name space and the Internet address space. These two vital elements of the Internet architecture have rather different characteristics that color the management problems they generate. Domain names have semantics that numbers may not imply; and thus a means of determining who can use which names is needed. As a result, speculators on Internet names often claim large numbers of them without intent to use them other than to resell them later. Alternate dispute resolution mechanisms,[25] if widely adopted, could significantly change the landscape here. Some of these problems have been mitigated through so-called anti-cybersquatting legislation in the U.S. and elsewhere.

The rapid growth of the Internet has triggered the design of a new and larger address space (the so-called IP version 6 address space; today's Internet uses IP version 4).[26] Although this address and packet format has been standardized for about 10 years, significant movement towards implementing the new version has only begun in the last year or two. The effort is particularly advanced in Asia and the Pacific Rim, notably in Japan and China. There is also increasing momentum in Europe and in the U.S. The Defense Department has adopted a target of 2008 to have full IPv6 implementation completed. Despite concerns to the contrary, the IPv4 address space will not be depleted for some time. Network Address Translation devices allow multiple computers to share a single IP address as if they were part of a single, multiprocessor computer. These NAT mechanisms interfere, however, with end-to-end protocol designs and in particular with security. Further, the use of Dynamic Host Configuration Protocol to dynamically assign IP addresses has also cut down on demand for dedicated IP addresses. Nevertheless, there is growing recognition in the Internet technical community that expansion of the address space is needed, as is the development of transition schemes that allow concurrent use of and possible interoperation between IPv4 and IPv6 while migrating to IPv6.

In 1998, the Internet Corporation for Assigned Names and Numbers[27] was formed as a private sector, non-profit organization to oversee the orderly progression in use of Internet names and numbers, as well as certain protocol-related matters that required oversight. The birth of this organization, which was selected by the Department of Commerce for this function, has been difficult, embodying as it does many of the inherent conflicts in resolving discrepancies in this arena. However, there is a clear need for an oversight mechanism for Internet domain names and numbers, separate from their day-to-day management.

Many questions about Internet management remain. They may also prove difficult to resolve quickly. Of specific concern is what role the U.S. government and indeed governments around the world need to play in its continuing operation and evolution. A major conference organized by the United Nations called the World Summit on the Information Society (WSIS) was held in Geneva in December, 2003. Although the question of Internet governance played a prominent and hotly debated role in the preparatory sessions leading up to the WSIS, resolution of the matter was deferred and the Secretary General of the United Nations, Kofi Annan, was asked to establish a Working Group on Internet Governance in preparation for Phase II of the WSIS, planned for November 2005 in Tunis.

WHERE DO WE GO FROM HERE?

As we struggle to envision what may be commonplace on the Internet in a decade, we are confronted with the challenge of imagining new ways of doing old things, as well as trying to think of new things that will be enabled by the Internet, and by the technologies of the future.

In the next ten years, the Internet is expected to be enormously bigger than it is today. It will be more pervasive than the older technologies and penetrate more homes than telephone, television and radio programming. Computer chips are now being built that implement the TCP/IP protocols, and recently a university announced a two-chip web server. Chips like this are extremely small and cost very little. And they can be put into anything. Many of the devices connected to the Internet will be Internet-enabled appliances (mobile phones, fax machines, household appliances, hand-held organizers, digital cameras, etc.) as well as traditional laptop and desktop computers. Information access will be directed to digital objects of all kinds and services that help to create them or make use of them.[28]

Very high-speed networking has also been developing at a steady pace. From the original 50,000 bit-per-second ARPANET, to the 155 million bit-per-second NSFNET, to today's 2.4 – 9.6 billion bit-per-second (Gb) commercial networks, we routinely see commercial offerings providing Internet access at increasing speeds. Demonstrations of 40 Gb per second have been made and commercial equipment that can support that speed is now emerging from Internet equipment vendors. Experimentation with optical technology using wavelength division multiplexing is underway in many quarters; testbeds operating at speeds of terabits per second (that is trillions of bits-per-second) are being constructed.

The Internet is already carrying data from very far away places, like Mars. Design of the interplanetary Internet as a logical extension of the current Internet and NASA's Deep Space Network is part of the NASA Mars mission program now underway at the Jet Propulsion Laboratory in Pasadena, California.[29] By 2009, we should have a well functioning Earth-Mars network that serves as a nascent backbone of the interplanetary Internet.

Wireless communication has exploded in recent years with the rapid growth of mobile telephony. Increasingly, Internet access is becoming available over these networks. Alternate forms for wireless communication, including both ground radio and satellite, are in development and use, and the prospects for increasing data rates look promising. Recent developments in high data rate systems appear likely to offer ubiquitous wireless data services in the 1-2 Mb per second range. In the last several years, wireless local area networks have become very popular in airport lounges, hotels, coffee shops and other public spaces as well as at home to permit "nomadic" use of the Internet. Based on IEEE standard 802.11 and popularly known as "Wi-Fi", these networks may become the primary way most people get access to the Internet. There are a number of other wireless standards under development by IEEE, including metropolitan area networks known as "WiMAX" that may provide alternatives to broadband Internet access currently supplied by Digital Subscriber Loops (DSL), cable modems, and conventional T1 (or DS1) and ISDN service.

A developing trend that seems likely to continue in the future is an information centric view of the Internet that can live in parallel with the current communications centric view. Many of the concerns about intellectual property protection are difficult to deal with, not because of fundamental limits in the law, but rather by technological and perhaps management limitations in knowing how best to deal with these issues. A digital object infrastructure that makes information objects "first-class citizens" in the packetized "primordial soup" of the Internet is one step in that direction. In this scheme, the digital object is the conceptual elemental unit in the information view; it is interpretable (in principle) by all participating information systems. The digital object is thus an abstraction that may be implemented in various ways by different systems. It is a critical building block for interoperable and heterogeneous information systems. Each digital object has a unique and, if desired, persistent identifier that will allow it to be managed over time. This approach is highly relevant to the development of third-party value added information services in the Internet environment.

Of special concern to the authors is the need to understand and manage the downside potential for network disruptions, as well as cybercrime and terrorism. The ability to deal with problems in this diverse arena is at the forefront of maintaining a viable global information infrastructure. "IOPS.org"[30] – a private-sector group dedicated to improving coordination among ISPs - deals with issues of ISP outages, disruptions, and other trouble conditions, as well as related matters, by discussion, interaction and coordination between and among the principal players. Other operational groups have formed, such as the North American Network Operators Groups and European, Asian, South American and African counterparts.[31] After a 1988 "worm" attack on many of the UNIX hosts of the Internet, DARPA created the Computer Emergency Response Team at Carnegie-Mellon University.[32] There are a number of similar groups within government and in the private sector, all devoted to identifying vulnerabilities and offering thoughtful solutions to them. Security has become a high priority as the Internet has become an increasingly critical infrastructure in the conduct of global communication and business. Business, the academic community and government all need as much assurance as possible that they will be able to conduct their activities on the Internet with high confidence that security and reliability will be present. The participation of many organizations around the world, including especially governments and the relevant service providers will be essential here.

The success of the Internet in society as a whole will depend less on technology than on the larger economic and social concerns that are at the heart of every major advance. The Internet is no exception, except that its potential and reach are perhaps as broad as any that have come before.

ENDNOTES

[1] Leonard Kleinrock's dissertation thesis at MIT was written during 1961: "Information Flow in Large Communication Nets", RLE Quarterly Progress Report, July 1961 and published as COMMUNICATION NETS: STOCHASTIC MESSAGE FLOW AND DELAY (1964). This was one of the earliest mathematical analyses of what we now call packet switching networks.

[2] J.C.R. Licklider & W. Clark, "On-Line Man Computer Communication", August 1962. Licklider made tongue-in-cheek references to an "inter-galactic network" but in truth, his vision of what might be possible was prophetic.

[3] Paul Baran, et al, *On Distributed Communications*, Volumes I-XI, RAND Corporation Research Documents, August 1964. Paul Baran explored the use of digital "message block" switching to support highly resilient, survivable voice communications for military command and control. This work was undertaken at RAND Corporation for the U.S. Air Force beginning in 1962.

[4] L. Roberts & T. Merrill, "Toward a Cooperative Network of Time-Shared Computers", Fall AFIPS Conf., Oct. 1966.

[5] D.W. Davies, K.A. Bartlett, R.A. Scantlebury, and P. T. Wilkinson. 1967. "A Digital Communication Network for Computers Giving Rapid Response at Remote Terminals," *Proceedings of the ACM Symposium on Operating System Principles*. Association for Computing Machinery, New York, 1967. Donald W. Davies and his colleagues coined the term "packet" and built one node of a packet switching network at the National Physical Laboratory in the UK.

[6] Barry M. Leiner, Vinton G. Cerf, David D. Clark, Robert E. Kahn, Leonard Kleinrock, Danial C. Lynch, Jon Postel, Larry G. Roberts, Stephen Wolff, *A Brief History of the Internet*," www.isoc.org/internet/history/brief.html and see below for timeline.

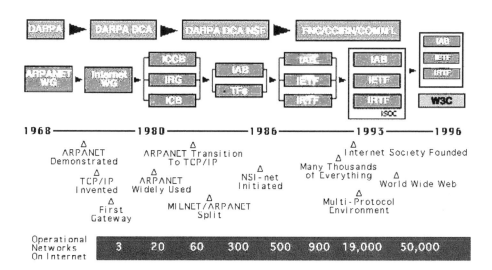

[7] Authors' note: with mobile telephony and roaming, as well as the so-called "free phone" numbers, telephone numbers have become identifiers that do not, in and of themselves, reveal how a call should be routed. Telephone numbers today are just general identifiers and have to be looked up in a large, shared table to find out where they touch the telephone network. Today's telephone number is more like a domain name, today, than an Internet address.

[8] A draft paper by the authors describing this approach was given at a meeting of the International Network Working Group in 1973 in Sussex, England; the final paper was subsequently published by the Institute for Electrical and Electronics Engineers, the leading professional society for the electrical engineering profession, in its Transactions on Communications in May, 1974. [Vinton G. Cerf and Robert E. Kahn, *A Protocol for Packet Network Intercommunication,* IEEE Transactions on Communications, Vol. COM-22, May 1974.] The paper described the TCP/IP protocol.

[9] The Internet Engineering Task Force is an activity taking place under the auspices of the Internet Society (www.isoc.org). See www.ietf.org

[10] From the BITNET charter: "BITNET, which originated in 1981 with a link between CUNY and Yale, grew rapidly during the next few years, with management and systems services provided on a volunteer basis largely from CUNY and Yale. In 1984, the BITNET Directors established an Executive Committee to provide policy guidance."
(see http://www.geocities.com/SiliconValley/2260/bitchart.html)

[11] Usenet came into being in late 1979, shortly after the release of V7 Unix with UUCP. Two Duke University grad students in North Carolina, Tom Truscott and Jim Ellis, thought of hooking computers together to exchange information with the Unix community. Steve Bellovin, a grad student at the University of North Carolina, put together the first version of the news software using shell scripts and installed it on the first two sites: "unc" and "duke." At the beginning of 1980 the network consisted of those two sites and "phs" (another machine at Duke), and was described at the January Usenix conference. Steve Bellovin later rewrote the scripts into C programs, but they were never released beyond "unc" and "duke." Shortly thereafter, Steve Daniel did another implementation in C for public distribution. Tom Truscott made further modifications, and this became the "A" news release.
(see http://www.ou.edu/research/electron/internet/use-soft.htm)

[12] A few examples include the New York State Education and Research Network (NYSERNET), New England Academic and Research Network (NEARNET), the California Education and Research Foundation Network (CERFNET), Northwest Net (NWNET), Southern Universities Research and Academic Net (SURANET) and so on.

[13] UUNET was formed as a non-profit by a grant from the UNIX Users Group (USENIX).

[14] Corporation for National Research Initiatives was founded in 1986 by Robert Kahn and Keith Uncapher. CNRI has devoted its research programs to the development and evolution of information infrastructure technologies.

[15] UUNET called its Internet service ALTERNET. UUNET was acquired by Metropolitan Fiber Networks (MFS) in 1995 which was itself acquired by Worldcom in 1996. Worldcom later merged with MCI to form MCI WorldCom in 1998. In that same

year, Worldcom also acquired the ANS backbone network from AOL, which had purchased it from the non-profit ANS earlier.

[16] PSINET was a for-profit spun out of the NYSERNET in 1990.

[17] CERFNET was started by General Atomics as one of the NSF-sponsored intermediate level networks. It was coincidental that the network was called "CERF"Net - originally they had planned to call themselves SURFNET, since General Atomics was located in San Diego, California, but this name was already taken by a Dutch Research organization called SURF, so the General Atomics founders settled for California Education and Research Foundation Network. Cerf participated in the launch of the network in July 1989 by breaking a fake bottle of champagne filled with glitter over a Cisco Systems router.

[18] Ironically, the network resources were later acquired by UUNET in a three-way deal involving AOL and CompuServe.

[19] See www.fnc.gov. October 24, 1995 Resolution of the U.S. Federal Networking Council.

[20]The Domain Name System was designed by Paul Mockapetris and initially documented in November 1983. Mockapetris, P., "Domain Names - Concepts and Facilities", RFC 882, USC/Information Sciences Institute, November 1983 and Mockapetris, P.,"Domain Names - Implementation and Specification", RFC 883, USC/Information Sciences Institute, November 1983. (see also http://soa.granitecanyon.com/faq.shtml)

[21] Actually, a pre-existing list of two-letter codes was adopted. This list is maintained on behalf of the UN Statistics Department by the International Standards Organization, and is referred to as ISO 3166. The entries on this list (specifically, 3166-1) refer to countries or areas of economic interest. See http://www.iso.ch/iso/en/prods-services/iso3166ma/

[22] The Handle System - see www.handle.net

[23] See Leiner, et al., "A Brief History," *supra* note 6.

[24] See www.iana.org for more details. See also www.icann.org.

[25] See www.doi.org

[26] Version 5 of the Internet Protocol was an experiment which has since been terminated.

[27] See www.icann.org for details.

[28] See Robert E Kahn and Robert Wilensky, *A Framework for Distributed Digital Object Services*, at www.cnri.reston.va.us/cstr/arch/k-w.html

[29] The interplanetary Internet effort is funded in part by DARPA and has support from NASA. For more information, see www.ipnsig.org and www.dtnrg.org

[30] See www.iops.org for more information on this group dedicated to improving operational coordination among Internet Service Providers.

[31] www.nanog.org and http://www.nanog.org/orgs.html

[32] See www.cert.org.

III. THE END OF END-TO-END:

PRESERVING THE ARCHITECTURE OF THE INTERNET
IN THE BROADBAND ERA

INTRODUCTION

Broadband Internet access is the holy grail of media companies.[1] In the early 1990s, before it took the Internet seriously, the established entertainment industry proposed to deliver high-bandwidth content (movies, music, and other forms of video and audio) to the public over an "information superhighway" attached to television sets. While many companies held trials and roll-outs of video-on-demand products,[2] the idea of interactive video over television never really caught on. By the mid-1990s, the attention of most content providers had switched to the Internet. While the Internet revolutionized communications, bandwidth constraints have, until quite recently, prevented its widespread use for streaming audio and video content.

Two new technologies promise to offer consumers broadband access to the Internet, enabling the fast and easy use of computer networks for audio and video content delivery. Those two technologies use the two data pipes currently connected to most homes: the phone line and the cable television line. Digital subscriber lines (DSL) use existing copper telephone connections to send a high-bandwidth digital signal to and from households within a covered service area. Unfortunately, the scope of DSL is currently limited both by the number of telephone switches that have been updated to accommodate the technology and by the requirement that customers live within approximately three and one-half miles of an updated telephone switching station. The second technology, cable modems, does not suffer from a similar geographic restriction, but it does require certain updates to the existing cable television network. Further, access to a cable modem requires that a cable television line be connected to a consumer's house.

At the present time, at least 80 percent of U.S. households have access to a cable system.[3]

How these technologies are developed, and the speed with which they are deployed, are critical to the future design of the Internet. Curiously, the law has so far treated DSL and cable modems very differently on the important question of whether the owner of the data pipe may exercise control over the way in which its customers access the Internet. Telephone companies are required to provide access to competing DSL providers on an open and nondiscriminatory basis. This prevents telephone companies from bundling broadband access with other services they would also like to sell to consumers. By contrast, cable companies have so far been permitted to impose whatever conditions they desire on their customers. The two largest cable companies, AT&T and Time Warner, have exercised, or have threatened to exercise, that power by bundling cable modem service with Internet Service Provider (ISP) service. If you want Internet cable access from AT&T, you must agree to use their captive, in-house ISPs, @Home or Roadrunner. While Time Warner has not yet imposed a similar rule, it strongly indicated that it intended to do so once its merger with America Online (AOL) was complete.[4] The Federal Trade Commission (FTC) recently approved the merger on the condition that the merged company agree to open broadband cable access to multiple competing ISPs.[5]

We believe that there is no justification in law or policy for giving cable companies special treatment. The current regime is simply a historical accident resulting from the different regulatory schemes traditionally imposed on telephone and cable television companies.[6] In this Article, we argue that the government should resist efforts by cable companies to leverage their control over cable lines into control over adjacent markets, such as the market for ISPs. If cable companies are allowed to dictate a consumer's choice of an ISP, and therefore eliminate competition among ISPs in the broadband market, prices will increase and innovation will be harmed. Further, and more fundamentally, allowing bundling will compromise an important architectural principle that has governed the Internet since its inception: the principle of "end-to-end" design (e2e).[7] The effective structure of the Internet itself is at stake in this debate.

The Federal Communications Commission's (FCC's) analysis to date does not consider the principle of the Internet's design. It therefore does not adequately evaluate the potential threat that these mergers present. Neither does the FCC's approach properly account for the FCC's role in creating the conditions that made the Internet possible. Under the banner of "no regulation," the FCC threatens to permit the Internet to calcify as earlier telecommunications networks did. Finally, and ironically, the FCC's supposed "hands off" approach will ultimately lead to more, not less, regulation.

We do not yet know enough about the relationship between the e2e principle and the innovation of the Internet. But we should know enough to be skeptical of changes in the Internet's design. There should be a strong presumption in favor of preserving the architectural features that have produced this extraordinary innovation. We should be wary of allowing a single company with bottleneck control over broadband pipes to undo these design principles without a clear showing that centralizing control would not undermine the Internet's innovation. The FTC's recent approval of the AOL–Time Warner merger subject to stringent open access conditions is a large step in the right direction. But it is only one step in the continuing debate over open access.

In December 1999, we filed a declaration with the FCC in connection with the proposed merger of AT&T and Media One that articulated some of these arguments.[8] In it, we suggested that the FCC condition approval of the merger on a commitment by AT&T to reverse its policy of linking cable modem service to the use of its in-house ISP, @Home. The declaration has received a great deal of attention in the scholarly community from both proponents and opponents of open access.[9] In this Article, we articulate the argument for open access in a formal way for the first time. We also respond to a variety of objections to open access.[10]

In Part I of this Article, we describe the design principles of the Internet and how they differ from the principles animating traditional telephone networks. We also explain the nature of the problem presented by cable company policies. In Part II, we explain why permitting cable companies to bundle ISP service with network access threatens the structure of the Internet. Finally, in Part III we respond to arguments suggesting that requiring cable companies to permit ISP competition is either a bad idea, or alternatively that it is a good idea but that government shouldn't adopt it.

WHY THE ISP MARKET SHOULD REMAIN COMPETITIVE

THE ARCHITECTURE OF THE INTERNET: END-TO-END NETWORK DESIGN

The Internet is the fastest growing network in history. In its thirty years of existence, its population has grown a million times over. Currently, it is the single largest contributor to the growth of the U.S. economy and has become the single most important influence linking individuals, and commerce, internationally. The Internet is not, however, the first communications network. There have been other networks before the Internet that did not experience the same extraordinary growth. These networks followed different design principles.

It is the view of many in the Internet community, ourselves included, that the extraordinary growth of the Internet rests fundamentally upon its design principles. Some of these principles relate to the openness of the Internet's standards and the openness of the software that implemented those standards. Some are engineering principles, designed to make the Internet function more flexibly and efficiently. But from the very beginning, these principles have been understood to have a social as well as a technological significance. They have, that is, been meant to implement values as well as enable communication. In our view, one aspect of this social significance is the competition in innovation the Internet enables. The tremendous innovation that has occurred on the Internet, in other words, depends crucially on its open nature.

Among the Internet's design principles is one that is particularly relevant to the bundling of broadband cable services. This is the end-to-end design principle that has been latent in system design for many years, but was first articulated explicitly as a principle in 1981 by Professors Jerome Saltzer, David Reed, and David Clark.[11] The e2e argument organizes the placement of functions within a network. It counsels that the "intelligence" in a network should be located at the top of a layered system— at its "ends," where users put information and applications onto the network. The communications protocols themselves (the "pipes" through which information flows) should be as simple and as general as possible.

One consequence of this design is a principle of nondiscrimination among applications. Lower-level network layers should provide a broad range of resources that are not particular to or optimized for any single application—even if a more efficient design for at least some applications is thereby sacrificed. As described in a subsequent paper by Reed, Saltzer, and Clark,

> end-to-end arguments have . . . two complementary goals: [(1)] Higher-level layers, more specific to an application, are free (and thus expected) to organize lower level network resources to achieve application-specific design goals efficiently (application autonomy); [(2)] Lower-level layers, which support many independent applications, should provide only resources of broad utility across applications, while providing to applications useable means for effective sharing of resources and resolution of resource conflicts (network transparency).[12]

While the e2e design principle was first adopted for technical reasons, it has important social features as well. E2e expands the competitive horizon by enabling a wider variety of applications to connect to and to use the network. It maximizes the number of entities that can compete for the use and applications of the network. As there is no single strategic actor who can tilt the competitive environment (the network) in favor of itself, or no hierarchical entity that can favor some applications over others, an e2e network creates a maximally competitive environment for innovation. The e2e design of the Internet has facilitated innovation. As Reed, Saltzer, and Clark argue,

> had the original Internet design been optimized for telephony-style virtual circuits (as were its contemporaries SNA and Tymnet), it would never have enabled the experimentation that led to protocols that could support the World Wide Web, or the flexible interconnect that has led to the flowering of a million independent Internet service providers. Preserving low-cost options to innovate outside the network, while keeping the core network services and functions simple and cheap, has been shown to have very substantial value.[13]

THE CONSEQUENCES OF THESE ARCHITECTURAL PRINCIPLES

The effect of the design of the Internet—including, but not exclusively, e2e—has been profound. By its design, the Internet has enabled an extraordinary creativity precisely because it has pushed creativity to the ends of the network. Rather than relying upon the creativity of a small group of innovators working for companies that control the network, the e2e design enables anyone with an Internet connection to design and implement a better way to use the Internet. Because it does not discriminate in favor of certain uses of the network and against others, the Internet has provided a competitive environment in which innovators know that their inventions will be used if useful. By keeping the cost of innovation low, it has encouraged an extraordinary amount of innovation in many different contexts. By keeping the network simple, and its interaction general, the Internet has facilitated the design of applications that could not originally have been envisioned. To take just a few examples, Internet telephony, digital music transfer, and electronic commerce are all applications far outside the range of expectations of those who designed the Internet (or even those who, much later, created the World Wide Web). Indeed, e-mail itself, the first true "killer app" of the Internet, was an unintended by-product hacked by early users of the network, not the point of the network itself. By keeping the cost of innovation low in the future— especially in the context of broadband media—the design of the Internet should continue to facilitate innovation not dreamed of by those who built it.

E2e design also prevents fears of strategic capture from chilling innovation. Innovation is most likely when innovators can expect to reap rewards in a fair marketplace. Innovation will be chilled if a potential innovator believes the value of the innovation will be captured by those that control the network and have the power to behave strategically. To the extent an actor is structurally capable of acting strategically, the rational innovator will reckon that capacity as a cost to innovation.

If that strategic actor owns the transmission lines itself, it has the power to decide what can and cannot be done on the Internet. The result is effectively to centralize Internet innovation within that company and its licensees. While there is a debate in the economic literature about the wisdom of centralizing control over improvements to any given innovation,[14] we think the history of the Internet compellingly demonstrates the wisdom of letting a myriad of possible improvers work free of the constraints of a central authority, public or private. Compromising e2e will tend to undermine innovation by putting one or a few companies in charge of deciding what new uses can be made of the network.

COMPARING THE ARCHITECTURAL PRINCIPLES OF THE OLD TELEPHONE NETWORK

The Internet's design principles are different from the design principles that governed the telephone network prior to the series of actions by the FCC and the Antitrust Division of the U.S. Department of Justice that resulted in the break-up of AT&T.[15] Prior to that break-up, the telephone network was not governed by the Internet's principle of e2e. It was instead governed by a different end-to-end philosophy—that the telephone company controlled the network from end to end. This meant that AT&T would not be neutral about the uses to which the telephone system could be put. For much of the history of the telephone network, it was forbidden to use the network in ways not specified by AT&T. It was unlawful, for example, to attach devices that performed services not offered by AT&T or to provide services that competed with the services provided by AT&T.[16] In the 1940s, even the telephone book was owned by AT&T.

Innovation under the old design was thus controlled by AT&T. If a person with a competing conception of how a communications network should be designed wanted to implement that competing conception, he or she would have to either work for AT&T or convince AT&T of the merits of this alternative design. AT&T was, therefore, a bottleneck on creativity in network architecture. While undoubtedly AT&T did much to advance telecommunications, through Bell Labs and other research, it also decided which innovations would be deployed. Its decisions turned in part upon the expected effect a new technology would have on AT&T's own business model.

The early history of the Internet itself was affected by AT&T's control over telecommunications innovation. An early design idea for the Internet was proposed to AT&T by RAND researcher Paul Baran in the early 1960s. Resistance to his design was strongest from AT&T.[17] As John Naughton reports, Baran recalls one particularly telling instance of AT&T's opposition:

> [AT&T's] views were once memorably summarized [sic] in an exasperated outburst from AT&T's Jack Osterman after a long discussion with Baran. "First," he said, "it can't possibly work, and if it did, damned if we are going to allow the creation of a competitor to ourselves."[18]

This resistance is perfectly understandable. From AT&T's perspective, maximizing its control over its network was profit-maximizing. We should expect corporate entities to behave in a profit-maximizing manner. But AT&T's strategy made economic sense only because the network was not end-to-end. Had the network been e2e, AT&T would have had no incentive to disable one use of the network it controlled in favor of another.

The same point about the relationship between innovation and the concentration of control can be made more obviously about the Internet in foreign countries even today. It is no accident that the Internet first reached prominence in the United States, because in practically every other nation the telephone architecture was controlled by state-sponsored monopolies. These monopolies, no less than AT&T, possessed no interest in facilitating the design of a network that would free individuals from their control. For many years, it was a crime in parts of Europe to connect a modem to a telephone line. Even today, the franchise in Germany for public phones permits the provider to control how access to the Internet occurs.[19]

THE GOVERNMENT'S ROLE IN CREATING THE COMPETITIVE ENVIRONMENT FOR THE INTERNET

It is fashionable today to argue that innovation is ensured if government simply stays out of the way. The FCC's current hands-off policy appears largely to be motivated by this prevailing ideological vogue. The view is that the best way for the government to guarantee growth in Internet broadband is to let the owners of networks structure broadband as they see fit.

We believe this view is misguided. It ignores the history that gave the Internet its birth and threatens to reproduce the calcified network design that characterized our telecommunications network prior to the Internet. The restrictions on innovation that marked the AT&T telephone monopoly were not removed by the government doing nothing. They were removed by active intervention designed to ensure the possibility of innovation. It was the FCC and the Department of Justice that cut the knot that tied innovation on the telecommunications network to the innovation favored by AT&T. Their action eventually freed the network from the control of a single strategic actor and opened it up for the innovation of many.[20] Beginning in 1968,[21] the FCC increasingly pursued a policy that forced AT&T to open its network to competing uses and providers. In 1984, actions by the Antitrust Division forced AT&T to unbundle its long distance service from its local telephone service.[22] This decree led to the break-up of the largest monopoly in American history.[23]

These actions together transformed the telephone network from a network whose use was controlled by one company—AT&T—into a general purpose network whose ultimate use was determined by end users. In effect, the government's activism imposed a principle analogous to e2e design on the telephone network. Indeed, though it masquerades under a different name (open access), this design principle is part and parcel of recent efforts by Congress and the FCC to deregulate telephony. The fundamental goal of the FCC in deregulating telephony is to isolate the natural monopoly component of a network—the actual wires—from other components in which competition can occur. By requiring the natural monopoly component at the basic network level to be open to competitors at higher-levels, intelligent regulation can minimize the economic disruption caused by that natural monopoly and permit as much competition as industry will allow.

Without these changes brought about by the government, the Internet, as we know it would not have been possible. These changes reversed the trend in telecommunications away from more centralized control over the communications network. In 1972, for example, network theorist Robert Fano wrote that unless there was a change in the trend in the network, existing institutions would further isolate computer and communications technologies from broad-based control.[24] But by seeding the development of a network within a different communication paradigm, and then opening the existing communication network so that it might deploy this different communication paradigm, the government created the conditions for the innovation that the Internet has realized.

This is not to say that the government created the innovation that the Internet has enjoyed. Nor is it to endorse government, rather than private, development of Internet-related technologies. Obviously, the extraordinary innovation of the Internet arises from the creativity of private actors from around the world. Some of these actors work within corporations; many have been associated with the Free Software and Open Source software movements;[25] others have been entrepreneurs operating outside of any specific structure. The creativity that these innovators produced, however, could not have come to fruition without the opening of the communications network by the government.

We certainly do not claim that a communications network would have been impossible without the government's intervention. We have had telecommunication networks for over a hundred years, and as computers matured, we no doubt would have had more sophisticated networks. The design of those networks would not have been the design of the Internet, however. The design would have been more like the French analogue to the Internet—Minitel.[26] But Minitel is not the Internet. It is a centralized, controlled version of the Internet, and it is notably less successful.

THE RELEVANCE OF LEGACY MONOPOLIES

While no one fully understands the dynamics that have made the innovation of the Internet possible, we do have some clues. One important element of that innovation is a structure that disables the power of existing monopolies to influence the future of a network design. This was the essence of the architecture upon which the Internet was originally built.

By freeing the telecommunications network from the control of one single actor, the government enabled innovation free from the influences of what one might call "legacy" business models. Companies develop core competencies, and most of them tend to stick to what they know how to do. Companies faced with a potential for radical change in the nature of their market might recoil, either because they do not know how to adapt to changing conditions or because they fear that they will lose dominance in the old market, as it becomes a new playing field. Their business planning is, in short, governed by the legacy of their past success. These legacy business plans often affect a company's response to innovation. In a competitive environment, these plans will often disadvantage a company that fails to respond rapidly enough to changed circumstances.

In some markets, companies have no choice but to respond to changed circumstances. It is a mark of Microsoft's success, for example, that its chairman, Bill Gates, succeeded in radically shifting the company's development toward the Internet in the face of changed competitive circumstances, despite the fact that these changes resulted in the termination of projects at other times deemed central to Microsoft's future. By contrast, commentators attribute Apple's relative failure during the early 1990s to its refusal to give up old models of business success.[27] Legacy models hindered Apple's development; the refusal to be captured by legacy models was a key to Microsoft's success.

In a market in which a company has power over the competitive environment itself, however, the rational incentives of a business might be different. If the business has control over the architecture of that competitive environment, then it will often have an incentive to design that architecture to enable better its legacy business models. As Charles Morris and Charles Ferguson describe it,

> Companies that control proprietary architectural standards have an advantage over other vendors. Since they control the architecture, they are usually better positioned to develop products that maximize its capabilities; by modifying the architecture, they can discipline competing product vendors. In an open-systems era, the most consistently successful information technology companies will be the ones who manage to establish a proprietary architectural standard over a substantial competitive space and defend it against the assaults of both clones and rival architectural sponsors.[28]

A company in this position can and will resist change in order to keep doing what it knows best.

This was the problem with the telephone company prior to its breakup by the government. AT&T enjoyed substantial returns from its existing network architecture. Regulators feared that these returns would make AT&T unwilling to experiment with other architectures that might better serve communication needs. As we have said, there is at least some evidence that AT&T in fact resisted the emergence of the Internet because it feared its effect on AT&T's own business model. Certainly it resisted the development and interconnection of other technologies to its telephone network. The regulators who pushed to free the telecommunication network believed that the market would choose differently from how AT&T, as controller of the network, would choose.

Time has proven these regulators correct. Once freed from the strategic control of an entity that had a particular business plan to protect, the communications network has evolved dramatically. The competitive process was enabled by making the network neutral about its uses, and by giving competitors access to the network so that they could compete in an effort to put the resources of the network to their best use. The same wires that AT&T used to send only analog voice are now being used to deliver stock quotes, music, fantasy games, reference information—in short, the whole content of the Internet. Left alone, AT&T might have made some content available over the telephone network, but it probably would not have shifted to packet-switched data,[29] and it certainly would not have developed or licensed all of the content that can now be found on the Internet.

The lesson from this explosion of innovation is critically important. An architecture that maximizes the *opportunity* for innovation maximizes innovation. An architecture that creates powerful strategic actors with control over the network and what can connect to it threatens innovation. These strategic actors might choose to behave in a procompetitive manner; there is no guarantee that they will interfere to stifle innovation. But without competition or regulation to restrict them, we should not assume that they will somehow decide to act in the public interest.

THE TECHNOLOGICAL FUTURE OF END-TO-END

More recently, technological developments have led some to question whether the Internet's end-to-end architecture is sustainable. While the e2e architecture of the Internet is fundamentally in place, users and network administrators are introducing intelligence into the network for a variety of reasons. Firewalls, proxy servers, Network Address Translators (NATs), and other systems are designed to determine the content and origin of packets and discriminate between packets. These changes, which may be inevitable given security concerns and the growth of e-commerce, make the network less transparent than the e2e model envisions.[30] While many of these developments exist at the software applications layer (that is, they are imposed at one end of the network or another), there have also been moves to build content-distinguishing intelligence into the network layer itself.[31] Clark and others are concerned about the effect of these trends on future innovation in the network. But as a practical matter, building security features and other content-distinguishing elements may be inevitable, at least at the applications level.

Flexibility in design is a feature of digital networks. The use of the network becomes a question of software implementation separable in fundamental ways from the ownership or even the nature of the network itself. François Bar and Christian Sandvig explain:

> In past networks, the communication platform and its configuration were "hard-wired" in the specific arrangement of electro-mechanical devices that formed a particular communication network—the logical architecture of the network precisely reflected its physical architecture. One had to own the network to change that arrangement. By contrast, platform configuration in digital networks depends on ability to program the network's control software. Control over network configuration thus becomes separable from network ownership. Multiple network platforms, supporting a variety of communication patterns, can simultaneously co-exist on a single physical infrastructure.[32]

Thus, the decision to build intelligence into the network may not be an all-or-nothing proposition. Rather, we can preserve the viability of e2e systems by keeping intelligence out of the hardware design and instead building it into some software layers on an as-needed basis.

As Werbach explains, this layered approach to Internet architecture means that the outmoded horizontal regulatory framework, in which cable, wireline, wireless, and satellite are all different forms of media with different regulatory structures, must give way to a vertical model of regulation.[33] This vertical model would distinguish between four different layers that comprise communications media: physical, logical, applications or services, and content.[34] Werbach argues that the goal of regulatory policy should be to prevent any one party from controlling the interface between different vertical layers.[35] This approach would permit competition at the higher-level layers (especially applications and content, but also potentially between different logical dataflow structures), notwithstanding the existence of a technical bottleneck at the physical layer. [Editor's note: Current terminology reverses the use of the terms vertical and horizontal, but the basic idea is the same. Regulation of horizontal layers would prevent parties at a lower layer from interfering (vertically) in higher levels].

This layered model will work only if control of the layers is not vertically integrated. Thus, as Bar and Sandvig point out,

> This newfound separability between a network's logical
> architecture and its physical layout . . . calls for a new policy
> bargain between control and access, that allows non-
> discriminatory *ability to design* the architecture of a
> communication platform, not only for those who own and
> control network infrastructures, but also for end-users or
> third parties.[36]

It is precisely this ability to design at the software layer that constitutes the
central issue in the debate over open access to cable networks.

IMPLICATIONS FOR BROADBAND CABLE

THE THREAT POSED BY ALLOWING CABLE COMPANIES TO BUNDLE ISP SERVICE

Some cable companies deploying broadband technology currently
prevent users from selecting an ISP of their choice, and more are likely to
do so in the future.[37] For customers of these cable companies, Internet access
is technologically bundled with ISP service. The broadband cable network
thus discriminates in the choice of services that it allows. This kind of
discrimination could have profound consequences for the competitive future
of the Internet.

To see the potential problem with this architecture, we must first
understand the importance of an ISP. ISPs serve a number of functions in
the existing narrowband residential market. Some ISPs primarily focus on
access to the Internet. Customers connect to the ISP through their local
telephone exchange. The ISP delivers Internet access at speeds limited
only by the local telephone exchange. Some ISPs supplement this access
with promises of user support—both the support to ensure the Internet
connection is maintained, and in some cases, help with the use of certain
Internet applications. Some ISPs further supplement this access with server
capabilities—giving users the ability to build web pages on the ISP's servers
or to support more expansive Internet activities. Finally, other ISPs provide,
or bundle, content with access. The most notable of these providers are
AOL, the Microsoft Network, CompuServe, and Prodigy.

The existing narrowband residential market is competitive.
Customers have a wide range of needs and the market responds with many

different packages of services. Nationwide there are some six thousand ISPs. In any particular geographic region, there can be hundreds that compete to provide service.

The functions performed by ISPs, however, are not fixed. They have no inherent nature. Hence as bandwidth changes from narrow- to broadband, we should expect the range of services offered by ISPs to change. As deliverability becomes more critical in video services, for example, ISPs could compete based on caching services. As the character of the available content increases, we might imagine some ISPs catering to certain content (video content) with others specializing elsewhere (new users).

The functions of ISPs, then, must not be conceived of too narrowly. Their importance, for example, does not have to do only with hosting "home pages" on the World Wide Web or the portal sites they might now provide. Their importance is also in the range of services they might bundle and offer competitively—from content (including video and audio services) and help functions to reference functions and special caching needs. In short, ISPs are engines for innovation in markets we do not yet imagine.

ISPs thus could be important middle-level competitors in the Internet economy. They could provide an ongoing competitive threat to actors at their borders. In the terms defined by Timothy Bresnahan, ISPs could become vertical competitors in an industry marked by highly concentrated markets at each horizontal level.[38] For example, AOL, a traditional online content provider and ISP, now threatens Microsoft in the operating system platform market. The size of AOL's market makes it an effective platform competitor. This threat could not have been predicted three years ago, but the fluidity of borders between markets on the Internet preserved the potential for new forms of competition.

Preserving competition is especially important given how little we know about how the broadband market will develop. The Internet market generally has been characterized by massive shifts in the competitive center. Hardware companies (IBM) have been displaced by operating system companies (Microsoft); operating system companies have been threatened by browser corporations (Netscape) and by open-platform "meta"-operating systems (Sun's Java). As Bresnahan notes, we have no good way to know which layer in this chain of services will become the most crucial. Thus, multiplying the layers of competition provides a constant check on the dominance of any particular actor. As Bresnahan puts it, "Far and away the most important [factor in market structure] is that competition came . . .

from another horizontal layer."[39]He therefore recommends, "one (modest) policy goal would be to make the threat of [vertical competition] more effective."[40]

The architecture proposed by AT&T and Time Warner for their broadband cable services compromises this vertical competition. By bundling ISP service with access, and by not permitting users to select another ISP, the architecture removes ISP competition within the residential broadband cable market. Without this competition, the architecture excludes an important check upon any strategic behavior that AT&T or Time Warner might engage in once the merger with AOL is complete. The architecture thus represents a significant change from the existing e2e design for a crucial segment of the residential Internet market. Furthermore, there is, in principle, no limit to what a cable company could bundle into its control of the network. As ISPs expand beyond the functions they have traditionally performed, AT&T or Time Warner might be in a position to foreclose all competition in an increasing range of services provided over broadband lines. The services available to broadband cable users would then be determined by the captive ISPs owned by each local cable company. These captive ISPs would control the kind of use that customers might make of their broadband access. They would determine whether, for example, full-length streaming video is permitted (it presently isn't), whether customers may resell broadband services (as they presently may not), and whether broadband customers may become providers of web content (as they presently may not).[41] These ISPs would have the power to discriminate in the choice of Internet services they allow, and customers who want broadband access would have to accept that choice.

Giving this power to discriminate to the owner of the actual network wires is fundamentally inconsistent with e2e design. These cable-owned ISPs would influence the development and use of cable broadband technology. They would be exercising that influence not at the ends of the network, but at the center, therefore shifting control over innovation from a variety of users and programmers to a single network owner. This design would contradict the principle that the network should remain neutral and empower users. It further could constitute the first step in a return to the failed architecture of the old AT&T monopoly.

The Costs of Violating Architectural Principles

The costs of undermining the e2e principle are hard to quantify. We simply do not know enough to gauge how sensitive the innovation of the Internet is to changes in this competitive architecture. Obviously, in part the significance turns on how the broadband market develops. But given trends as we can identify them now, the risks are great. In this part, we detail some of these risks.

The first risk is the cost of losing ISP competition. The benefits of this competition in the Internet's history should not be underestimated. The ISP market has historically been extraordinarily competitive. This competition has driven providers to expand capacity and to lower prices. Also, it has driven providers to give highly effective customer support. This extraordinary build-out of capacity has not been encouraged through the promise of monopoly protection. Rather, the competitive market has provided a sufficient incentive, and the market has responded.

The loss of ISP competition means more than the loss of the attractive, low-cost services we see today. One should not think of ISPs as providing a fixed and immutable set of services. Right now, ISPs typically provide customer support as well as an Internet protocol (IP) address that channels the customer's data. Competition among ISPs focuses on access speed and content. AOL, for example, is both an access provider and a content provider. Earthlink, on the other hand, simply provides access. In the future, however, ISPs could be potential vertical competitors to access providers who could provide competitive packages of content, differently optimized caching servers, different mixes of customer support, or advanced Internet services. ISP competition would provide a constant pressure on access providers to optimize access.

The second risk is that legacy monopolies will improperly affect the architecture of the Internet in an effort to protect their own turf. Broadband Internet service is a potential competitor to traditional cable video services. Traditional cable providers might well view this competition as a long-term threat to their business models and might not want to adapt to that competitive threat. By gaining control over the network architecture, however, cable providers are in a position to affect the development of the architecture so as to minimize the threat of broadband to their own video market. For example, a broadband cable provider that has control over the ISPs its customers use might be expected to restrict customers' access to streaming video from competitive content sources, in order to preserve its market of traditional cable video. AT&T has announced just such a policy. When asked whether users of the AT&T/MediaOne network would be permitted to stream video from competing providers across their network, Internet Services President Daniel Somers reportedly said that AT&T did not spend $56 billion to get into the cable business "to have the blood sucked out of our vein."[42]

Even absent a deliberate intent to restrict some forms of innovation, giving the owners of the pipes control over the nature of the network will inherently skew innovation in the network. As Bar and Sandvig observe, "those who control communication networks tend to design communication platforms which support the patterns of interaction that further their interest [and that] reflect their own history and technical expertise."[43] The old Bell System did not design a packet-switched alternative to the telephone system, because it simply did not think in those terms. Similarly, cable companies should be expected to design the systems they control in ways that are consistent with their experience and their interests. But in doing so, they will disadvantage other approaches, even if they do not intend to do so.

The third risk of giving control of the network to a strategic actor is the threat to innovation. Innovators are less likely to invest in a market in which a dominant player has the power to behave strategically against it. One example of this cost to innovation is the uncertainty created for future applications of broadband technology. One specific set of applications put in jeopardy are those that count on the Internet being always on.[44] Applications are being developed, for example, that would allow the Internet to monitor home security or the health of an at-risk resident. These applications would depend upon constant Internet access. Whether it makes sense as a software designer to develop these applications depends in part upon the likelihood that they could be deployed in broadband cable contexts. Under the e2e design of the Internet, this would not be a question. The network would carry everything; the choice about use would be made by the user. But under the design proposed by the cable industry, AT&T and Time Warner affiliates would have the power to decide whether these particular services would be "permitted" on the cable broadband network. AT&T has already exercised this power to discriminate against some services.[45] It has given no guarantee of nondiscrimination in the future. Thus if cable companies decided that certain services would not be permitted, the return to an innovator would be reduced by the proportion of the residential broadband market controlled by cable companies.

The point is not that cable companies would necessarily discriminate against any particular technology. Rather, the point is that the possibility of discrimination increases the risk an innovator faces when deciding whether to design for the Internet. Innovators are likely to be cautious about how they spend their research efforts if they know that one company has the power to control whether that innovation will ever be deployed.[46] The increasing risk is a cost to innovation, and this cost should be expected to reduce innovation.

Finally, it is worth thinking about how the elimination of ISP competition in broadband markets might affect the architecture of the Internet as a whole. We have extolled the virtues of decentralization as a spur to innovation. But the decentralization of the Internet has social policy effects as well. It is much harder for the government to censor a vibrant, decentralized ISP market than a market in which only a few ISPs serve all customers. Concentration of the ISP market might make government intervention to control certain forms of speech easier and therefore more likely.[47] Enabling government control could be a good or a bad thing, depending on one's perspective. But for those who doubt the government's motives in regulating speech, it should be a cause for concern.[48]

Perhaps some of these costs of preventing ISP competition in the cable market could be ameliorated by competition from other broadband providers. If cable companies restrict the nature of ISP service for broadband cable, then to the extent there is competition from DSL, DSL might have a competitive advantage over cable. We are not terribly persuaded by this argument, for reasons we discuss below.[49] But even if the broadband market were competitive, not all of the costs from denying ISP competition in broadband cable could be remedied by competition from other broadband providers. In particular, the cost to innovation would not be remedied by competition among providers. That cost is borne by the market as a whole, not by particular consumers in the market. Consumers individually do not feel any cost from innovation that does not occur. They therefore have no additional incentive to move from one kind of provider (cable) to another (DSL). Thus, if the increase in strategic power dampens the willingness to invest in broadband technologies, there is no mechanism by which that effect will be felt, and remedied, by broadband consumers directly.

ARGUMENTS MADE AGAINST PERMITTING ISP COMPETITION

We have been surprised by the number of objections raised to what strikes us as the rather intuitive arguments made above, and in particular by the vigor with which those objections have been asserted not only by the cable companies, but by groups within the FCC and scholarly communities. In this part we address those arguments in detail. Before responding to these objections, though, it is worth noting one important fact. None of the objections raised offer any reason to believe that either permitting ISP competition or preserving the e2e character of the Internet is a bad idea. Rather, these objections fall into three basic categories: (1) government doesn't need to act because the market will solve the problem, (2) ISP competition is good, but permitting cable companies to eliminate that competition is on balance desirable in order to give them incentives to deploy broadband more quickly, and (3) requiring cable companies to permit ISP competition might be a good thing, but the law simply doesn't permit it.

No Government Action Is Needed Because the Market Will Solve the Problem

In its initial consideration of access to broadband cable services, and in the most recent reports from the Cable Services Bureau of the FCC, the FCC has taken the position that it would best facilitate competition in this market by simply doing nothing. The FCC calls this a policy of "regulatory restraint."[50] In our view, this approach profoundly underplays the importance of the FCC's activism in ensuring competition in the past, and will jeopardize the innovative prospects for broadband Internet service in the future. It is based on a fundamentally misguided assumption also shared by many other commentators: that if we leave the cable industry alone, the market will take care of the problem. This argument comes in several flavors.

Cable Companies Will Open Access on Their Own

First, James Speta has argued that the economics of telecommunications are such that cable companies will open their networks to multiple ISPs.[51] Speta claims that cable companies actually have no incentive to bundle upstream content or services with broadband Internet access, even if they are in a monopoly position with respect to such access: "[A] broadband network . . . does not have incentive to foreclose providers of complementary information services, even if the platform provider markets its own information services. It is against the platform owner's interest to attempt to monopolize content—even if the platform owner is a monopolist in transmission service."[52]

Speta bases this argument on a theory that he calls "indirect network externalities."[53] Essentially, his model is one in which the cable company's customers derive value both from interconnection and from the content provided over that connection. Speta argues that this means that cable companies have an incentive to provide the most efficient set of content possible. He challenges advocates of ISP competition for failing to make arguments consistent with his theory: "Those asserting that cable television systems and other providers of broadband access will use their ownership of wires or other platforms to impede competition in other markets fail to provide an economic model to support those claims. The most plausible model, in fact, suggests otherwise."[54]

Similarly, he criticizes us for failing to explain why cable companies would want to restrict access to ISP competition, and concludes that "economic theory holds that" cable companies "will have no incentive to do so."[55] Stripped to its essence, what Speta and others argue is that cable companies have an incentive to act in a way that maximizes competition, and so they will. The difficulty with this argument is that cable companies have *already* closed the ISP market to competition. We are not concerned with a hypothetical future risk here. Speta's theory therefore has a rather large prediction problem. Obviously, the cable companies haven't seen the market in the way he suggests they should.[56] One should be skeptical of a theory whose predictions are so demonstrably at odds with reality.[57]

There are two possible explanations for why cable companies have not acted in accordance with Speta's predictions. First, Speta's theoretical model could be wrong. It turns out, in fact, that there is good theoretical reason to be skeptical of Speta's analysis. Speta seems to conflate the provision of content with the provision of ISP services. He is surely right to say that cable companies will want to give cable modem customers access to the Internet and, therefore, to a host of content other than their own. But it doesn't follow that cable companies will permit competition among ISPs to connect consumers to that content. Rather, a cable company's incentive is to maximize its profit by striking the best deal it can with one or more ISPs. That deal will most likely involve ISP exclusivity, with the cable company sharing in the monopoly profits the ISP will charge.[58] The cable company might have an incentive to choose an efficient ISP, but it emphatically does not have an incentive to minimize the cost to consumers or to give them a choice of ISPs.[59]

Network effects don't change this story. In the first place, it is not clear the extent to which broadband cable really involves network effects.[60] Certainly, access to the Internet is desirable largely because of its potential to interconnect users, and so the Internet itself is characterized by network effects. This effect carries over to speed and bandwidth of Internet service: broadband service is more valuable to a consumer if there is a great deal of content (say, streaming video) that makes use of that bandwidth, and content providers are in turn more likely to provide that content if there are a large number of broadband users. So far, so good. But for any given broadband cable provider, the network benefits collapse rather quickly because of the technology involved. The more people with cable modems sharing a single cable loop, the less bandwidth available to each of them. For subscribers on any given local loop, then, it is emphatically not the case that they benefit from adding more users to the network beyond a certain minimum subscription base. Rather, consumption is locally rivalrous. In such a market, cable companies benefit from charging a supercompetitive price to a smaller number of users of each loop.

Second, even if Speta is right as a theoretical matter that a hypothetical cable company behaving rationally should open its lines to ISP competition, it is not necessarily the case that cable companies will do the rational thing. The rationality assumption has historically been central to law and economics, but it has recently come under fire even within the discipline of economics. The "behavioral law and economics" literature offers strong reason to believe that at least in certain circumstances, people don't always do the rational thing. Rather, systematic biases can infect decision making.[61] In the business context, these biases often take the form of what might be called a "corporate endowment effect." Businesses have core competencies—areas in which they are experienced and in which they know how to make money.[62] They may discount the value of radically new ideas that would require them to move their business in a new direction, particularly when the proposed shift would cannibalize an existing revenue stream.[63] We saw one example of this in AT&T's behavior as a legacy monopoly.[64]

In this case, it is quite possible that the endowment effect is at work. Even if network effects are at issue here, and even if Speta is right that these effects should prompt cable companies to open their networks, it is not clear that the cable companies will see it that way. Cable companies might believe they will not lose the benefit of those effects simply by mandating that consumers use a single ISP. While in earlier times ISPs often promoted their own content, in the modern era ISP access is mostly valuable because it connects users to the Internet. A cable company might well believe that one ISP can accomplish that just as well as another, and therefore that consumers won't lose the benefits of network access by being forced to use the ISP the cable company has chosen. As we have argued, we think such a decision ignores the potential for future innovation to be spurred by ISP competition. But cable companies might not focus on such benefits, just as AT&T in an earlier era didn't focus on the computer applications of its telephone lines. In addition, from the cable company's perspective even some perceived reduction in network benefits might be offset by a differentially greater impact on rivals.[65] It seems wrong to suggest that an appreciation for these network effects will necessarily compel cable companies to open their access.

We believe, then, that it is wrong to assume that cable companies will necessarily have incentives to promote a vibrant and competitive ISP market, particularly when they own certain competitors in that market. But even if one is skeptical of our theoretical explanation, the fact that the cable companies have voted with their feet—and seem to agree with us— should give one pause. In short, it doesn't really matter whether cable companies are rational or irrational in refusing to open their networks. What really matters is that they have resisted doing so.

One potential response in other contexts to this "voting with their feet" argument might be to say that if cable companies are foolish or presumptuous enough to act against the dictates of theory, they are merely being inefficient and the market will discipline them. But this brings us to a critical problem for advocates of the theory that the market will fix everything: There is no effective competitive market for cable services. Cable companies are regulated monopolies. The natural monopoly characteristics associated with local wire distribution impose a formidable barrier to entry. The theory must instead be that some other, noncable provider of broadband services will recognize the wisdom of open access, and that their competition will be enough to force cable companies to abandon their policy of using captive ISPs. We address this argument in the next part.

Other Broadband Services Will Preserve ISP Competition

Cable companies are not the only ones providing broadband Internet access.[66] Telephone companies (and independent companies using collocated equipment) provide broadband access through DSL. Other potential (though as yet largely unrealized) sources of broadband competition include satellite and wireless services.[67] Given these potentially competitive services, one might ask, why worry at all about what cable companies do with their broadband wires? If the cable companies don't permit competition among ISPs, the argument goes, they will simply be driven out of the market by other companies that do. Indeed, the Cable Services Bureau Report (Bureau Report) on cable open access makes this argument.[68]

There are other sources of broadband Internet access than cable modems, and that fact might constrain what cable companies do with their lines. We think, however, that it is unwise to rely on this potential facilities based competition as an excuse for permitting cable companies to prevent downstream competition among ISPs. In our view, a principle is respected if respected generally, not occasionally. And the benefits of a principle come from the expectation that it will be respected. Further, competition in a small subset of the broadband market is no substitute for competition in the entire broadband market. This is particularly true if (as the Bureau Report itself suggests) the characteristics of the competing media differ.

In the first place, one should be careful not to overstate the effectiveness of these alternate means of competition. The current market share of cable in the residential broadband market is high. As of 2000, it accounted for 70 percent of the broadband market.[69] So while other broadband technologies do exist, and more may be deployed, for most consumers the reality of the marketplace is that broadband access means a cable modem.[70] Further, not all consumers face even potential competition between cable modems and other forms of broadband service. For consumers outside a wireless or satellite service area, or more than three miles from a converted telephone switching station, cable is the only possible choice for broadband service.[71]

Second, because cable and DSL use different technologies, they have different strengths and weaknesses. The content and services that fit best with broadband are just being developed. DSL can compete with cable modems for some kinds of broadband services, but not for others. DSL, for example, will probably not be competitive for streaming video on demand. Its competitive strength is not uniform.

Finally, given how cable companies have behaved so far, it is reasonable to ask why other broadband providers should be expected to behave any differently. Wireless and satellite providers might well have similar incentives and decide to maximize profits by closing off access to ISPs, just as cable companies have done. As each new broadband technology enters the Internet market, the FCC's position with respect to cable would imply that that new technology too could violate the principle of e2e design. Only DSL would be required (because of existing statutory obligations) to maintain the principle of e2e design with respect to ISP choice.

It is true that DSL lines are currently open to certain indirect forms of ISP competition.[72] But this is not the result of the operation of the market. Rather, it is the result of regulation. DSL service is provided by phone companies, and Congress and the FCC have historically been willing to regulate phone companies and to require open interconnection during their deregulation. It would be ironic if competition over DSL lines were to be cited as an example of the market at work, when in fact those DSL lines are open to competition only because regulators have forced them to be.

Given that historical accident, should we assume that DSL and the future wireless and satellite technologies provide enough competition that we don't need to encourage any more? We think not. First, it is admittedly true that the existence of facilities-based competition lessens the harm cable companies will do by closing the ISP market. But lessening the harm is not the same thing as eliminating it. Even if DSL does provide a partially competitive market for some ISPs who want to serve broadband access to some customers, it simply makes no sense as a matter of economic policy to foreclose the largest possible market for ISP competition, particularly when doing so serves no good end.[73] Second, it seems manifestly unfair to give cable and satellite companies a free ride because we have already imposed regulation on their competitors. One of the principal lessons of telecommunications convergence is that we are better off treating like things alike.[74] Third, it is not clear that DSL-ISP access will remain competitive. Several scholars have already argued that phone companies should not have to open their wires to ISP competition because they will be constrained by the existence of cable companies who will discipline them if they act anticompetitively.[75] This is a neat switch on the arguments made above. It seems we have potential competition everywhere, but the only broadband market structure in which ISP competition actually exists is the one in which regulators have required infrastructure providers to permit it.

The FCC Should Take a "Wait and See" Approach

Finally, one commentator has endorsed the idea of "regulatory restraint" by arguing for a presumption of inaction. In a broader, theoretical context, Stuart Benjamin argues that Congress and the agencies should presumptively not act "proactively" when the harm sought to be remedied is speculative.[76] Benjamin identifies proposals to open access to broadband cable as an example of attempts to regulate based only on a potential future harm.[77] The FCC seems to have endorsed this "wait and see" approach in the cable context. The Bureau Report reasons that if things turn out for the worse—if cable companies in fact implement a closed system as they say they intend, and if cable becomes an important aspect of the broadband market—then the government can pursue open access to cable after the fact, presumably through antitrust litigation.

Benjamin's concern is more plausible than Speta's. There is good reason not to act precipitously. While the question of ISP competition in the broadband cable market is not a hypothetical one—AT&T is precluding ISP competition today—it is true that the risks we identify in Part II have not yet come to pass. In large measure this is because the broadband Internet market itself is in its nascency. Still, Benjamin is right to be concerned as a general matter about predictions of future harm as a determinant of policy. It is too easy to predict disaster on either side of a debate.

We do not believe, however, that the presumption he suggests is the right one here. Benjamin concerns himself with the government asserting its interests in order to justify the suppression of speech.[78] There is no government regulation of speech at issue here.[79] We do not propose that cable modems must carry certain content to all customers, as in *Turner Broadcasting Systems, Inc. v. FCC*.[80] Rather, the question is one of technical interconnection: whether the cable company is entitled to control the means by which consumers access the same content—the Internet.

Even in the speech context, the U.S. Supreme Court has permitted evidence of a threat to future competition to justify the must-carry requirement in the cable context.[81] The Court had good reasons for rejecting the "wait and see" approach. Benjamin's approach discounts the cost of regulating ex post. In the structural context in which antitrust and regulatory activities generally arise, it is much harder to undo a problem once it has become entrenched than it is to prevent that problem from arising in the first place. In their present state, the ISPs that AT&T and Time Warner would rely upon are independent business units. Once the cable companies have integrated their ISPs, the regulatory costs of identifying nondiscriminatory rates would be much higher than they would be under the existing structure. Rather than the complexity that DSL regulation involves, imposing a rule of open access now would be relatively less costly. The same is even more true of independent ISPs. If the vibrant market for ISPs in narrowband access is weakened or destroyed because they cannot provide broadband service, those ISPs and their innovative contributions will disappear. If they do, we won't magically get them back by deciding later to open the broadband market to competition. It is for this reason that antitrust and regulatory laws provide mechanisms for stopping threats to competition "in their incipiency,"[82]rather than waiting until competition has disappeared entirely and then trying to rebuild it.

Whether one believes the government is justified in its suit against Microsoft or not, one cannot avoid the conclusion that the existing systems for dealing with monopoly problems in the networked economy ex post are extremely inefficient. Among the costs of using antitrust litigation to design markets are precisely the costs of uncertainty that the Bureau discusses in relation to cable. To say there is no reason to use a seat belt because there is always the care of an emergency room is to miss the extraordinary costs of any ex post remedy. There is little evidence that the government is in a position to intervene to undo entrenched monopoly power in an efficient and expeditious manner.

Moreover, the costs of dislodging an existing monopoly power are always significant, and always higher than the costs of preventing the monopoly from forming. This is particularly true in this context, in which if we must regulate ex post we will face integrated, bundled broadband providers that will have to be broken up, and ways will have to be found to recreate the competition the FCC will have allowed to languish.

Indeed, if the FCC does in fact decide to regulate this industry because access does not magically become open, we will end up with more, not less, regulation, because the FCC will have to regulate not only access to the wires but also a whole host of industries that could have been competitive had they not become bundled to the network itself. We will find ourselves, in short, in a new era of regulation reminiscent of the old days of the Bell System.

A second problem with the "wait and see" approach in this context is that it is not at all clear we *will* see the costs of eliminating ISP competition. It may be impossible to measure the loss of innovation that results from stifling ISP competition and regularizing innovation along the lines of what cable companies think is optimal. Any ex post assessment will face the difficult problem of evaluating a negative—what things didn't happen as a result of this change.[83]

In the cable modem context, we think "wait and see" should have a different meaning. The Internet already has a certain architecture; it is the cable companies that are attempting to remake that architecture in fundamental ways. If we truly do not know enough about the consequences of this effort, we are better off maintaining a status quo that we know to have been successful. This is particularly true because the costs of action and inaction are not symmetrical. If we are right, permitting the cable companies to eliminate ISP competition could do untold damage to innovation and competition on the Internet. But if we are wrong, so what? Requiring cable companies to permit ISP competition is not hard to achieve.[84] It doesn't cost anyone a lot of money. And while a myriad of commentators have objected to the FCC mandating such competition, not one has identified a single reason to believe that using captive ISPs furthers some important policy goal that could not be furthered any other way.[85] Given this imbalance, we think any uncertainty offers good reason not to let the cable companies proceed with eliminating competition.

MONOPOLY CONTROL PROVIDES NEEDED INCENTIVES

The only argument we have been able to find suggesting that eliminating ISP competition might actually be desirable is that eliminating competition gives cable companies supercompetitive revenues that in turn will encourage them to deploy broadband Internet access more quickly. Howard Shelanski raised this issue in the telecom context, noting that requiring competition may reduce the incentives for incumbent carriers to build out their systems and make them available for broadband use.[86] Speta and Phil Weiser developed and relied upon this argument in more detail. Speta argues that cable companies will deploy broadband access and open it to competition, but only if they are "able to charge unaffiliated ISPs and other content providers the full monopoly price for interconnection and access."[87] Speta's argument is grounded not so much on indirect network effects as on an assumption about "priming the pump." Speta assumes that no one will buy broadband cable services initially unless the cable company itself provides high-bandwidth content.[88] And the cable companies will have no incentive to invest in developing broadband infrastructure unless they can reap monopoly profits from that endeavor. The FCC repeats the threat of cable companies that they will not invest as quickly if they are forced to open access.[89] In effect, the argument is that we must expand the cable companies' monopoly over the wires into competitive markets in order to give them an incentive to implement broadband access.

The need for investment incentives is a fair point. But it is worth noting at the outset that this "monopoly incentives" argument contradicts every other argument made by opponents of ISP competition. For cable companies to reap monopoly returns from prices charged to ISPs means, among other things, that the cable companies will not voluntarily open their lines to ISP competition.[90] If cable companies are collecting monopoly profits from ISPs, it means that facilities-based competition by other forms of broadband Internet access has not served to restrict cable's power over price. It means that broadband cable service is a monopoly, and therefore within the jurisdiction of the antitrust laws. And it assumes that, contrary to the Chicago-school theory of tying,[91] cable companies will make more money from bundling ISP service with the provision of access than they would merely by charging an unregulated price for access alone.[92]

The question then becomes whether giving cable companies the power to eliminate ISP competition is the only way to provide the requisite incentives. We think not. It is possible to grant sufficient incentives by letting cable companies set the appropriate price to consumers for use of the wires themselves. By contrast, allowing cable companies to gain that incentive by monopolizing an adjacent competitive market offers no guarantee of giving the appropriate incentive. It also poses significant risks to competition and innovation.

We also suspect that the cable companies protest too much. We have heard many times the argument that an industry will never develop—or will collapse—if it is not given preferential treatment by the government. Most of those arguments turn out to be illusory. In the late 1970s, Hollywood argued to Congress that the movie business would not exist in ten years unless VCRs were banned. The courts wisely decided not to ban VCRs, and Hollywood is doing better than ever. More recently, some argued as late as 1996 that no one would ever put any valuable content on the Internet unless Congress passed special copyright protections for Internet works.[93]

The amazing variety of useful material on the Internet today, despite Congress's failure until recently to give special perks to copyright owners, belies the argument. It may well be that cable companies will provide broadband Internet access whether or not we give them special incentives to do so, particularly because the costs of build-out are not all that great in the cable context. [94] Indeed, a variety of companies are veritably racing to deploy broadband Internet services—even phone companies, whose DSL service is theoretically hobbled by the inability to charge monopoly prices to ISPs. Some commentators have even suggested that competition, not monopoly, is actually the best spur to investment by incumbents in telecommunications and related fields.[95]

Further, the speed of investment in broadband services is not the only economic and social value at stake. The environment for innovation in other sorts of products and services is also affected by the competitive environment of the Internet. If the cost of a faster deployment of broadband is a reduction in Internet innovation, then it is not clear the benefit is worth the cost. And if the cost is a reduction in innovation in Internet services, the long-term risk to social welfare is even greater. The extraordinary returns that AT&T enjoyed as a monopoly provider before the 1984 consent decree may well have sped its investment in its conception of what a communications network should be; it does not follow that there was a net benefit to society from that increased incentive to invest. Indeed, the vibrant, innovative markets that have sprung up since the break-up of AT&T suggest that competition is a better spur to innovation than monopoly.

The monopoly incentives argument is one piece of a much larger debate in the economics literature over the relative value of monopoly and competition in spurring innovation. On the one hand are those who believe that competition dissipates research incentives, and therefore that monopoly is desirable because it spurs research. Advocates of this view, with which the cable industry has aligned itself, point to Joseph Schumpeter's statement that "perfect competition is not only impossible but inferior."[96]   On the other hand are those who hold, with Kenneth Arrow, that monopolists tend to be lazy, and that it is the threat of competition that spurs new innovation.[97] In the related context of intellectual property law, this debate plays out in a difference between those who argue that granting broad initial intellectual property rights encourages the initial inventor to develop improvements,[98] and those who believe that improvements will be encouraged by allowing a competitive market to develop.[99]

As Howard Shelanski has observed, this is not a question that can be answered a priori, but only by reference to actual cases.[100] We believe the empirical evidence suggests quite strongly that it is competition, not monopoly, that best spurs creativity.[101]   Shelanski's study of ten technological innovations in the U.S. telecommunications industry demonstrates not only that innovation does occur under competitive conditions, but that in the cases he studied innovations were deployed faster in competitive markets than in monopoly markets.[102] We think the evidence is even stronger in the case of the Internet. As discussed above, the tremendous innovation associated with the Internet not only came about in a competitive marketplace, but in a fundamental sense *resulted* from the competitive, end-to-end character of that market.

Finally, one important and subtle point is that the kinds of innovation that occur are likely to differ in each regime. Monopoly firms might have the *ability* to spend more on research and development than competitive firms, but the economic evidence demonstrates that the money they spend tends to follow established research paths that lead to what one might call "regularized innovation"—optimization along existing lines.[103] By contrast, competition is much more likely to spur innovation that marks a radical departure from the past. It is that latter, serendipitous kind of innovation that we fear will be lost if the ISP market is eliminated.

THE GOVERNMENT CANNOT PREVENT BUNDLING

A third set of arguments against action by the FCC focuses on the legal or technical competence of the government to act. These advocates generally claim that the FCC is legally barred from acting to preserve competition, even if as a policy matter it should do so.

Only Antitrust Law Governs Broadband Cable

The first assumption that opponents of cable open access seem to make is that the FCC's authority to act in this area is coterminous with antitrust law. They speak, for example, in terms of roof of monopoly power or the essential facilities doctrine. We address those antitrust objections below.[104] But antitrust law applies in this context only as a back-stop for the failures of regulatory policy. Cable companies are certificated and regulated natural monopolies. Both federal and local governments have not only the power but the obligation to regulate cable companies in the public interest. Some commentators have argued that the Communications Act of 1934[105] actually forbids the FCC from regulating in this area. Speta, for example, argues that broadband Internet access is actually a form of "programming service" (and therefore a subset of the larger "cable service") similar to other sorts of cable content t raditionally provided over cable wires.[106] As such, he believes the act precludes the FCC from treating a cable company's provision of Internet access as the actions of a "common carrier or utility."[107] He further argues that a rule permitting ISP competition would in effect treat the cable company as a common carrier.[108]

We are not specialists in the intricacies of the Communications Act, and are therefore reluctant to essay our own explanation of what the act is intended to do.[109] We doubt Speta's chain of inferences in two critical respects, however. First, it does not seem to us that a cable company is providing a "cable service" by offering access to the Internet.[110] A telephone company surely does not offer "cable service" merely by providing Internet access; it is not clear to us why the result should be different merely because the company in question also provides cable programming services. Our reading is bolstered by the only appellate decision to have considered the issue. In *AT&T v. City of Portland*,[111] decided after Speta wrote his article, the court held that "[t]he essence of cable service . . . is one-way transmission of programming to subscribers generally. This definition does not fit @Home . . . Internet access."[112] Instead, the court concluded that @Home was providing two separate services bundled together: the "information services" provided by traditional ISPs, and a "telecommunications service" similar to that provided by telephone companies.[113] The court explained that the common carrier status imposed on telecommunication services under the act was consistent with the architecture of the Internet.[114]

Second, even if the Supreme Court were to conclude that broadband Internet access is a form of cable programming, it does not follow that broadband access via cable modem falls entirely outside the FCC's regulatory purview. Rather, the only restriction that would be imposed is one that forbids the FCC from imposing "common carrier" or "utility" obligations on the cable company. But permitting ISP competition is not equivalent to imposing common carrier status on cable companies. As Speta acknowledges, common carriers are subject to rate regulation, tariffs, collocation rules, and the like.[115] He believes that any open access rule would necessarily include rate regulation, in part because he equates a rule requiring nondiscriminatory pricing with actual government oversight and approval of the prices charged.[116] It seems to us that this assumption misunderstands what the debate is all about. As we explain more fully below, Speta and others might be misled by the term "open access" into believing that we propose cable companies should be subject to all the same interconnection requirements as telephone companies. This is simply not the case. All we propose is that cable companies be permitted to charge consumers for access to their wires, but not be permitted to bundle ISP services together with wire access. This is an unexceptional principle in other areas. To take a similar example, modem makers do not sell their equipment only on the condition that consumers also buy ISP services from them. Should they attempt to do so, we don't need to solve the problem by creating a complex rate structure to determine a fair price for the bundle. We just need to prohibit the bundling.

Antitrust Law Is Inapplicable

A related fallacy seems to infect the arguments of ISP competition opponents about antitrust law. Phil Weiser, Greg Sidak, and others suggest that antitrust law comes into play in the cable modem context only if the cable lines are determined to be an "essential facility" to which the law might compel access.[117] The standards for making an essential facilities argument are quite high, and with good reason. We could debate whether or not those standards are met here,[118] but let us assume for the sake of argument that they are not. Opponents of ISP competition seem to have forgotten that there is more to antitrust law than the essential facilities doctrine.

The bundling of cable line access and ISP service instead presents a straightforward claim of tying. Tying violates the antitrust laws when four conditions are satisfied: there are two separate products or services, the customer is required to purchase one in order to get the other, the tying party has market power in the tying product market (here cable wires), and there is likely to be an effect on the market for the tied product (here ISP services).[119] None of these elements seem to us to be in serious doubt. We have not seen anyone suggest that access to cable lines and the provision of ISP services are really the same thing, or even that there is some significant technological benefit to be gained from packaging them together.[120] Cable companies do have monopolies over cable wires in their local service area by government fiat.[121] The question becomes whether there is likely to be an effect[122] on ISP competition. We find it hard to believe that there could not be such an effect, given that the best source of broadband access will be foreclosed to all but a single ISP. Even if the market were defined so broadly that closure by a small cable company did not have the requisite effect, certainly closure by the two largest cable companies (AT&T and Time Warner) and the dominant ISP provider (AOL) should be of competitive concern.[123]

Some academics have suggested that tying should not be illegal at all, because it is premised on a concept of monopoly leveraging that makes no sense as a matter of economic theory.[124] Louis Kaplow has deconstructed that argument rather effectively, explaining among other things that the economic criticism of leveraging theory assumes a static market for both tied goods.[125] Kaplow's argument has particular force here, where both markets are subject to rapid evolution, and where the broadband ISP market is itself in the early formative stages.[126] Further, the one circumstance in which it seems everyone can agree that tying does make economic sense is when it is used to leverage monopoly power from a regulated to an unregulated market—precisely what the cable companies are doing in this situation.[127]

The application of antitrust law to isolate a natural monopoly and to minimize its market effects is hardly surprising. It is the principle that underlies both *MCI Communications Corp. v. AT&T*[128] and the Modified Final Judgment against AT&T itself.[129] The idea is to wall off the monopoly market from the competitive market, a process Joe Farrell has referred to as "quarantin[ing] the monopoly lest it infect the competitive segments."[130] William Baxter, who no one would call an antitrust liberal, endorsed this idea as the least restrictive alternative, and we think it makes sense as a general principle of antitrust law.[131]

In any event, it is simply wrong to characterize this debate as one in which cable companies are being forced to share their private property. All we propose is that they have to obey the same rules everyone else does: They cannot bundle two different products or services together in circumstances in which doing so will reduce competition. This proposal will not affect the price cable companies can charge for bandwidth. It merely prevents them from controlling which ISP a consumer uses to take advantage of the bandwidth they have paid for.

Regulating Bundling Is Not Feasible

The FCC in its Report repeats technological arguments made by the cable companies themselves about why open access is not feasible in the context of broadband cable. Speta makes a variant of these arguments, suggesting that allowing the cable company to tie ISP services to cable access will permit it to ensure that only those Internet services that "perform well on the platform" will be available to consumers.[132]   This is a curious argument to juxtapose with Speta's first objection—that cable companies will open access on their own. If open access is not feasible, it is not clear how or why they would open access.

We think the argument is a red herring and that it is misleading to suggest that there is any technological need for this tie. As AOL explained in its October 1999 filing with the city of San Francisco, less than a month before it agreed to merge with Time Warner (and thus switched sides), "there is no technical reason why the City could not adopt an open access policy for multiple ISPs."[133]

First, the fact that cable is a "shared medium," while DSL is dedicated, should not affect ISP choice. The Internet itself is a shared medium. Its performance, as AOL's filing notes, "var[ies] depending on the number of actual subscribers using the Internet connection at the same time."[134] The only difference between DSL and cable is the place where one enters the shared pool. It is true that cable is architected to share bandwidth among local users, whereas DSL is not. But whether that difference results in a difference in performance is simply a function of how many users the cable company decides to connect and not of whether the users it connects have different ISPs. Given a certain profile of usage, cable broadband providers can guarantee an effective equivalent of unshared access simply by not overselling the access they attach at any single node. More to the point, the cable companies can control usage whether or not they also own the ISPs, merely by limiting the number and size of network subscriptions. So the shared medium argument does not justify bundling of ISP service with access to the network.

Second, the Bureau argues that security on a cable node is less effective than on a DSL connection, because data from other computers passes by all computers on a network node (as is the case, for example, with an Ethernet network). This argument too is misleading. There is a difference in the security approaches necessary to implement broadband cable securely, because users on a particular node are all exposed to the same network traffic. But cable companies are already developing technologies to eliminate that security risk. There is no reason to believe that a properly implemented cable system would be any less secure than a comparable DSL system. And again, there is no reason to believe that cable control over ISPs is necessary to achieve this goal.

In fact, it seems that open access is technically feasible.[135] The real question is how hard it will be to achieve. As Shawn O'Donnell points out, that question depends in significant part on how the cable infrastructure itself is designed.[136] This architecture is being built as we write. Indeed, the cable industry itself is developing open standards not just for "Layer III" interconnections (for example, DOCSIS cable modems), but for higher-level interoperability.[137] O'Donnell argues that the architecture should be constructed in a way that facilitates rather than impairs access by others.[138] Interconnection of cable modems with multiple ISPs might take work, but it surely is not impossible.

––––––––––

What strikes us as most notable about the open access debate is the great lengths to which the FCC and so many commentators are willing to go to justify the behavior of cable companies. Indeed, cable advocates are making arguments that are internally inconsistent: that cable modems face serious competition from DSL, but that controlling the ISP market will give them monopoly incentives to invest; that open access is not feasible, and yet cable companies can be expected to open access on their own.

Given that almost none of these arguments actually suggest that ISP competition itself is a bad thing, it is worth asking why so many people feel a burning need to defend its abolition. In our view, much of this debate has been shaped by two misapprehensions that have more to do with terminology than with reality.

First, much of the debate seems to have been side-tracked by the use of the term "open access." The term is apparently a red flag of sorts to those who spend their lives in telecommunications law, carrying a whole series of connotations from the history of telecommunications deregulation. In the context of cable modems and ISP competition, open access advocates are actually asking for something different and far more limited. Thus, much of the response to open access requests seems to focus on what the respondent thinks open access means, and not on what its proponents are in fact asking for.[139]

In our view, open access is simply shorthand for a set of competitive objectives. The objectives sought in the DSL context are perfectly adequate to apply in this context, at least as a starting point. But they are not the only possible approach. The relevant question that the FCC should address is how to ensure that customers have an easy choice among relevant competitors, so as to preserve competition in the broadband market. The DSL requirements ensure that. The FCC can impose open access conditions on cable companies without replicating the complex regulatory scheme necessary to implement sections 251 and 252 of the Telecommunications Act of 1996.[140] Interconnection to a cable modem network, even by multiple ISPs, involves nothing more than the development of an Internet connection between an ISP and a router. It does not necessarily require price regulation of cable lines or collocation of equipment, nor would open access conditions require cable companies to honor requests for interconnection at special locations within the network.[141] So long as unaffiliated ISPs are allowed to interconnect at the same place—and at the same price—as affiliated ISPs, the e2e principle will not be compromised.[142]

The second terminology problem has to do with the fact that proponents of ISP competition are asking for regulation. "Regulation" seems to be a dirty word in many sectors these days. There are some good reasons for that. Government has in the past unquestionably regulated too many industries and too many aspects of those industries. It has been too quick to assume that an industry was a natural monopoly and that price regulation was the only way of creating a simulacrum of competition. The FCC has been part of the problem in some respects, and has justly been criticized for attempting to do such things as regulate broadcast content and impose equal time rules.[143]

   We fear, however, that the FCC has gone overboard in taking these criticisms to heart and now fears doing anything that might be tarred with the label "regulation."[144]   The fact is that the structural characteristics of the cable and telecommunications markets require some form of regulatory oversight over the use of the local distribution networks themselves. The error of past eras was not that they regulated these industries at all, but that they regulated too much. For most of the twentieth century, the FCC took its mandate to be the exclusion of competition from the telephone market and the regulation of AT&T as a monopoly provider not just of access to local wires, but of local telephone services, long-distance service, and telephone equipment.[145] Beginning in the late 1960s with the *Carterfone* decision,[146] the FCC began to allow competition into first the equipment and then the long-distance segments of the market. Competition in those areas—and the principle of nondiscriminatory interconnection—were cemented in the consent decree breaking up AT&T.[147] Once the single phone network was divided into seven regional Bell operating companies (plus some independents) in charge of local phone service, and a potentially unlimited number of long-distance carriers, it was evident to all that interconnection was at the heart of the phone system. This did not mean there was no place for regulation—merely that many of the things the FCC used to regulate could in fact be competitive markets. What stood in their way for seventy years was the fact that these different products and services were bundled and sold together.

   Broadband Internet access is not precisely analogous to telecommunications, of course. But cable regulators should learn one important lesson from the history of telecommunications regulation: if we let natural monopoly services be bundled together with potentially competitive services, we will end up having to regulate not only the monopoly services but the competitive ones as well. Thus, it is ironic that the FCC now seems willing to allow cable companies to tie their natural monopoly service to a competitive one. Ironic because in the name of deregulation, the FCC is embarking upon a course of action that will lead in the end to more regulation, and what is worse, to unnecessary regulation. If one is generally predisposed to keep the government's hands off the market, this is exactly the wrong way to go about it.

CONCLUSION

Everyone seems to agree about one important fact: We know less than we should about how this market functions. Ten years ago, no one would have predicted how network architecture would matter to the Internet; as late as 1995, Microsoft itself confessed it had missed the significance of the Internet. We are faced in the Internet with a phenomenon we do not fully understand, but that has produced an extraordinary economic boom.

In the face of this uncertainty, the question we should ask is what presumptions we should make about how this market is functioning. In our view, these assumptions should reflect the design principles of the Internet. The Internet has been such a fast-growing network because it has enabled extraordinarily innovative competition. It has been architected, through the e2e design, to enable this competition. This principle of the initial Internet should guide the government in evaluating changes to the Internet's architecture, or acquisitions that threaten to change this effective architecture. The presumption should be against changes that would interfere with this e2e design. The aim should be to keep the footprint of monopoly power as small as it can be, so as to minimize the threats to innovation.

These principles should guide the FCC in the context of mergers and regulations affecting ownership of significant aspects of the Internet. If a regulated entity threatens to force the adoption of an architecture that is inconsistent with the Internet's basic design, and if that action affects a significant portion of a relevant Internet market, then the burden should be on the party taking that action to justify this deviation from the Internet's default design. The presumption should be against deviating from these principles.

As with any principle, these presumptions should apply unless there is clear evidence that displacing them in a particular case would be benign. The burden should not be upon those who would defend the existing design. The existing design has done quite enough to defend itself. If there is good reason to allow AT&T, Time Warner, and others to change the cable network into a version of the old telephone network, it is incumbent on those who seek this change to justify a return to the past. In our view, the cable industry has not come close to meeting that burden.

ENDNOTES

[1] Broadband Internet access is a term of art that refers to high-speed Internet access provided over either cable modems, high-bandwidth satellite transmissions, or a Digital Subscriber Line (DSL) configured telephone wire

[2] Cf. Mitchell Kapor, Where Is the Digital Highway Really Heading, WIRED, July–Aug. 1993, available at http://www.wired.com/wired/archive/1.03/kapor.on.nii_pr.html. For later criticism of this approach, see Evan I. Schwartz, People Are Supposed to Pay for This Stuff?, WIRED, July 1995, available at http://www.wired.com/wired/archive/3.07/cable.html.

[3] See Comments of SBC Communications Inc. at 14, *In re* Applications of Am. Online, Inc. & Time Warner Inc. for Transfers of Control (FCC Apr. 26, 2000) (No. 00-30), *available* *at* http://gullfoss2.fcc.gov/prod/ecfs/retrieve.cgi?native_or_pdf=pdf&id_document=6011257512. There are other possible sources of broadband communications competition. Both wireless and satellite communications can conceivably be used for broadband Internet access. To date, however, there has been little deployment of these technologies that is both two-way and offers significant bandwidth. Nonetheless, these wireless technologies certainly bear watching as potential forms of competition.

[4] Time Warner has announced its intention to merge with America Online (AOL), the world's largest Internet service provider (ISP). AOL, which formerly opposed bundling by cable companies, withdrew its opposition after the merger was announced, leading to speculation that the merged entity might require bundling. *See, e.g.*, Peter S. Goodman & Craig Timberg, *AOL Ends Lobbying for Open Access*, WASH. POST, Feb. 12, 2000, at A1. When pressured by Congress in hearings on the merger, the companies said there would be no "fixed limit" on the number of ISPs that could connect, but refused to make a binding commitment. *AOL, Time Warner Vow on ISP Access to Broadband Cable Seen as Positive Step*, 5 ELECTRONIC COMM. & L. REP. 239 (2000). More recently, after further regulatory pressure, AOL said it would be willing to open part of its bandwidth to some (but not all) competing ISPs. It finally reached a deal with the Federal Trade Commission (FTC) in November 2000 to open access to a significant number of ISPs under government supervision.

[5] *In re* Am. Online, Inc. & Time Warner Inc., No. C-3989, 2000 WL 1843019 (FTC Dec. 14, 2000).

[6] See François Bar & Christian Sandvig, Rules from Truth: Post-Convergence Policy for Access (Sept. 2000) (unpublished manuscript, on file with authors) (noting the accidental nature of different regulatory schemes in an era of convergent technologies).

[7] *See* David P. Reed et al., *Commentaries on "Active Networking and End-to-End Arguments,"* 12 IEEE NETWORK 66, 69–71, *available at* http://ieeexplore.ieee.org/iel4/65/15117/00690972.pdf (May–June 1998).

[8] *See* Written *Ex Parte* of Professor Mark A. Lemley and Professor Lawrence Lessig, *In re* Application for Consent to the Transfer of Control of Licenses MediaOne Group, Inc. to AT&T Corp. (FCC Dec. 15, 1999) (No. 99-251), *reprinted in* Mark A.

Lemley & Lawrence Lessig, *Open Access to Cable Modems*, 22 WHITTIER L. REV. 3 (2000).

⁹ *See, e.g.*, Written *Ex Parte* of Professor James B. Speta at 1, *In re* Application for Consent to the Transfer of Control of Licenses MediaOne Group, Inc. to AT&T Corp. (FCC Dec. 15, 1999) (No. 99-251), *available at* http://www.law.nwu.edu/faculty/fulltime/speta/papers/fcccomments.pdf [hereinafter Speta, *Ex Parte*]; Mark Cooper, *Open Access to the Broadband Internet: Technical and Economic Discrimination in Closed, Proprietary Networks*, 71 U. COLO. L. REV. 1011 (2000); James B. Speta, *The Vertical Dimension of Cable Open Access*, 71 U. COLO. L. REV. 975 (2000) [hereinafter Speta, *The Vertical Dimension*]; Phil Weiser, *Competing Paradigms in Telecommunications Regulation*, 71 U. COLO. L. REV. 819 (2000). For an analysis very similar to our own, see François Bar et al., *Defending the Internet Revolution in the Broadband Era: When Doing Nothing Is Doing Harm*, BRIE Publications, *at* http://brie.berkeley.edu/~briewww/pubs/wp/wp137.html (Aug. 1999).

¹⁰ "Open access" has become a contentious and ill-defined term. We discuss what we believe it means *infra* notes 139–142 and accompanying text.

¹¹ *See* J.H. Saltzer et al., *End-to-End Arguments in System Design*, *available at* http://web.mit.edu/Saltzer/www/publications/endtoend/endtoend.pdf (Apr. 8, 1981), *reprinted in* INNOVATION IN NETWORKING 195–206 (Craig Partridge ed., 1988).

¹² Reed et al., *supra* note 7, at 70.

¹³ *Id.* Note that the initial Advanced Research Projects Agency Network (ARPANET) did not implement end-to-end (e2e) perfectly into its design. It was because of changes in the 1970s, suggested by Vince Cerf and David P. Reed, that the network we now recognize as the Internet conformed to e2e.

¹⁴ *See infra* notes 96–99 and accompanying text.

¹⁵ *See* United States v. AT&T, 552 F. Supp. 131 (D.D.C. 1982), *aff'd sub nom.* Maryland v. United States, 460 U.S. 1001 (1983).

¹⁶ *See In re* Use of the Carterfone Device in Message Toll Tel. Serv., 13 F.C.C.2d 420 (1968); *see also* Hush-A-Phone Corp. v. United States, 238 F.2d 266 (D.C. Cir. 1956).

¹⁷ *See* John Naughton, A BRIEF HISTORY OF THE FUTURE: FROM RADIO DAYS TO INTERNET YEARS IN A LIFETIME 106–07 (1999).

¹⁸ *Id.* at 107. Katie Hafner and Matthew Lyon recount a similar resistance. *See* KATIE HAFNER & MATTHEW LYON, WHERE WIZARDS STAY UP LATE 52–66 (1996).

¹⁹ *See* Regulatory Auth. For Telecomms. & Posts, *Technical Telecoms Regulation*, *at* http://www.regtp.de/en/ (last modified Mar. 9, 2001).

²⁰ For discussions of the history of telecommunications deregulation and its lessons for the modern day, see Tom W. Bell, *The Common Law in Cyberspace*, 97 MICH. L. REV. 1746 (1999); Steve Bickerstaff, *Shackles on the Giant: How the Federal Government Created Microsoft, Personal Computers, and the Internet*, 78 TEX. L. REV. 1 (1999); Jim Chen, *The Magnificent Seven: American Telephony's Deregulatory Shootout*, 50 HASTINGS L.J. 1503 (1999); Jim Chen, *Titanic Telecommunications*, 25 SW. U. L. REV. 535 (1996); and Bar et al., *supra* note 9.

[21] *See Carterfone*, 13 F.C.C.2d 420; *see also Hush-A-Phone Corp.*, 238 F.2d 266 (reversing a Federal Communications Commission (FCC) order that had prevented the use of a product that would compete with Bell system equipment).

[22] *See* United States v. AT&T, 552 F. Supp. 131 (D.D.C. 1982), *aff'd sub nom.* Maryland v. United States, 460 U.S. 1001 (1983).

[23] The government has eliminated price regulation and has opened markets to competition subject to open access requirements in other industries as well, notably in the energy industry. *See, e.g.,* Joseph D. Kearney & Thomas W. Merrill, *The Great Transformation of Regulated Industries Law*, 98 COLUM. L. REV. 1323 (1998). While the history of energy deregulation is well beyond the scope of this Article, it is worth noting that open access in telecommunications is hardly sui generis.

[24] *See* Robert M. Fano, *On the Social Role of Computer Communications*, PROC. IEEE, Nov. 1972, at 1249, *reprinted in* PROC. IEEE, Dec. 1999, at 2130.

[25] For background on these movements, see Free Software Foundation, Inc., *GNU's Not Unix!—the GNU Project and the Free Software Foundation (FSF)*, *at* http://www.gnu.org (last modified June 28, 2001).

[26] For information about Minitel (in French), see France Telecom Intelmatique, *Si Vous Êtes en France, Utilisez le Minitel Nouvelle Génération*, *at* http://www.minitel.fr (last visited Jan. 29, 2001).

[27] *See generally* James Daly, *101 Ways to Save Apple*, WIRED, June 1997, *available at* http://www.wired.com/wired/archive/5.06/apple.html (referring to the well-worn criticism of Apple for failing to open its operating system).

[28] Charles R. Morris & Charles H. Ferguson, *How Architecture Wins Technology Wars*, HARV. BUS. REV., Mar.–Apr. 1993, at 86, 88–89.

[29] The Internet delivers data in discrete packets that are independently routed, while the telephone network dedicates entire circuits to real-time communication. The former is called "packet switching," and the latter "circuit switching." *See, e.g.,* JOSHUA EDDINGS, HOW THE INTERNET WORKS 19 (1994).

[30] For a detailed discussion of these changes, see, for example, David D. Clark & Marjory S. Blumenthal, Rethinking the Design of the Internet: The End to End Arguments vs. the Brave New World (Aug. 10, 2000) (unpublished manuscript, on file with authors); and Hans Kruse et al., *The InterNAT: Policy Implications of the Internet Architecture Debate*, Proceedings of the 28th Research Conference on Communication, Information and Internet Policy, *at* http://www.csm.ohiou.edu/kruse/publications/InterNAT_v4.pdf (last visited Mar. 16, 2001).

[31] *See* Clark & Blumenthal, *supra* note 30, at 11–12.

[32] Bar & Sandvig, *supra* note 6, at 22.

[33] *See* Kevin Werbach, A Layered Model for Internet Policy 18 (Aug. 17, 2000) (unpublished manuscript, on file with authors).

[34] *See id.* at 20.

[35] *See id.* at 25–26.

[36] Bar & Sandvig, *supra* note 6, at 22; *see also* Werbach, *supra* note 33, at 26.

[37] Specifically, this is the policy of one of the two largest cable companies in the United States today, AT&T, and would have been the policy of Time Warner after its

merger with AOL if not for the intervention of the FTC. *See supra* note 4 and accompanying text.

[38] See Timothy F. Bresnahan, New Modes of Competition: Implications for the Future Structure of the Computer Industry, at http://www.pff.org/microsoft/bresnahan.html (June 1998).

[39] *Id.*

[40] *Id.*

[41] These limitations are imposed by @Home Corporation. *See* @Home Corp., *@Home Acceptable Use Policy, at* http://www.home.com/support/aup/ (last modified May 8, 2000); @Home Corp., *@Home Frequently Asked Questions, at* http://www.home.com/qa.html (last visited Jan. 9, 2001).

[42] David Lieberman, *Media Giants' Net Change Major Companies Establish Strong Foothold Online*, USA TODAY, Dec. 14, 1999, at B3 (quoting Daniel Somers).

[43] Bar & Sandvig, *supra* note 6, at 22.

[44] François Bar and others believe these potential developments are so significant they constitute an entirely new "third phase" of the Internet's development. *See* Bar et al., *supra* note 9.

[45] For example, @Home's policy limits the amount of video its consumers can download, limits total upstream traffic, precludes running a server of any sort, and prevents the use of corporate local area networks over the cable connection. *See, e.g., id.* (listing @Home's policies). These policies are presumably driven by bandwidth limitations. We have no evidence on how these policies have been enforced by @Home in practice.

[46] *Cf.* Mark A. Lemley, *The Economics of Improvement in Intellectual Property Law*, 75 TEX. L. REV. 989, 1048–65 (1997) (noting that giving one company the power to centrally coordinate improvements on an existing product is likely to reduce innovation in those improvements). In economic terms, a potential innovator of a product that must interoperate with a bottleneck monopolist faces reduced incentive to innovate compared to an innovator facing a competitive industry. This is true because the innovator's only option in the bottleneck setting is to sell out to the monopolist, who in this case will act as a monopsonist in the market for the innovation. It is well established that monopsonists purchase products at artificially low prices. *See* HERBERT HOVENKAMP, FEDERAL ANTITRUST POLICY: THE LAW OF COMPETITION AND ITS PRACTICE 14 (1994).

[47] *See* Kruse et al., *supra* note 30, at 18–20; *cf.* Lawrence Lessig & Paul Resnick, *Zoning Speech on the Internet: A Legal and Technical Model*, 98 MICH. L. REV. 395 (1999).

[48] *See generally* LAWRENCE LESSIG, CODE AND OTHER LAWS OF CYBERSPACE (1999) (making this architectural point on a number of different fronts).

[49] We address these arguments in more detail *infra* Part III.A.2.

[50] *See* DEBORAH A. LATHEN, CABLE SERVICES BUREAU, BROADBAND TODAY 43 (1999), *available at* http://www.fcc.gov/Bureaus/Cable/Reports/broadbandtoday.pdf.

[51] *See* James B. Speta, *Handicapping the Race for the Last Mile?: A Critique of Open Access Rules for Broadband Platforms*, 17 YALE J. ON REG. 39, 76 (2000).

Others have endorsed this theory as well. *See* Weiser, *supra* note 9, at 834 (calling Speta's argument "persuasive").

[52] Speta, *supra* note 51, at 76.

[53] *Id.*

[54] *Id.* at 78.

[55] Speta, The Vertical Dimension, supra note 9, at 997.

[56] Interestingly, the cable companies themselves periodically say that they would be fools to close the ISP market to competition. *See* Weiser, *supra* note 9, at 834 n.65 (quoting statements of AT&T Chief Executive Officer Michael Armstrong). It is worth taking these comments with a rather large grain of salt. Not only were they made while the cable companies were trying to persuade Congress and the FCC to allow them to merge, but they don't reflect what the cable companies are actually doing. Neither AT&T nor Time Warner has opened access to ISPs. The few concessions they have made have been as a result of regulatory, not market, pressure. *See, e.g.*, Cooper, *supra* note 9, at 1029–32, 1036–40. And AOL, which used to be the chief proponent of open ISP competition over cable modems, changed its tune once it agreed to merge with Time Warner. *See, e.g., id.* at 1040.

[57] Mark Cooper makes the same point. *See* Cooper, *supra* note 9, at 1030–31.

[58] Indeed, the vertical integration of cable companies and ISPs, as has happened with AT&T and is currently happening with Time Warner and AOL, is merely an efficient means of capturing this revenue stream.

[59] *See* Jean-Jacques Laffont & Jean Tirole, COMPETITION IN TELECOMMUNICATIONS 161–73 (2000).

[60] For a detailed discussion of network effects, see Joseph Farrell & Garth Saloner, *Standardization, Compatibility, and Innovation*, 16 RAND J. ECON. 70 (1985); Michael L. Katz & Carl Shapiro, *Network Externalities, Competition, and Compatibility*, 75 AM. ECON. REV. 424 (1985); and S.J. Liebowitz & Stephen E. Margolis, *Network Externality: An Uncommon Tragedy*, J. ECON. PERSP., Spring 1994, at 133. For a discussion in the legal context, see Mark A. Lemley & David McGowan, *Legal Implications of Network Economic Effects*, 86 CAL. L. REV. 479 (1998).

[61] *See, e.g.*, BEHAVIORAL LAW AND ECONOMICS (Cass R. Sunstein ed., 2000); Jennifer Arlen, *The Future of Behavioral Economic Analysis of Law*, 51 VAND. L. REV. 1765 (1998); Samuel Issacharoff, *Can There Be a Behavioral Law and Economics?*, 51 VAND. L. REV. 1729 (1998); Russell Korobkin, *Inertia and Preference in Contract Negotiation: The Psychological Power of Default Rules and Form Terms*, 51 VAND. L. REV. 1583 (1998); Russell B. Korobkin & Thomas S. Ulen, *Law and Behavioral Science: Removing the Rationality Assumption from Law and Economics*, 88 CAL. L. REV. 1051 (2000); Jeffrey J. Rachlinski, *The New Law and Psychology: A Reply to Critics, Skeptics, and Cautious Supporters*, 85 CORNELL L. REV. 739 (2000).

[62] For a review of this literature, see Robert P. Merges, *Rent Control in the Patent District: Observations on the Grady-Alexander Thesis*, 78 VA. L. REV. 359, 371–73 (1992), which collects economic literature suggesting that a company with a successful invention will choose to focus on one or two basic applications of that invention, rather than investing money and effort on researching implications of its invention that lie outside its core competencies.

[63] Companies might also be less likely to act rationally in monopoly settings because they do not face the discipline of the market.

[64] *See supra* note 17 and accompanying text.

[65] Thus, Carl Shapiro explains that exclusive dealing should be of greater, not less, antitrust concern in network markets. *See* Carl Shapiro, *Exclusivity in Network Industries*, 7 GEO. MASON L. REV. 673 (1999); *cf.* Joseph Farrell, *Creating Local Competition*, 49 FED. COMM. L.J. 201, 203– 04 (1996) (pointing out that the Bell System's exclusion of rivals who wanted to interconnect benefited it on balance, even though it reduced the aggregate network benefits).

[66] We assume here that broadband Internet access is a separate market from narrowband access. Whether this is true as an economic matter depends on the cross-elasticity of supply between broadband and narrowband services. Treating broadband and narrowband separately seems intuitive to us, given the different uses to which the two will be put, but in any event it is explained more rigorously in Bar et al., *supra* note 9. *See also* Marcus Maher, Comment, *Cable Internet Unbundling: Local Leadership in the Deployment High Speed Access*, 52 FED. COMM. L.J. 211, 219–21(1999).

[67] A good summary of broadband services can be found in Speta, *supra* note 51, at 48–61.

[68] *See* LATHEN, *supra* note 50, at 34.

[69] See Daniel L. Rubinfeld & Hal J. Singer, Vertical Foreclosure in High Technology Industries: A Case Study of the AOL Time Warner Merger, 16 BERKELEY TECH. L.J. tbl.2 (forthcoming 2001); see also Cable Takes the Early Lead, INDUSTRY STANDARD, Oct. 11, 1999, at 119 (80 percent). For a higher estimate, see Randy Barrett, Cable, Phone Lines in Battle for Supremacy, INTER@CTIVE WEEK, Jan. 25, 1999, at 69, and Bar et al., supra note 9 (94 percent). By contrast, cable is not widely deployed in the business market, because the existing cable lines are virtually all residential.

[70] It is clearly correct that broadband services are just beginning. The vast majority of Internet users are narrowband users. Thus, the situation in several years could possibly look very different.

[71] *See* Bar et al., *supra* note 9 (noting that as of 1999, 40–50 percent of local telephone loops would not support DSL).

[72] It is generally *not* the case that DSL providers open their lines to multiple ISPs. Rather, the competition that exists in DSL is proxy competition that results from the FCC's requirement that local exchange carriers permit competing DSL providers to collocate their equipment on phone company premises.

[73] Daniel Shih makes the perverse argument that we should eliminate ISP competition in cable in order to make noncable methods of data transmission more attractive by comparison. *See* Daniel Shih, Comment, *Open Access or Forced Access: Should the FCC Impose Open Access on Cable-Based Internet Service Providers?*, 52 ADMIN. L. REV. 793, 807 (2000). Far from being an argument against open access, we think the market attractiveness of openness proves our point.

[74] See, e.g., Thomas G. Krattenmaker & L.A. Powe, Jr., Converging First Amendment Principles for Converging Communications Media, 104 YALE L.J. 1719 (1995).

[75] *See* Jerry A. Hausman & J. Gregory Sidak, *A Consumer-Welfare Approach to the Mandatory Unbundling of Telecommunications Networks*, 109 YALE L.J. 417, 489–90 (1999) ("Because cable companies' lines currently pass more than ninety-five percent of U.S. homes, it follows that mandatory unbundling of the ILECs' [(incumbent local exchange carriers')] broadband networks is not necessary for competition in broadband services, nor would competition be impaired if the ILECs' broadband networks were not unbundled."). Why this "follows," the authors do not explain. *See also* Howard A. Shelanski, *The Speed Gap: Broadband Infrastructure and Electronic Commerce*, 14 BERKELEY TECH. L.J. 721, 743 n.99 (1999) ("There is intuitive appeal to the argument that if providers of one major broadband technology (cable modem) are not regulated, nor should the providers of the competing (DSL) technology be.").

[76] Stuart Minor Benjamin, *Proactive Legislation and the First Amendment*, 99 MICH L. REV. (forthcoming 2000).

[77] *See id.*

[78] *See generally id.*

[79] Harold Feld effectively deconstructs the idea that the owners of cable lines ipso facto have a first amendment right to control ISP choice over those lines, an argument that if accepted would require us to eliminate the entire concept of common carriers in telephony as well. *See* Harold Feld, *Whose Line Is It Anyway? The First Amendment and Cable Open Access*, 8 COMMLAW CONSPECTUS 23 (2000). For this reason, we are not persuaded by Raymond Ku's argument that the First Amendment must protect both ISPs and cable companies, or neither. *See* Raymond Shih Ray Ku, *Open Internet Access and Freedom of Speech: A First Amendment Catch-22*, 75 TUL. L. REV. 87 (2000). We don't see the case for open access as a first amendment argument at all, but rather as an antitrust and regulatory issue. We note, however, that one district court has come to a different conclusion, striking down a local "open access" ordinance on first amendment grounds. *See* Comcast Cablevision v. Broward County, 124 F. Supp. 2d 685 (S.D. Fla. 2000).

[80] 512 U.S. 622 (1994) [hereinafter *Turner I*]; Turner Broad. Sys., Inc. v. FCC, 520 U.S. 180 (1997).

[81] *See Turner I*, 512 U.S. at 662.

[82] Clayton Act, Pub. L. No. 98-443, § 7, 98 Stat. 1708 (1984) (codified at 15 U.S.C. § 18 (1994)); *see also* Cargill, Inc. v. Monfort of Colo., Inc., 479 U.S. 104, 124–25 (1986) (Stevens, J., dissenting) (analyzing the legislative history of section 7 of the Clayton Act).

[83] To be fair, we acknowledge that it is similarly difficult to prove the positive—that innovation occurred only because of the structure of the Internet.

[84] *See infra* Arguments Against Permitting ISP Competition.

[85] Indeed, the only credible argument that closing access is a good thing at all is that it gives needed incentives to cable companies. We discuss that argument in the next part.

[86] *See* Shelanski, *supra* note 75, at 739.

[87] Speta, *The Vertical Dimension*, *supra* note 9, at 995. Speta continues:" If the price is unregulated, then cable companies should experience increased profits with open access. If the price they may charge for access is limited, however, then cable

companies may in fact experience decreased profits, and price controls could well affect a cable operator's willingness to provide new, upgraded services." .*Id.*; *see also* Speta, *supra* note 51, at 87 ("[O]pen access rules that attempt to mimic perfectly competitive markets may decrease the broadband access provider's incentives to deploy the platforms in the first instance."); Weiser, *supra* note 9, at 830 ("Imposing an unbundling mandate on cable modems . . . will undoubtedly deter investment in those areas—after all, why invest in new facilities, intellectual property, or a customer base when you will not be able to appropriate all returns on this investment?"); GLENN WOROCH, ECONOMIC IMPACTS OF OPEN ACCESS RULES ON THE RACE TO DEPLOY BROADBAND INFRASTRUCTURE (working paper 2001, on file with authors).

A curious variant of this argument is that cable companies must be able to control ISP access in order to make the cable companies themselves more valuable and, therefore, more attractive targets for acquisition by others. *See* Shih, *supra* note 73, at 806.

[88] *See* Speta, *supra* note 51, at 83 ("[V]ertical integration of access providers may be necessary. Especially in initial periods of deployment, broadband access providers must ensure a supply of complementary information services. . . . [A] broadband provider must either provide those goods itself or arrange for a source of supply."). Speta goes on to argue that internal content development by cable companies might be more efficient and that it may serve to guarantee the existence of goods that take advantage of broadband services. *See id.*

[89] *See* LATHEN, *supra* note 50, at 45.

[90] *See* Speta apparently assumes that cable companies will open their lines to all ISPs at a monopoly price. *See* Speta, *The Vertical Dimension*, *supra* note 9, at 995. This is implausible, however. In the first place, charging a monopoly price to ISPs to permit them to interconnect will necessarily exclude some ISPs from the market. If it did not restrict provision of ISP services, it would not be a monopoly price. Second, the cable company can maximize revenue from the ISP market by choosing one ISP, not by taking money from many different ISPs. Granted, the ISP it chooses might be the most efficient one—and therefore the one able to pay it the most money. But that does not mean consumers will be as well off as they would be under competitive conditions. And in fact, cable companies will probably have incentives to do what AT&T has done—use the ISP they already own.

[91] *See* Robert H. Bork, THE ANTITRUST PARADOX: A POLICY AT WAR WITH ITSELF 372–74 (1978).

[92] If not, there is no additional incentive provided by bundling that cable companies could not achieve in a competitive ISP market.

[93] *See* Info. Infrastructure Task Force, INTELLECTUAL PROPERTY AND THE NATIONAL INFORMATION INFRASTRUCTURE: THE REPORT OF THE WORKING GROUP ON INTELLECTUAL PROPERTY RIGHTS (1995).

[94] *See* Bar et al., *supra* note 9 (noting the substantial profits that cable companies are making now and the limited cost associated with broadband cable "build-out"). It is worth noting that Shelanski makes his argument primarily in the context of telephone, not cable, incentives. *See* Shelanski, *supra* note 75, at 739; *cf.* Thomas M. Jorde et al.,

Innovation, Investment, and Unbundling, 17 YALE J. ON REG. 1 (2000) (making a similar argument against unbundling requirements in telecommunications).

[95] *See, e.g.*, Glenn A. Woroch, Competition's Effect on Investment in Digital Infrastructure (1999) (unpublished manuscript, on file with the authors). Harry M. Shooshan and others present evidence that capital investment in telecommunications infrastructure increased dramatically after the break-up of AT&T, a fact at odds with the infrastructure investment argument. *See* Harry M. Shooshan III et al., *MaCable.com: Closed v. Open Models for the Broadband Internet, at* http://www.spri.com/pdf/reports/opennet/macable.pdf (Oct. 15, 1999).

[96] JOSEPH A. SCHUMPETER, CAPITALISM, SOCIALISM, AND DEMOCRACY 106 (1st ed. 1942). Strictly speaking, this is only one interpretation of Joseph Schumpeter's classic work, one that might be termed "East-coast Schumpeterianism." By contrast, "West-coast Schumpeterians" are more skeptical of the value of monopoly over competition in inducing innovation.

[97] *See* Kenneth J. Arrow, *Economic Welfare and the Allocation of Resources for Invention*, in THE RATE AND DIRECTION OF INVENTIVE ACTIVITY 609, 620 (Nat'l Bureau of Econ. Research ed., 1962), *reprinted in* 5 KENNETH J. ARROW, COLLECTED PAPERS OF KENNETH J. ARROW: PRODUCTION AND CAPITAL 104, 115 (1985). For a nice discussion of the debate in the context of telecommunications policy, see Jim Chen, *Standing in the Shadows of Giants: The Role of Intergenerational Equity in Telecommunications Reform*, 71 U. COLO. L. REV. 921, 947–51 (2000).

[98] For arguments in favor of allowing one central party to coordinate the market for subsequent improvements, see Edmund W. Kitch, *The Nature and Function of the Patent System*, 20 J.L. & ECON. 265 (1977). Doug Lichtman recently argued that facilitating competition in goods complementary to a network market is actually undesirable because it results in a price that is too high given the network effects. He proposes that the network monopolist be permitted to control the market for complementary goods in order to coerce a lower price in that market. *See* Douglas Lichtman, *Property Rights in Emerging Platform Technologies*, 29 J. LEGAL STUD. 615 (2000). If Lichtman is correct—and we are not persuaded that any system manufacturer that has actually sought to control complementary goods has done so in order to *reduce* prices—his argument would be a reason to oppose reverse engineering in one specific class of cases: complementary goods to strong network markets. *But see* Jeffrey Church & Neil Gandal, *Systems Competition, Vertical Merger, and Foreclosure*, 9 J. ECON. & MGMT. STRATEGY 1 (2000) (arguing that control by a hardware manufacturer over complementary software goods leads to monopolization of the complementary goods and higher prices). It is not clear, however, that the markets Lichtman discusses bear much resemblance to this one, a point on which Lichtman would likely agree.

[99] For arguments against giving an initial inventor control over subsequent improvements, see Lemley, *supra* note 46, at 1042–72, and Robert P. Merges & Richard R. Nelson, *On the* Complex Economics of Patent Scope, 90 COLUM. L. REV. 839 (1990).

[100] See Howard A. Shelanski, Competition and Deployment of New Technology in U.S. Telecommunications, 2000 U. CHI. LEGAL F. 85.

[101] We should emphasize here that this conclusion has no direct bearing on the very different question of intellectual property incentives. Intellectual property grants incentives to invent by promising *future* market control in the invented product; it has nothing to say about the structure of the market in which the putative inventor operates ex ante.

[102] *See* Shelanski, *supra* note 100, at 98–99, 104, 110. Shelanski cautions that it is difficult to compare the deployment paths of different innovations and that his data cannot itself be taken as proof of causation. It is also worth noting that cable industry advocates have recently taken to arguing that DSL is "fast-growing" and therefore providing cable companies with a significant source of facilities based competition. *See, e.g.*, Milo Medin, Executive Vice President of Excite@Home, Presentation to Regulating on the Technological Edge (Oct. 20, 2000). But the growth of DSL belies the argument that monopoly incentives are necessary to induce investment, because DSL is subject to open access requirements.

[103] Shelanski, *supra* note 100, at 94–96 (collecting data from prior studies).

[104] *See infra* Part III.C.2.

[105] Ch. 652, 48 Stat. 1064 (codified as amended at 47 U.S.C. §§ 151–613 (1994)).

[106] *See* Speta, *The Vertical Dimension*, *supra* note 9, at 989–90. The relevant statutory provision is 47 U.S.C. § 522(6).

[107] 47 U.S.C. § 541(c).

[108] See Speta, The Vertical Dimension, supra note 9, at 990.

[109] For an argument that the Communications Act actually compels open access to cable modems, see Earl W. Comstock & John W. Butler, *Access Denied: The FCC's Failure to Implement Open Access to Cable as Required by the Communications Act*, 8 COMMLAW CONSPECTUS 5 (2000).

[110] *See id.* at 13–17; Jason Whiteley, AT&T Corp. v. City of Portland*: Classifying "Internet Over Cable" in the "Open Access" Fight*, 2000 BYU L. REV. 451 (arguing that cable modems are not a "cable service," and should instead be regulated as a telecommunication service).

[111] 216 F.3d 871 (9th Cir. 2000).

[112] *Id.* at 876.

[113] *See id.* at 876–77.

[114] *See id.* at 879. Jim Chen has penned a thoughtful and scholarly analysis of this problem. *See* Jim Chen, *The Authority to Regulate Broadband Internet Access Over Cable*, 16 BERKELEY TECH. L.J. (forthcoming 2001). Chen flatly rejects the argument that broadband cable access is a "cable service" within the meaning of the Telecommunications Act of 1996, Pub. L. No. 104-104, 110 Stat. 56 (codified at 47 U.S.C. §§ 151–614 (Supp. II 1997)). Rather, he believes that broadband services are best characterized as an "advanced telecommunications capability" under section 706(c)(1) of the Telecommunications Act.

[115] See Speta, The Vertical Dimension, supra note 9, at 990.

[116] *See id.* at 991

[117] *See, e.g.*, Hausman & Sidak, *supra* note 75, at 467; Weiser, *supra* note 9, at 830 (assuming that open access advocates need "[t]o establish that cable modems constitute an essential facility"); *see also* Speta, *Ex Parte*, *supra* note 9, at 8–12 (arguing

against our regulatory filing on the grounds that AT&T does not control an essential facility). On the essential facilities doctrine in antitrust law generally, see IIIA PHILIP AREEDA & HERBERT HOVENKAMP, ANTITRUST LAW ¶¶ 772–74 (1996). To be fair, Weiser goes on to acknowledge that other, nonantitrust arguments can be based on the principle of interconnection, not on an essential facilities argument. *See* Weiser, *supra* note 9, at 835. He does not discuss tying, however.

[118] Some have suggested that the traditional models of neoclassical economics overstate the possibility of competition in the telecommunications industries because of their static assumptions. *See* Ashutosh Bhagwat, *Unnatural Competition?: Applying the New Antitrust Learning to Foster Competition in the Local Exchange*, 50 HASTINGS L.J. 1479 (1999).

[119] *See, e.g.*, Eastman Kodak Co. v. Image Technical Servs., Inc., 504 U.S. 451 (1992); Jefferson Parish Hosp. Dist. No. 2 v. Hyde, 466 U.S. 2 (1984).

[120] *But cf.* United States v. Microsoft Corp., 147 F.3d 935, 950 (D.C. Cir. 1998) (crediting Microsoft with a contrary argument that there is a benefit to integrating a Web browser with an operating system).

[121] It is possible, of course, that the tying product could be defined more broadly for these purposes, including other forms of wires into the home. Even if the market were defined to include all broadband access points, however, the evidence suggests that cable has a dominant share of that broader market too. *See supra* note 69 (noting a market share of 70–94 percent). And certainly cable companies have a monopoly over broadband access in the significant parts of the country where DSL access is unavailable

[122] Under current law, even a dangerous probability of monopolization of the tied market is not required. *See Jefferson Parish Hosp.*, 466 U.S. 2.

[123] Rubinfeld and Singer's model of the AOL–Time Warner demonstrates significant anticompetitive effects in the ISP market resulting from the merger absent an open access condition. *See* Rubinfeld & Singer, *supra* note 69.

[124] *See* BORK, *supra* note 91, at 373–74.

[125] See Louis Kaplow, Extension of Monopoly Power Through Leverage, 85 COLUM. L. REV. 515 (1985).

[126] *See also* Herbert Hovenkamp, *Antitrust Policy After Chicago*, 84 MICH. L. REV. 213 (1985).

[127] Admittedly, cable programming service is no longer subject to general price regulation. However, cable programming services are regulated in a variety of other ways. While the incentives to leverage in order to escape nonprice regulation are presumably less than the incentives to escape price regulation, they might still be greater than zero.

[128] 708 F.2d 1081 (7th Cir. 1983).

[129] *See* United States v. AT&T, 552 F. Supp. 131 (D.D.C. 1982), *aff'd sub nom.* Maryland v. United States, 460 U.S. 1001 (1983).

[130] Farrell, *supra* note 65, at 207; *see also* Roger G. Noll & Bruce M. Owen, *The Anticompetitive Uses of Regulation: United States v. AT&T, in* THE ANTITRUST REVOLUTION 290 (John E. Kwoka, Jr. & Lawrence J. White eds., 1989).

[131] William Baxter was the head of the Antitrust Division of the U.S. Department of Justice who oversaw the break-up of AT&T.

[132] *See* Speta, *supra* note 51, at 85.

[133] Open Access Comments of America Online, Inc., before the Department of Telecommunications and Information Services of San Francisco, Cal., Oct. 27, 1999, at 5.

[134] *Id.* at 19.

[135] *See* Shawn O'Donnell, Broadband Architectures, ISP Business Plans, and Open Access 2 (Sept. 25, 2000) (unpublished manuscript, on file with authors) (coming to this conclusion).

[136] *See id.*

[137] *See* David Reed, Presentation to Regulating on the Technological Edge, Berkeley Center for Research on Telecommunications Policy (Oct. 20, 2000). This David Reed works for Cable Labs, and is not the same as the David Reed cited above as a coauthor with Jerome H. Salzer and David C. Clark.

[138] *See* O'Donnell, *supra* note 135, at 2.

[139] For example, Speta clearly seems to assume that "open access" or "unbundling" in this context carries with it all of the baggage of traditional cost-of-service regulation. *See* Speta, *supra* note 51, at 85. Indeed, Speta suggests in a later paper that the economics of cable modems "suggest only an interconnection obligation, not the 'open access' rules being pushed." James B. Speta, A Common Carrier Approach to Internet Interconnection 2 (Sept. 2000) (unpublished manuscript, on file with authors). We think Speta misunderstands what advocates of cable open access are actually asking for. An obligation to interconnect ISPs is precisely the heart of open access.

[140] Pub. L. No. 104-104, 110 Stat. 56 (codified at 47 U.S.C. §§ 151–614 (Supp. II 1997)).

[141] *See* Christopher K. Ridder, AT&T Corp. v. City of Portland, 15 BERKELEY TECH. L.J. 397, 409–12 (2000) (arguing that "open access" isn't the equivalent of common carriage); Bar et al., *supra* note 9.

[142] *See* Cooper, *supra* note 9, at 1023 (noting that cities "have not sought to impose full common carriage obligations on broadband internet services"). To be sure, Bar and others point out that merely nondiscriminatory pricing may not be sufficient should the cable company decide to price its captive ISP services below cost. *See* Bar et al., *supra* note 9. But there are other antitrust remedies for such an act.

[143] *See, e.g.*, Thomas G. Krattenmaker & Lucas A. Powe, Jr., REGULATING BROADCAST PROGRAMMING 237–96 (1994).

[144] *See, e.g.*, Bar et al., *supra* note 9 (citing comments by FCC Chairman William Kennard that his mandate was to "do no harm").

[145] *See In re* Policy & Rule Concerning Rates for Dominant Carriers, 4 F.C.C.R. 2873, 2882–88 (1989) (reviewing this history); *see also* Farrell, *supra* note 65, at 204–06.

[146] *See In re* Use of the Carterfone Device in Message Toll Tel. Serv., 13 F.C.C.2d 420, 424 (1968); *see also* Hush-A-Phone Corp. v. FCC, 238 F.2d 266, 269 (D.C. Cir. 1956) (allowing attachment of non-AT&T equipment that did not affect the phone or the network).

[147] *See* United States v. AT&T, 552 F. Supp. 131, 227 (D.D.C. 1982), *aff'd sub nom.* Maryland v. United States, 460 U.S. 1001 (1983).

PART II:
EMPIRICAL STUDIES,
THE ROLE OF OPEN ARCHITECTURE
IN STIMULATING INNOVATION

IV. MAKING THE NETWORK CONNECTION

Using Network Theory To Explain The Link Between Open Digital Platforms And Innovation

PURPOSE AND OUTLINE

For almost two decades consumer advocates have been among the leading proponents of open communications networks.[1] Unlike most consumer issues, where price is their central concern, in the matter of communications and the Internet, their primary focus has been on another aspect of market performance, innovation driven by consumer choice. Their analyses have demonstrated the benefits of open communications networks in terms of core Internet services, computer development, and broad spillovers into the economy.[2]

In the last quarter of the twentieth century the convergence of computers, communications and the Internet all deployed under design principles of open architecture created a digital communications platform that has revolutionized the environment for innovation. Nations and industries that seized the opportunity presented by the open digital communications platform have enjoyed much more vigorous economic growth than those that did not.[3] Policy choices that required open architecture and nondiscrimination in access to communications networks played a key role in creating the open communications environment.[4]

Unfortunately, policymakers in the U.S. have not shown a deep appreciation for the fundamental importance of the principle of open communications architecture or the role that policy played in promoting it. In the U.S., federal regulators seem to have accepted the proposition that the owners of advanced telecommunications facilities should no longer be obligated to provide non-discriminatory access to their networks.[5] Federal Communications Commission Chairman Michael Powell has declared four Internet freedoms that he believes must be preserved, but he was unwilling to make them mandatory.[6] Thus, the principle of open architecture in communications networks is still in play. A deeper appreciation of its importance remains vital in the policy debate.

This Chapter argues that allowing network owners to discriminate against communications, content, equipment or applications represents a dramatic change that would render the information environment much less conducive to innovation. "The mere threat of discrimination dramatically affects incentives and *imposes a burden on innovation today.*"[7]

This paper makes the case for open communications networks by combining two recent analytic frameworks. The first perspective highlights the source of the benefits of open communications based on the emerging field of network theory.[8] The second perspective is provided by analysis of network economics – primarily its positive aspects in network effects and feedback loops. Negative concerns about network effects that may enhance the market power and anticompetitive behavior of firms that dominate critical locations in the network are described in a separate paper. By describing the underlying network principles that created the conditions for a technological revolution, the paper endeavors to highlight critical policy decisions that helped to create and sustain the dynamic innovation environment.

The next section briefly outlines the consumer view of open communications networks. It identifies key characteristics that are essential to a dynamic, consumer-friendly information environment and argues that communications networks are a uniquely important platform or "bearer service" that supports and plays a critical role in a broad range of economic activities in the 21st century digital economy. It offers a basic description of the digital communications platform and the positive economic characteristics to which it gave rise. This is the positive externalities side of network economics. The section also offers a longer historical perspective on the role of open communications networks in the development of capitalist economies. It suggests that increasingly interconnected and open communications networks have played an important part in furthering economic growth.

Section II turns to the emerging field of network theory to explain the fundamental institutional underpinning of the dramatic economic developments associated with the open digital communications platform. Across a range of physical and social sciences, this theory offers a policy relevant explanation of robust (successful) institutions based on an understanding of the principles of network architecture. The discussion identifies multiscale connectivity as a key architectural feature of "ultrarobust" networks. This is the central characteristic of the digital communications platform that is critical to the new information environment.

Section III combines the network and Internet analyses in a discussion of innovation in high technology industries. It shows that the transformation of the information environment by the open digital communications platform facilitates and accelerates technological innovation. It argues that the digital communications platform is a critical enabling technology and that interconnection, interoperability and maximization of available functionality to end-users are essential ingredients for the continued flow of dynamic innovation.

Section IV examines the role of Internet Service Providers (ISPs) in the development and penetration of the Internet. One of the most frequent things students of network structure do is count hubs and endpoints. ISPs are the initial hubs on the periphery of the Internet closest to the end-points. ISPs played a critical role in the adoption of Internet services by the public. Moreover, because the focal point of change in the Internet revolution has been at the periphery of the communications network, we should not be surprised to find the most pronounced effect of a change in policy there. Certainly the conflict over open architecture has been centered in a battle between ISPs and network owners. In the context of network theory, ISPs are an obvious target for analysis.

OPEN COMMUNICATIONS AND
THE DIGITAL INFORMATION REVOLUTION

PUBLIC POLICY AND THE INFORMATION REVOLUTION

In the late 1980s, consumer advocates helped push back efforts by the dominant telephone companies to assert control over the Internet through control of the telecommunications network. The consumer advocates believed that there was a critical choice to be made between a centralized and a decentralized approach to providing information services.[9] They warned that the approach advocated by the communications companies "could set the information age development back by undermining the diversified, innovative process of the current decentralized approach."[10] The characteristics of the decentralized approach that the consumer analyses singled out proved to be the essential characteristics of the Internet:

> Pragmatic: Most of these new, innovative services have close substitutes. Why not give individuals maximum flexibility in the choice of equipment and services allowing them to develop applications at the periphery of the network?

> Decentralized: Decentralized decisions will select the most cost-effective technologies for specific applications.

> Periphery: Intelligence is more concentrated in homes and businesses and on the premises of service providers who connect their services through a local transmission network.

> Applications: Specific applications will be required to be cost effective. There will be successes and failures, but the process of trial and error driven by profit will generate lowest cost and minimize public cost risks of network applications.

> Individualized: Costs are more highly individualized, borne by those who develop the applications and those who choose to subscribe to them, either through or around the public network.[11]

The consumer analysis argued that fundamental changes in technology had created the basis for a dynamic information environment. In particular, "the fact that a great deal of the necessary intelligence is currently located on the periphery of the information age network has led to a pragmatic, decentralized pattern of development."[12]

Many participants in the debate over advanced telecommunications services (that underlie high-speed Internet services) have pointed out that for three decades the FCC played a key role in creating the dynamic environment that supported the development of the Internet through policies set in its "Computer Inquiries."[13] In these proceedings, the FCC kept the underlying telecommunications facilities open and available, ensuring that first computer data services, then enhanced services and later information services could grow without the threat of foreclosure or manipulation by network operators. Lawrence Lessig is blunt about the government's role, noting that "[p]hone companies…did not play… games, because they were not allowed to. And they were not allowed to because regulators stopped them."[14] Thus, a determined commitment to open communications networks was critical to the widespread development of the Internet – "The government's activism imposed a principle analogous to [end-to-end] design on the telephone network... By requiring the natural monopoly component at the basic network level to be open to competitors at higher levels, intelligent regulation can minimize the economic disruption caused by that natural monopoly and permit as much competition as industry will allow."[15]

Government activism was also crucial in promoting the spread of the open architecture of the Internet.[16] Not only was a decentralized communications network conceived by an arm of the Defense Department and pushed over the objection of the dominant communications companies, but a requirement that open protocols be used by interconnecting networks as the Internet was rolled out to institutions in civil society led to a deeply embedded open architecture in the Internet.

Telephone companies did not get their way at the start of Internet commercialization. Communications networks remained open and the telephone companies' ability to leverage control over the communications infrastructure remained constrained by public policy. The network was interconnected and accessible to producers and consumers, free from the domination of centralized network operators and not Balkanized by proprietary standards. Decentralized activities and widespread experimentation were encouraged by very few restrictions on use.

What emerged was a digital communications platform comprised of a highly interrelated set of activities in the communications, computer, and information industries. Indeed, technological convergence has blurred the distinction between these activities. In the economics literature, the set of information and communications technologies (ICT) are widely seen as creating not merely a new environment in which information is produced and distributed, but also a revolutionary change in a wide range of economic activities.[17]

After a remarkable decade of commercial success, the open architecture of the Internet was again challenged by the owners of a new telecommunications network – cable operators. Controlling the dominant facilities for advanced telecommunications functionalities, they sought to operate the network on a closed, proprietary basis. Consumer groups were among the first to oppose this effort to abandon the principle of open communications networks:

> Today… [t]here is no bundling of connectivity (telephone service) and content (Internet service). Any Internet service provider can advertise a phone number and be reached by a local phone call. It is that unfettered access that has been the seedbed of Internet creativity. It is that access that is threatened by the closed access model the cable industry is pursuing.
>
> The central consumer concern is that AT&T [the largest cable operator at the time] is pursuing policies that… will extend the cable model of a closed, proprietary network to broadband Internet services…
>
> The cable TV model, based on private carriage, is quite different. Closed system operators choose who has access. Unaffiliated suppliers of content have no way to sell directly to the public. They must negotiate with the owner of the transmission system who sets the terms and conditions of interconnection and can keep them off their networks.
>
> As a result of these restrictive policies, the offer of commercial services is being retarded and consumers are losing crucial alternatives.
>
> These practices are anticompetitive and will damage the free flow of services on the Internet… The abusive treatment of unaffiliated ISPs that will occur in a market populated with closed systems will undermine the fundamental nature of the Internet.[18]

After five years of debate, the FCC officially abandoned its extremely successful policy of requiring open communications networks. It first proposed to allow the cable modem service to be closed.[19] It then proposed that telephone companies be allowed to deny access to their advanced telecommunications networks.[20]

The decision about access to the advanced telecommunications networks remains an open, front burner issue, however. Recently, the U.S. Court of Appeals for the Ninth Circuit reaffirmed it original decision to reject the FCC's view of cable modem service.[21] The FCC has not issued a final order in its telephone DSL proceeding. Thus, there is still time to reconsider the fundamental question of open access to the advanced telecommunications network.

THE STRUCTURE OF THE DIGITAL COMMUNICATIONS PLATFORM

To appreciate the dramatic shift that took place in the information environment with the emergence of the digital communications platform, it is helpful to view the platform as consisting of four layers (see Figure 1):[22] the physical layer, the logic or code layer, the applications layer and the content layer. It is a platform because there are strong complementarities between the layers and each layer sustains broad economic activity in the layer above it.[23] Shane Greenstein notes "[a] platform is a common arrangement of components and activities, usually unified by a set of technical standards and procedural norms around which users organize their activities. Platforms have a known interface with respect to particular technologies and are usually 'open' in some sense."[24] The digital communications platform is an important platform because of the special role that communications and information play in the 21st century economy. Moreover, public policy plays an important role because platforms "are typically associated with substantial externalities whose value is difficult to capture."[25]

The physical layer is composed of three elements. It has (1) a transmission medium (e.g. wires or spectrum) that links (2) communications equipment in the network with (3) appliance or display devices at the consumer premises (PC, TV). Direct communications between appliances is also an increasingly feasible activity. The logic (or code) layer involves the codes and standards with which communications equipment and display devices interconnect, interoperate, and communicate. Protocols interpret

Figure 1:

Layers Of The Digital Communications Platform

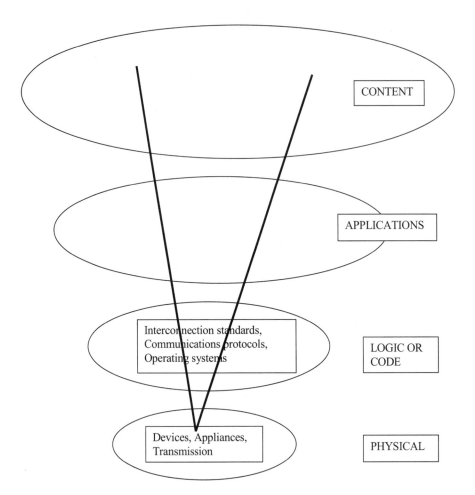

the signals. Operating systems allocate and coordinate the resources of the system. The operating systems and communications protocols can be resident in communications equipment and devices or network equipment or both. Applications constitute the third layer. Applications are programs that execute a sequence of steps to solve a problem or perform a task for the user (like e-mail or file-sharing). The content layer is made up of the specific task or problem solved in a given execution of an application. The end-user or a service provider can provide content.

The emergence of the digital communications platform altered the relative cost and importance of the factors of information production. The growth of the Internet and its underlying technologies changed the fundamental economics of information production and later the economics of technological change. At the physical layer, cheap, powerful computers, routers, switches and high capacity fiber optic cable are the rapidly proliferating physical infrastructure of the digital economy that allow communications at rising speeds with falling costs.[26] In the code and applications layer, a software revolution is the nervous system that enables the messages to be routed, translated, and coordinated.[27] Open protocols facilitate communications. Standardized and pre-installed bundles of software appear to have allowed the rapidly expanding capabilities of computer hardware to become accessible and useful to consumers with little expertise in computing. At the content layer, every sound, symbol, and image can now be digitized.[28] The more complex the sound or image, the more data has to be encoded and decoded to accomplish the digital representation.[29] However, when computing speeds, storage capacity and transmission rates become big enough, fast enough, and cheap enough, it becomes feasible to move huge quantities of voice, data, and video over vast distances.

Communications and computer industries have always exhibited network effects and strong economies of scale.[30] By increasing the number of units sold, the cost per unit falls dramatically.[31] Cost savings may apply not only to initial production costs, but also to service and maintenance costs. Digitization may reinforce these economic characteristics because economies of scope reinforce economies of scale. Adding service to the bundle lowers average costs.

Computer industries exhibit other characteristics. As the installed base of hardware and software deployed grows, learning and training in the dominant technology is more valuable since it can be applied by more users and to more uses.[32] As more consumers use a particular technology, each individual consumer can derive greater benefit from it. In addition to the direct network effects, larger numbers of users seeking specialized applications create a larger library of applications that become available to other users, and secondary markets may be created. These are all the positive benefits of network externalities.

The power of the digital communications platform stems in part from the fact that information production exhibits unique characteristics.

It is significantly non-excludable.[33] Once information is distributed, it is difficult to prevent it from being shared by users. It is nonrivalrous.[34] The consumption of information (reading or viewing) by one person does not detract from the ability of others to derive value from consuming it. It has high first copy costs.[35] The cost of distribution is low relative to the cost of producing information. It exhibits positive externalities.[36] Putting information into the world enables subsequent production at lower cost by its original producers or others. In some respects, information is also subject to network effects.[37] The production and distribution of information becomes more valuable as more people gain access to it. Information is a major input to its own output, which creates a feedback effect.[38] Where network effects and feedbacks are direct and strong, they create positive feedback loops.

The effect of the digital platform also was driven by the fact that the three major components of the digital platform – the personal computer (PC), the Internet/Web and the telecommunications network – were largely open during their initial deployment and commercial success. By open, I mean that the architectural interfaces to access the component were available to all potential users on identical terms and conditions.[39] Users did not have to negotiate rates, terms and conditions or request permission to deploy new components or services. Individuals seeking to plug into or develop an application for the platform could not be discriminated against.

The orders of magnitude of change that underlies the growth in the computer and communications industries are enormous.[40] Since the first desktop computers entered the residential market about thirty years ago, desktop computers have undergone a remarkable transformation. "The cost of processing information and data that once might have been hundreds of thousands, if not millions, of dollars is rapidly falling to zero. The IBM-370-168 mainframe (circa 1975) sold for $3.4 million; today a personal computer with an Intel Pentium chip retails for about $1,500 and is nearly 1,000 times faster."[41] The cost has been cut in half in the two years since this observation was made. Data transmission costs have fallen dramatically as well.

THE BROADER IMPACT

When such a dramatic change takes place in a technology that is critical to a variety of activities, the effects are felt throughout society.

Historically, dramatic changes in communications and transportation technology have affected society deeply.[42] The ongoing technological revolution does so as well, but in a uniquely profound way.[43]

Although an obligation to provide nondiscriminatory access to communications networks has been a long-standing principle in the U.S., the most recent iteration of this policy had a particularly powerful effect because it interacted with the spreading technology (computer) and architectural principle of the Internet (end-to-end) to create a uniquely dynamic environment. The digital communications platform "links the logic of numbers to the expressive power and authority of words and images. Internet technology offers new forms for social and economic enterprise, new versatility for business relationships and partnerships, and new scope and efficiency for markets."[44]

The Internet unleashed competitive processes and innovation exhibiting the fundamental characteristics of audacious or atomistic competition.[45] Decentralized experimentation by users who had command over increasing computing power created the conditions for a dramatic increase in innovation.[46] Openness of the communications network was central to this newly dynamic environment.

Because computing intelligence can be distributed widely, and the activities of the end-points communicated so quickly, interactivity is transformed. "As rapid advances in computation lower the physical capital cost of information production, and as the cost of communications decline, human capital becomes the salient economic good involved in information production."[47] Users become producers as their feedback rapidly influences the evolution of information products.

> It is a proven lesson from the history of technology that users are key producers of the technology, by adapting it to their uses and values, and ultimately transforming the technology itself, as Claude Fischer . . . demonstrated in his history of the telephone. But there is something special in the case of the Internet. New uses of the technology, as well as the actual modifications introduced in the technology, are communicated back to the whole world, in real time. Thus, the timespan between the process of learning by using and producing by using is extraordinarily shortened, with the result that we engage in a process of

learning by producing, in a virtuous feedback between the diffusion of technology and its enhancement.[48]

The institutional forms that will expand are those that economize on the most valuable factor of production (now human capital) by facilitating communications to reduce cost or maximizing output.[49] Alternatively, the scarcest or most critical input to production becomes the focal point of attention in economic activity.[50] This makes it possible for a wholly new form of information production – based on peer-to-peer relationships – to exist on a sustainable basis.[51] By drawing on a broad and diverse supply of human capital, a loose, collaborative approach can provide a potent mechanism for production.

The impact of this shift in information production is not limited to new organizational forms. Those who have studied corporate changes in the last quarter of the twentieth century have found similar patterns.[52] The new thrust of corporate organization, based on distributed intelligence and a flat structure, reflects these forces.[53] Hierarchy is out; horizontal is in.[54] The ability to coordinate at a distance dramatically alters the nature of centralized control, transferring much decision-making to dispersed management. A Harvard Business School Press publication, graphically titled *Blown to Bits*, summarized the dramatic change compelling corporate adjustment as follows: "Digital networks finally make it possible to blow up the link between rich information and its physical carrier. The Internet stands in the same relation to television as television did to books, and books to stained glass windows. The traditional link . . . between the economics of information and the economics of things – is broken."[55]

Thus, the revolution in communications and computing technology combined with the institutional innovation of the Internet to create not only a potentially profound change in the environment in which information is produced and distributed, but it opened the door to greater competition among a much wider set of producers and a more diverse set of institutions. We find that the deeper and more pervasively the principle of openness is embedded in the communications network, the greater the ability of information production to stimulate innovation.

In 1994, just as the commercial Internet was taking off, a National Research Council publication referred to the Internet as a "bearer" service. It underscored the concept of open access: "An open network is one that is capable of carrying information service of all kinds from suppliers of all kinds to customers of all kinds, across network service providers of all kinds, in a seamless accessible fashion."[56]

Figure 2 presents the graphic the NRC used to convey the importance of the bearer service. It draws attention to the fact that the open data network (ODN) and protocols at the neck of the hourglass are the link between diverse networks and a broad range of applications. Not surprisingly, the NRC chose the then current example to make its point: "The telephone system is an example of an open network, and it is clear to most people that this kind of system is vastly more useful than a system in which the users are partitioned into closed groups based, for example, on the service provider or the user's employer."[57] The principles of openness it identified bear repeating:

> *Open to users.* It does not force users into closed groups or deny access to any sectors of society, but permits universal connectivity, as does the telephone network.
>
> *Open to providers.* It provides an open and accessible environment for competing commercial and intellectual interests. It does not preclude competitive access for information providers.
>
> *Open to network providers.* It makes it possible for any network provider to meet the necessary requirements to attach and become a part of the aggregate of interconnected networks.
>
> *Open to change.* It permits the introduction of new applications and services over time. It is not limited to only one application, such as TV distribution. It also permits new transmission, switching, and control technologies to become available in the future.[58]

Interestingly, when the FCC officially abandoned its policy of ensuring open access to the communications networks, leading technology firms joined in the call to preserve open access. The High Tech Broadband Coalition asked the FCC to "protect important 'connectivity principles' that have made the Internet what it is today."[59] They offered four principles:

Figure 2:

The Internet As A Bearer Service

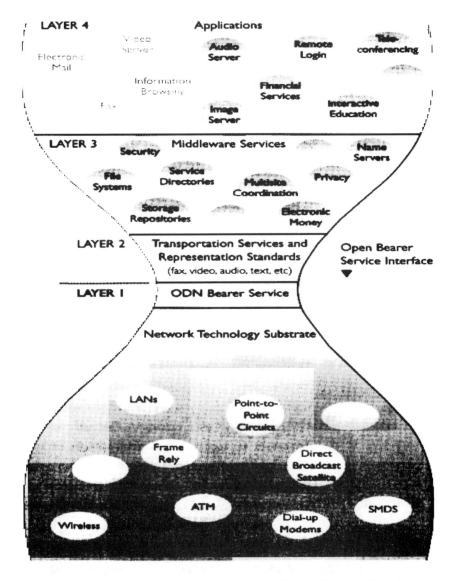

Source: Computer Science and Telecommunications Board, National Research Council, *Realizing the Information Future* (Washington, D.C. National Academy Press, 1994), p. 53.

Consumers have a right to meaningful information regarding technical limitations of their service.

Consumers should have unrestricted access to their choice of Internet content using the bandwidth capacity of their service plan.

Cable modem customers should be allowed to run applications of their choice, as long as they do not harm the provider's network and are within the bandwidth limits of their service plans.

Consumers should be permitted to attach any devices they choose, without prior permission, to their ISP connection, so long as they operate within the agreed bandwidth and do not harm the provider's network or enable the theft of services.[60]

The High Tech Broadband Coalition is made up of entities that supply most other non-transmission components for the digital platform. In essence, the Coalition is advocating nondiscrimination or neutrality of the network for consumers so that vigorous competition can continue between developers and suppliers of devices, applications and content. The effect of this "network neutrality" would be to restore or ensure the fundamental principle that service originating on one network would be able to interconnect with and utilize the functionality of all other networks, thereby preserving the Internet as a network of networks.

The Internet distribution technology or bearer service transforms economic activity, opens new markets, and supports even faster development than previous transportation and communications revolutions have typically done. As a business text observed:

Taken together these critical features of the Internet are understood by economics by generalizing the concept of the Internet's bearer service through the idea that the Internet acts as a general-purpose technology or platform technology. The reduced transaction costs and positive network externalities often found on the Internet enable new products to be brought to market more easily and quickly than in the past.[61]

Critical communications technologies have the most dramatic impact on society and there is a tendency to link them together as analogies when describing the impact of the Internet. For example, Mark Buchanan observes that "[t]he Internet has doubled in size yearly for ten straight years, which amounts to an explosive thousand-fold increase in the number of computers connected to it. In fact, it has grown in influence even more rapidly than did the telephone early in the twentieth century."[62] The implication is that the telephone had a major impact, but the impact of the Internet is even greater. Buchanan goes on to cite an observation by Peter Drucker from 1998 that compared the Internet and the railroad in a way that emphasizes the melding of technologies into communications platforms that transform society:

> As [Drucker] sees it, the computer is akin to the steam engine, and the Information Revolution is now at the point at which the Industrial Revolution was in the 1820s. Drucker points out that the most far reaching changes of the Industrial Revolution came not from the steam engine itself, but as a consequence of another unprecedented invention the engine made possible – the railroad. Similarly, he suspects, it is not computers or the Internet that will be world-changing, but rather one of their recent spin-offs: "e-Commerce is to the Information Revolution what the railroad was 170 years ago, e-commerce is creating a new and distinct boom, rapidly changing the economy, society and politics."[63]

Joel Mokyr points to electricity as a better referent.[64] Describing the semiconductor's "unusual properties" as "its ability to recombine with other techniques, its complementarity with downstream innovations, and its consequent pervasiveness in many applications,"[65] Mokyr concludes that it "merits the term general purpose technology."[66] Picking up a theme mentioned earlier, he argues:

> there have been few comparable macroinventions since the emergence of electricity in the late nineteenth century…What has happened is the emergence of a large

cluster of separate innovations with an unusual propensity to recombine with one another and to create synergistic innovations which vastly exceeded the capabilities of the individual component... The significance of ICT, then, is not just in its direct impact on productivity but that it is a *knowledge technology* and thus affects every other technique in use.[67]

OPEN COMMERCE AND COMMUNICATIONS NETWORKS: A CORNERSTONE OF CAPITALISM

In the half decade after Drucker's observation, e-commerce has lived up to its advanced billing. Interestingly, the railroads created both boom and bust cycles, but drove an industrial spiral upward, just as the Internet has. Moreover, dramatic transformations such as these also go hand-in-hand with major institutional transformations in the economy. The railroad age saw the growth of the corporation, as the digital communications platform is now transforming business organizations.[68] I argue in this section that critical decisions to ensure non-discriminatory access to the emerging dominant means of communications at the end of the 19th century – the railroad and telecommunications network – played a critical role in the subsequent success, just as the decision to keep the telecommunications network open for enhanced and information services at the end of the 20th century.

The dynamic effect of open communications networks in the digital age is only the most recent iteration of a broader process that has been unfolding over half a millennium. I have noted that the "Computer Inquiries" were an evolution of the common carrier principles to preserve open communications in the information age. We gain another perspective on the importance of open communications networks by placing recent developments in the longer sweep of history. By doing so we find that open communications and transportation networks are deeply embedded in the very DNA of capitalism.

As capitalism was dissolving feudalism, the emerging social order discovered an important new social, political and economic function – mobility. Physical and social mobility were anathema to feudalism, but essential to capitalism and democracy. Providing for open and adequate highways of commerce and means of communications were critical to allow commerce to flow, to support a more complex division of labor and to weave small distant places into a national and later global economy.

Legal obligations of common carriage and nondiscrimination were the solutions.[69] For example, under common law, innkeepers were obligated to serve all travelers, thereby supporting the movement of people, goods and services. Not only were all to be served on a nondiscriminatory basis, but when the innkeeper hung out his sign he brought upon himself the obligation to protect the property of the traveler. A legal text provides the following summary:

> There is also in law always an implied contract with a common innkeeper, to secure his guest's goods in his inn... Also if an innkeeper, or other victualer, hangs out a sign and opens his house for travelers, it is an implied engagement to entertain all persons who travel that way; and upon this universal *assumpsit,* an action on the case will lie against him for damages, if he without good reason refuses to admit a traveler.[70]

Inns were critical to commerce since, given the technology of the time, only short distances could be covered before rest and sustenance were needed. As critical as inns were to the flow of commerce, obviously roads and waterways were more important. Navigation projects, canals and turnpike trusts chartered under obligations of providing service to the public were the early vehicles of the capitalist political economy to provide for transportation projects.[71] Created in the 15th through 18th centuries and building on principles of common law, these were private undertakings with a public franchise to collect tolls on the section of a road or waterway whose upkeep was the responsibility of the trustee. Fees were assessed and access provided on a nondiscriminatory basis. While different rates could be charged to different types of traffic, discrimination within categories was forbidden.

By the 19th century, however, direct public responsibility for roads became the norm and provided nondiscriminatory access. Maintaining a network of transcontinental roads became a governmental responsibility, first city, then state, then national. Later, the principles of nondiscriminatory access were carried through to all national communications and transportation networks. Roads and highways, canals, railroads, the mail, telegraph, and telephone, some owned by public entities, most owned by private corporations, have always been operated as common carriers that are required to interconnect and serve the public on a non-discriminatory basis. An early court decision regarding telecommunications provides an interesting historical perspective:

> The telephone has become as much a matter of public convenience and of public necessity as were the stagecoach and sailing vessel a hundred years ago, or as the steamboat, the railroad, and the telegraph have become in later years. It has already become an important instrument of commerce. No other known device can supply the extraordinary facilities which it affords. It may therefore be regarded, when relatively considered, as an indispensable instrument of commerce. The relations which it has assumed towards the public make it a common carrier of news – a common carrier in the sense in which the telegraph is a common carrier – and impose upon it certain well defined obligations of a public character. All the instruments and appliances used by the telephone company in the prosecution of its business are consequently, in legal contemplation, devoted to a public use.[72]

The early date of this observation, 1886, is notable, since the telephone had just begun to penetrate, but so too is the comprehensive sweep of history. The telephone network was in its infancy but its vital nature brought the obligation of a common carrier upon it. Telephones would soon become a dominant means of business communication. Traditional practice did not excuse it from public interest obligations because it was new. Moreover, this citation also suggests the dual nature of communications networks as both a means of commerce and a means of democratic expression.

CONSTANCY OF THE PRINCIPLE, EVOLUTION OF ITS IMPLEMENTATION

Interestingly, the railroads, whose transcontinental network was completed only two decades before the decision cited above, had already brought upon themselves specific legislation to impose regulation beyond simple common carriage because of anticompetitive and discriminatory business practices. Because they practiced price gouging and discrimination against shippers and localities, direct regulation was imposed on them, first at the city level, but later at the state level and ultimately the national level.

These large corporate entities had failed to be restrained by the common law principles of common carriage or the common law principles were inadequate to the more complex reality of industrial society. As the Collum Committee found, "the paramount evil chargeable against the operation of the transportation system of the United States as now conducted is unjust discrimination between persons, places, commodities, or particular descriptions of traffic."[73] More discipline was needed to protect the public interest; society responded with specific obligations of nondiscrimination and interconnection and the provision of service at just and reasonable rates.

It is an important historical theme that the transformation of the economy in the second industrial revolution gave rise to new forms of economic organization that seemed unwilling to be bound by principles of commerce that were critical to the maintenance of a dynamic capitalist economy. Private contract and common law had failed to promote the public interest and were replaced by more direct public obligations. Moreover, as the nature of the economy and economic organization change, the nature of conduct that is considered anti-social changes as well. The American century was built, in part, on a repeated reaffirmation of the commitment to open communications and transportation networks (e.g. the Interstate Commerce Act (1887), the Mann Elkins Act (1910) and the Communications Acts (1934)) and to competitive principles (the Sherman Act (1880), the Clayton Act (1914) and the Federal Trade Commission Act (1914)).

Telecommunications has followed a path similar to the railroads with respect to regulation. Common law principles of nondiscriminatory access began to break down in the railroad industry in the 1850s, when railroads began to assert a right to carry their own goods and discriminate against shippers and geographic locations. Over the course of several decades, governments reacted by subjecting them to regulation that included, but went beyond, common carriage.

The dominant telecommunications entity also failed to provide nondiscriminatory interconnection at the end of the 19th century. Common law could not effectively force access and private entities could not negotiate it. By the early 20ᵗʰ century, states entered, imposing regulation that embodied common carrier principles and more. Eventually the federal government followed the same course. While advocates of proprietary carriage complain that the decision to impose public obligations cut off the public policy debate and short-circuited the private process, several decades of failure with an increasingly ubiquitous bearer service imposed substantial harm on localities and users of the network.

Almost a decade after the introduction of high-speed Internet into the mass market, the pattern is being repeated. A federal district court has twice ruled that advanced telecommunications should be subject to the obligation of non-discrimination, but the network owners are resisting. The Court could not have been clearer on this point:

> Among its broad reforms, the Telecommunications Act of 1996 enacted a competitive principle embodied by the dual duties of nondiscrimination and interconnection. See 47 U.S.C. s. 201 (a) ...s. 251 (A) (1)... Together, these provisions mandate a network architecture that prioritizes consumer choice, demonstrated by vigorous competition among telecommunications carriers. As applied to the Internet, Portland calls it "open access," while AT&T dysphemizes it as "forced access." Under the Communications Act, this principle of telecommunications common carriage governs cable broadband as it does other means of Internet transmission such as telephone service and DSL, "regardless of the facilities used." The Internet's protocols themselves manifest a related principle called "end-to-end": control lies at the ends of the network where the users are, leaving a simple network that is neutral with respect to the data it transmits, like any common carrier. On this role of the Internet, the codes of the legislator and the programmer agree.

As happened a century earlier, states and cities have entered the fray. Events may move a little faster because, in the age of the digital communications platform, harm mounts more quickly. Time speeds up and the platform has a more profound effect on the remainder of society, but the fundamental issue is the same.

Current arguments against obligations to provide nondiscriminatory access are based on the claim that competition exists between two networks and that that is all the American economy needs. That claim is wrong as a matter of historical fact and practical experience. Opponents of an obligation for nondiscrimination have mistakenly set up a mutually exclusive choice between competition and public obligations.[74]

The notion that two competitors are enough to ensure a vigorously competitive market is inconsistent with economic theory and decades of empirical evidence. Monopoly is not now and never has been a necessary legal condition for common carrier status. The existence of intermodal competition in other industries did not eliminate the obligation for nondiscrimination. The paramount concern is the nature of the service, not the conditions of supply. Public convenience and necessity is required of a service because it is a critically important, indispensable input into other economic activity. The function provided by and the network characteristics of transportation and communications industries are conducive to creating the conditions for "affecting the public interest."

Starting from the demand side to arrive at common carrier obligations does not mean that the conditions of supply do not matter. On the supply-side, a key characteristic of common carriers is the reliance on some public resource for the deployment of the network. Transportation and communications networks are typically the beneficiaries of public largesse or special considerations. The public support may take one of many forms, such as public funds, use of public property, the right to condemn private property, or the grant of a franchise.

The manner in which the service is offered to the public is also important. Service that is made widely available to the public becomes "affected with the public interest." The presence of market power over a vital service is another factor that leans in favor of common carriage status. However, viewed in this way, the presence of market power on the supply side is only one of several considerations in determining whether an obligation for nondiscrimination should be applied to a particular service, and by no means the most important.

Public roads competed against privately owned canals, but they were both subject to common carrier obligations. Private railroads were added to compete with canals and roads, and they were all subject to common carrier obligations. Telegraph, wireline telephone and wireless are all common carriers. In other words, we have layered alternative modes of communications one atop another, each using a different technology, each optimized for a somewhat different form of communications, and still we imposed the common carrier obligations to ensure access. Access to the means of communications was too important to allow discrimination. That access should play a critical role in the digital revolution is not surprising.

> Access in the form of search engines that allow an individual to find some known piece of useful knowledge at low cost becomes critical. Indeed, it must be true that had useful knowledge grown at the rate it did without changes in the technology of access, diminishing returns might have set in just due to the gigantic scale… It may be that the Internet 2 will be the culmination of this process, but in fact access has been improving for decades in the form of computer-based information databases such as computerized library catalogs, databases, and online access channels such as Medline. As people who carry out technological instructions – let alone those who write new ones – have access to more and more useful knowledge, the means by which they can access, sort, evaluate, and filter this knowledge is crucial.[75]

NETWORK THEORY

It is easy to look at the powerful technologies that have converged in the digital communications platform and assume that they are the engines of change. This is particularly the case in the presence of positive feedback loops. In this section I argue that the architecture of the network in which they have become embedded is at least as important. The technologies themselves would not be as powerful nor would the effect on the rest of society be as great if the platform had not evolved as an ultrarobust network. This section describes some of the key elements in the understanding of networks that has been emerging across a number of disciplines in the physical and social sciences. There are three primary reasons for turning to this literature.

First, the fact that science is finding a basic set of principles explaining the success of networks ranging from cells and simple life forms to the human brain and social institutions, like firms and social movements, highlights the importance of network principles. The architecture of the network dictates its robustness. The digital communications platform I have just described is a layered set of networks that exhibits particularly robust characteristics.

Second, individual networks are frequently part of a larger physical organism or social organization. In other words, networks of networks create larger systems. The digital communications platform is a critically important technology network that deeply affects the social, economic and political structure of society.

Third, the social scientific application of network theory has been policy oriented in the sense that it seeks to identify characteristics of social networks that can be changed to improve their robustness. The theory emphasizes success and failure based on the ability and willingness of institutions to adopt structures that adapt to changing environments and new challenges.

COMPLEX NETWORKS

Networks are built from nodes (or endpoints) connected through communications links.

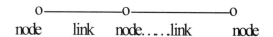

Interconnectivity is a critical feature of networks. It prevails because "most systems displaying a high degree of tolerance against failures share a common feature: their functionality is guaranteed by a highly interconnected network."[76] Simply put, it "seems that nature strives to achieve robustness through *interconnectivity*."[77] Robust networks are typified by the formation of hubs: "the few highly connected nodes that keep these networks together."[78]

The links between hubs are especially important as bridges that hold the network together.

In robust networks, hubs and links form modules.[79] Modules share strong internal ties and specialize in discrete functions, but have weak ties to the rest of the network through links between hubs. Modularity implies

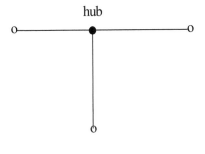

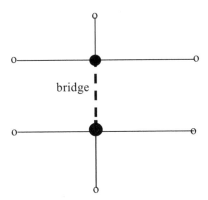

a division of labor.   That is, specialization allows modules to provide functions efficiently in the network.[80]

The modules in a robust network are hierarchically organized:

> Numerous small, but highly interlinked modules combine
> in a hierarchical fashion to a few larger, less interlinked
> modules.... Hierarchical modularity sheds new light on the
> role of the hubs as well: they maintain communication
> between the modules. Small hubs have links to nodes
> belonging to a few smaller modules. Large hubs... [are]
> bridging together communities of different sizes and
> cultures.[81]

Networks grow and establish structures according to rules that foster efficient structures. Hubs form because of preferential attachment,[82] but links are not added randomly because "building and maintaining new ties…leaves individuals less time for production; hence both congestion and ties are costly."[83]

Networks can be designed in various ways depending on the pattern of the links. The links can be connected in various ways including centralized (Figure 3a), decentralized (Figure 3b), and distributed (Figure 3c).

Networks gain robustness by creating links that reduce effort. Duncan Watt calls them shortcuts. The dictionary definition of a shortcut captures the essence of the process: "a method of doing or achieving something more directly and easily than by ordinary procedure… to make the work more simple and easy."[84] Watts notes that "[a]n obvious approach is to bypass the overtaxed node by creating a shortcut, thus rechanneling the congestion through an additional network tie."[85]

But, which links are most important to forge?[86] The answer that emerges is familiar to anyone who has studied the Internet: distributing communications increases efficiency. The expenditure of time and effort (energy) are critical factors in efficient structures. Watt's theoretical analysis finds that "[t]he addition of a single shortcut contracted the paths between many distant pairs of nodes simultaneously, thereby effectively reducing congestion along many long chains of intermediaries."[87] Buchanan notes that this is a pervasive principle: "Whatever the setting, computation requires information to be moved about between different places. And since the number of degrees of separation reflects the typical time needed to shuttle information from place to place, the small-world architecture makes for computational power and speed."[88]

> [T]he burden of any particular node can be relieved by the greatest possible amount by connecting the neighbors for whom it relays the most messages… Because the strategy always selects the most congested node to relieve, and because the nodes that it connects were handling those messages anyway, the effect is always to reduce overall congestion without increasing any individual's burden.[89]

We might call this the principle of distributed efficiency. There is a tension between preferential affiliation, in which hubs gain links, and

Figure 3:
Network Configurations

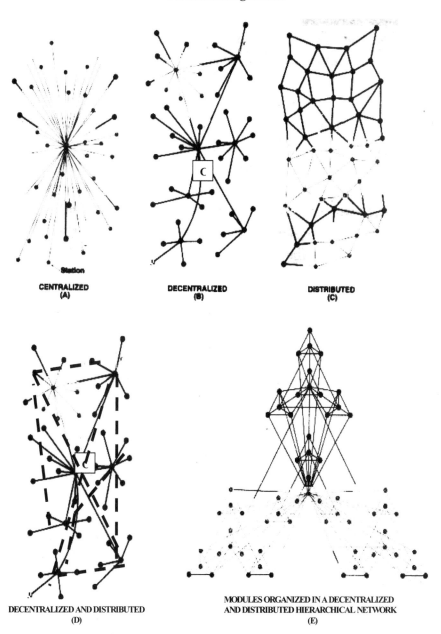

Sources: Barabasi, Albert-Laszlo, *Linked* (New York: Plume, 2002), A-C = p. 145, E = p. 233;

distributed efficiency, in which important shortcuts bypass hubs that have become congested or overburdened and allow nodes to communicate. Nevertheless, the value of distributed efficiency can be easily identified.

Figure 3d adds distributed efficiency links (dashed lines) into a decentralized hub-dominated network. Buchanan calls the links between hubs "bridges," drawing on Mark Granovetter's observation that "weak links are often of greater importance than strong links because they are the crucial ties that sew the social network together."[90]

Important shortcuts (bridges) meet the criteria of reducing traffic between neighboring hubs that are already in communication through a third hub. By adding bridges to the decentralized network, it gains the characteristics of a distributed network. The example in Exhibit 3d has the following characteristics:

(1)   By adding links at the periphery, congestion of the core is reduced. Communications capabilities are distributed to the nodes or end points.

(2)   The additional links can relieve a great deal of traffic that had flowed through the central hub (c). Therefore, the network should have the necessary resources to free up to form the new links.

(3)   Moreover, as configured, if module (c) is removed or rendered inoperative, all clusters could communicate with one another, a condition that did not obtain in the purely decentralized network.

(4)   Under routine functioning, no node is separated by more than two degrees (one link, one bridge) from any other hub.

(5)   Under stress, should any module be removed, no node is more than three steps (one link, two bridges) from any other hub.

(6)   No matter how many modules are taken out, all the remaining nodes can continue to communicate although it becomes more difficult since each communication must traverse more bridges.

While we tend to "see" networks as nodes and hubs and measure them by counting the quantity or assessing the quality of messages that flow between them, the architecture of the network is dictated by the rules of communications and connectivity. In the robust, efficient network, information flows because it can (connectivity) and should (functionality). The architecture makes the observed pattern of communications between nodes and hubs possible.

THE ARCHITECTURE OF ULTRAROBUST NETWORKS

Watts describes a special characteristic of robust networks that result from balancing these architectural principles as <u>multiscale connectivity</u>, and the network architecture that exhibits superior performance as an ultrarobust network. He describes the importance of multiscale connectivity in terms of avoiding or recovering from failure and also in facilitating success:

> Multiscale connectivity, therefore, serves not just one but two purposes that are essential to the performance of a firm in uncertain environments. By distributing the information congestion associated with problem solving across many scales of the organization, it minimizes the likelihood of failure [maximizes the chances for success]. And *simultaneously* it minimizes the effect of failures [maximizes the impact of successes] if and when they do occur... Because they exhibit this two-for-the-price-of-one robustness property, we call multiscale networks ultrarobust.[91]

The hierarchical, modular network that exhibits both decentralized and distributed communications traits allows experimentation at the periphery, without threatening the functionality of the network (see Figure 3e). Failure is not catastrophic; since it can be isolated and its impact minimized. Success can be pursued independently and exploited because of efficient communications. Successful nodes grow more rapidly through preferential attachment.

> Hierarchical modularity has significant design advantages. It permits parts of the network to evolve separately... The

impact of genetic mutations [experimentation or innovation], affecting at most a few genes at once, is limited to a few modules. If a mutation is an improvement, the organism with the superior module will flourish. If, however, tinkering with a gene decreases the module's fitness, the organism will fail to survive.[92]

Watts goes on to identify searchability as a critical and "generic property of social networks."[93] Searchability is facilitated by paying attention to one's neighbors (chosen by preferential attachment).[94] As he puts it: "By breaking the world down the way we do – according to multiple simultaneous notions of social distance – and by breaking the search process itself down into manageable phases, we can solve what seems to be a tremendously difficult problem with relative ease."[95]

Searchability is one of the key advantages of multiscale networks because "in ambiguous environments, information congestion related to problem-solving activities causes individuals – especially those higher in the hierarchy – to become overburdened. The local response of these individuals is to direct their subordinates to resolve problems on their own by conducting directed searches."[96] Watts argues that "[w]hen problem solving is purely local, requiring messages to be passed between members of the same work team, for example, or subscribers to the same ISP, congestion can be relieved effectively by a process that corresponds to *team building*."[97]

Lacking a central directory of organizational knowledge and resources, the subordinates rely on their informal contacts within their firm (or possibly in other firms) to locate relevant information... A direct consequence is that the internal architecture of the firm is driven away from that of a pure hierarchy by virtue of the new links that are being formed and consolidated over many repeated searches.

The equilibrium state of this process is a multiscale network for the simple reason that only when the network is connected across multiple scales is individual congestion – hence the pressure to create new connections – relieved... the process of ties at multiple scales also renders the network highly searchable, so that the multiscale state becomes effectively reinforcing.[98]

Albert Barabasi notes that the Internet "evolves based on local decisions on an as needed basis… The underlying network has become so distributed, decentralized, and locally guarded that even such an ordinary task as getting a central map of it has become virtually impossible."[99] Figure 4 presents a picture of what the publisher's note refers to as "the original proposal for the World Wide Web."[100] It is a module in the larger network whose function is to organize resources to manage information. It exhibits all of the characteristics of the networks I have described. It has hierarchy based on preferential affiliation (e.g. the "proposal mesh") with both

Figure 4:

The Original Proposal For The World Wide Web

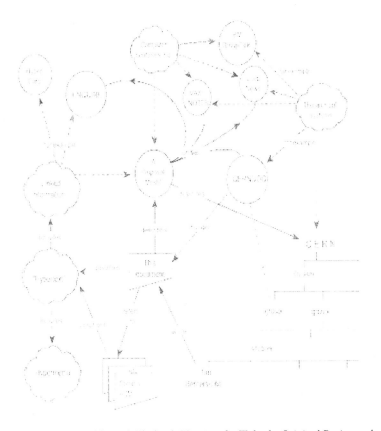

Sources: Berners-Lee, Tim, with Mark Fischetti, *Weaving the Web: the Original Design and Ultimate Destiny of the World Wide Web* (New York: Harper Business, 1999), p. 211.

decentralized clusters and bridges to achieve distributed efficiency. Note that not all bridges are built between hubs, reflecting the author's understanding of how information flows within the module. Only some bridges need to be built.

I have pointed out that several of the key components of the digital communications platform – the telecommunications facility, the appliance (PC), and the communications protocols (Internet and the web) – were open. The PC itself is considered a "platform," whose complementary elements exist in an open architecture. The Internet is a "stack" of protocols whose architecture is open. In other words, the digital communications platform is a nested set of open components that exhibit an unprecedented level of connectivity. It exhibits the modular, hierarchical, distributed, multiscale connectivity of an ultrarobust network.

INNOVATION IN HIGH TECHNOLOGY INDUSTRIES

THE TECHNOLOGY OF TECHNICAL CHANGE

Networks are critical to innovation, which "spreads from innovators [nodes] to hubs. The hubs in turn send the information out along their numerous links, reaching most people within a given... network."[101] Most importantly, "the structure of the network can have as great an influence on the success or failure of an innovation as the inherent appeal of the innovation itself."[102] The same tension exists for innovation as exists for all problems confronted by the network. "[T]he success of an innovation appears to require a trade off between local reinforcement and global connectivity."[103]

> Networks that are not connected enough, therefore, prohibit global cascades because the cascade has no way of jumping from one vulnerable cluster to another. And networks that are too highly connected prohibit cascades also, but for a different reason: they are locked into a kind of stasis, each node constraining the influence of any other and being constrained itself.[104]

Multiscale connectivity in hierarchical, modular architecture is the sweet spot between underconnected and overconnected networks and ideal for problem solving "by making problem solving itself a routine activity."[105]

Effective adoption of an innovation or response to a disaster requires the ability to search the network for solutions and synchronize the modules when one is found.[106]

> Routine problem solving both balances the information-processing burden across the individuals of an organization and sets up the conditions under which exceptional problems can be solved.

> The precise *mechanism* by which a firm's response to routine ambiguity generates ultrarobustness is, as yet, an unsolved puzzle, but it seems to bear a deep resemblance to the property of network searchability.[107]

I have already suggested the link between the Internet and innovation in the concept of a bearer network. Applying network theory establishes the link between the digital communications platform and the stimulation of innovation with much greater detail. Recent analyses of technological innovation provide strong evidence that the digital communications platform transformed the very fabric of the innovation process of what Arora calls "the changing technology of technical change."[108] Consider the following description of the innovation process:

> von Hippel notes that greater efficiency can be achieved by dividing the overall problem-solving effort into tasks, showing maximal interaction within them and minimal interactions across them. In doing so, one can reduce one fundamental source of inefficiency, notably that actions in one particular innovation stage or activity may require information or even exchanges of actions in several other innovation stages or activities. This is a source of inefficiency because of the extensive coordination and information flow that this process requires and the potential disruptions that may be brought about by these interdependencies... [H]e argues that the development of innovations often relies upon information that is in the domain of different agents (e.g. the user and the manufacturer), and that some of this information can be "sticky" in the sense that it can only be transferred at very

high costs to other parties. This information arises from tacit knowledge and the routines that are normally associated with the ordinary activities performed by each agent or organization.[109]

Technological innovation is framed as an information problem that challenges the network structure. There are two hurdles. First, knowledge is local and flowing it through hubs to solve problems creates inefficiency (uses energy). Second, the possibility of failure increases as the number of interrelated problems that must be solved sequentially increases, because of dependence on multiple solutions to problems across numerous nodes.

The solution to the first problem is to distribute responsibility:

> The traditional approach in this type of situation has been to try to move the sticky information…. [S]ystem developers would first undertake a great deal of work at the user site (e.g., a bank or an insurance company) to understand the needs for the system to be produced. Once they acquired this information, the developers returned to their company and designed it… [A] more effective approach would be to move the locus of the problem-solving effort. The user and the producer could then draw only upon their own local and idiosyncratic information sets, without having to move between locations.[110]

The parallel to the network problem is quite strong. Efficiency in technological innovation comes by breaking the problem down and solving it at the "local" level because local information is the ultimate source of the solution. The solution is efficient as long as one economizes on the need to flow information up through the hierarchy. When problem solving moves to the local level, the cluster must become modular. Modularity plays the same role in the context of technological innovation as it does in the broader network theory.

The solution to the second problem – sequential challenges – emerges from modularity with open interfaces. It loosens the dependence on simultaneous solutions to multiple problems:

> Modularity is a key component in a system of open architecture. Modularity in product design has received some attention in recent years due to its perceived

advantages for innovation, particularly in view of shorter product life cycles, which reduce time-to-market and the growing value of product customization...

This had natural implications for innovation. Most notably, provided one did not change the required interfaces, a great deal of innovation could take place in the components without requiring redesign of other components or of the entire architecture.[111]

The local nature of the robust network is not confined to the internal organization of firms. It extends to the network environment in which the firm exists. Silicon Valley has been described as a matrix,[112] essentially a multiscale network of firms of various sizes in which sticky knowledge spreads through links that "fall somewhere between market and firm. These hybrid links are most easily formed where interfirm relations are close, the lines between them dense."[113] The effect of "this sort of density is particularly important in fast-changing areas of the economy, in which all partners to a venture need to be able to change in coordinated fashion."[114] The proximity also facilitates modularity and specialization since "density... also allows people to differentiate finely between different firms, finding the most apt for a particular task or idea."[115] Key to the unbundling[116] of the production process is "the region's culture of open information exchange and interfirm mobility, which fosters a culture of recombination and new firm formation."[117] "Much of this innovative activity is less associated with footloose multinational corporations and more associated with high-tech innovative regional clusters, such as Silicon Valley, Research Triangle and Route 122."[118]

The most successful firms and regions take on the characteristics of layered multiscale networks:

The sum of these associations is a vast network composed of many small networks of contributors to the Valley's process for innovation and entrepreneurship... Tight links built up over time by the rich accumulation of shared conversations, projects, and deals have yielded a treasure trove of rich and productive relationships...

> The prevailing philosophy of Silicon Valley promotes openness and learning, sharing of information, the co-evolution of ideas, flexibility, mutual feedback, and fast responses to opportunities and challenges... a regional network-based industrial system that promotes collective learning and flexible adjustment among specialist producers of complex related technologies.[119]

A Broad-Based, Transformative Revolution

The technological revolution of the late twentieth century has altered the information environment to make distributed solutions more feasible. The uniquely user-focused character of the communications-intensive Internet solution recurs.

Eric von Hippel argues that "the primary irreversible factor that we speculate is making user-based design an increasingly attractive option is technological advance."[120] Ashish Arora et al. note that "the recent evolution of technology and knowledge bases... has created greater opportunities for task portioning."[121] This allows greater local autonomy in decision-making:

> Specifically, the main force behind the changing technology of technical change is the complementarity between increased computational power and greater scientific and technological understanding of problems.[122]

> Advances in scientific understanding decrease the costs of articulating tacit and context-dependent knowledge and reduce the costs of technology transfer. Further, such knowledge can be embodied in tools, particularly software tools, which make the knowledge available to others cheaply and in a useful form... [A]dvances in science and the tremendous increase in computational capabilities have greatly contributed to extending the division of innovative labor.[123]

Arora et al. argue that the "changing technology of technical change" allows technological innovation to move outside the firm; others argue that the form of organization changes as well:

[M]odularity in product design brings about modular organizations... the standard interfaces of a modular design provide a sort of "embedded coordination" among independent firms and innovators, which can coordinate their activities independently of a superior managerial authority. ... [M]odular systems that are also open (i.e., where the interfaces are not proprietary standards) make market leaders more vulnerable to competition. While modularity can accelerate overall product innovation, because of the contribution of several specialists, the presence of many specialists can also lead to tougher competition and greater entry.[124]

As hierarchical modularity in the network replaces vertically integrated hierarchy in the firm, complex digital platform industries have benefited from open network approaches: "The open system approach fuels the growth of many smaller innovative firms. The presence of several firms for each subsystem or component, and the narrow focus pursued by each firm will lead to higher degrees of experimentation and innovation with a faster rate of technical progress."[125] Vertical integration and extreme hierarchical structure lose their comparative advantage in the context of open digital communications networks, while modular flexibility and connectivity gain significant advantage:

Cross-functional interaction must take place concurrently, rather than sequentially, if firms are to cut time-to-market for new products and processes. Cross-functional and cross-departmental networks must be strengthened without causing information overload... If such activity becomes completely unstructured, it augments rather than displaces bureaucracy... With organizational sub-units cross-linked in this way, authority flows as much from knowledge as position in the organizational hierarchy. The challenge is to develop a culture which supports the establishment of cross-functional teams which draw on the requisite knowledge, wherever it may be located.[126]

The rewards to modules and networks that restructure effectively are clear. There is "a strong causal link between productivity gains in the

ICT sector and a spread of these productivity improvements throughout the economy via investment in ICT capital."[127]

> When we turn to the assertion that rigorous industrial restructuring in the pre-1990 period may have been beneficial to economic performance, we find that a lack of restructuring indeed appears to have affected economic growth of industries adversely, probably especially for the case of high tech industries… [M]anufacturing industries, especially high tech industries with relatively high speed of restructuring have, *ceteris paribus,* performed best.[128]

PINPOINTING THE KEY TECHNOLOGIES

While the overall thrust of network theory suggests that multiscale connectivity promotes ultrarobust networks, and the digital communications platform is the architecture that holds it together, it also leaves open the optimal mix between hierarchical networks and hierarchical firms.[129] What are the characteristics of technologies that are critical to broad-based progress? It is not hard to find the key to which technologies are important to make available. Arora et al. identify two situations in which the exploitation of available technologies and innovative opportunities can be problematic because private actions are not likely to achieve the optimal outcome. These are essentially collective action challenges.

First there is a strong "public goods" character to information and knowledge.

> The key here is that the knowledge has multiple potential applications, so that users do not compete. When knowledge is nonrival, protecting that knowledge through patents creates potential inefficiencies… A number of different potential users may have to get together to invest in creating knowledge. Such contracts are problematic because users will differ in the value they place upon the enterprises and, consequently, are likely to underreport their value.[130]

Second are transaction costs problems "in cumulative or systemic technologies," because "a commercializable innovation may require many different pieces of knowledge some of which may be patented and owned by people with conflicting interests."[131] This is the platform problem, where many complements must interoperate to achieve the full value of the platform:

> In a Coasian world with no transaction costs, given any initial distribution of property rights over the fragments, agents will bargain to a Pareto optimal solution. More realistically, the required collection of the property rights, although socially efficient, might not occur because of transaction costs and hold-up problems. An agent holding a patent on an important fragment ("blocking patent") may use the patent in an attempt to extract as much of the value of the innovation as possible...
>
> In other words, when several pieces of intellectual property have to be combined, the transaction costs implied could be so high as to prevent otherwise productive combinations.[132]

We could look to a variety of high technology industries to find examples of this process, but we should not be surprised to find that the best examples come from the components of the digital information platform. Interconnection and interoperability to maximize the availability of functionality have been the hallmarks of the open architecture of the digital communications platform.

> Things are different when a firm invests in developing a new platform interface...These are *enabling technologies.* They contain valuable content or information that probably could have value (i.e. price) in the marketplace. But protecting that content, such as by hiding the detailed specifications of the hardware or software interfaces, would defeat their entire *raison d'etre:* Interfaces exist to entice other firms to use them to build products that conform to the defined standards and therefore work efficiently with the platform.[133]

Intel's approach to platform leadership has been widely recognized and it provides a perfect example of the importance of open architecture. Intel "made a decision pretty early on that what we wanted was something that was *open* and *royalty-free* that the industry could adopt without huge concerns about infringing IP [intellectual property] or having to pay high royalties."[134]   The distinction from standard-setting bodies is clear. "Generally, their policy is that any interface IP that is introduced into a specification has to be licensed under 'reasonable and non-discriminatory terms.' But 'reasonable' is a very subjective term."[135]

Intel imposed a further requirement of reciprocity: "anyone who would have access to [our] IP – if they had any [of their own] in that area – would have to make their IP open and available to the industry as well."[136]

Of course, Intel was not the only company to arrive at platform leadership as the key to dynamic innovation. The "Silicon Valley system" is described as one "where relationships are based on a shared recognition of the need to ensure the success of a final product. Traditional supplier relationships are typically transformed by a decision to exchange long-term business plans and share confidential sales forecasts and cost information."[137]

In short, "where informal connections are dense and the mysteries of practice are in the air, the inefficiencies that keep ideas within isolated firms, hedged in by intellectual property strategies and closely related, are less of a constraint on mobility."[138]

It is interesting to reflect on the factors that drove Intel to its aggressive approach to platform leadership. The PC had been an open platform throughout its existence, but IBM had chosen that path out of expediency, rather than a conviction about the superiority of an open platform. Caught behind in the shift from mainframes to PCs, IBM was forced to outsource development and supply of many components of the PC to get to market quickly. Open architecture was the answer, but IBM's commitment to the concept was weak.

> IBM was attempting to evolve the PC architecture in a proprietary manner with a new bus project: MCA. That strategy was in line with IBM trying to maintain (or more precisely, to revert to) a "vertical" industry: that is a structure of industry competition where highly integrated firms made most of their own components and competed on the merits of distinctive, proprietary architecture...
>
> Intel, by contrast, did not try to benefit from proprietary architectural interface for the PC. Instead, the company

made sure that the new specification was free and open to everyone... It was in Intel's best interest for all PC manufacturers and developers of complementary products to plug their products together in the same way to make development of complements as easy and cheap as possible.[139]

A similar sequence of events played out in the development of the Internet's most important application, the World Wide Web. As the Internet moved out of the laboratory and into the commercial market, the specter of a closed interface arose. Tim Berners-Lee describes it as follows:

> It was about this time, spring 1993, that the University of Minnesota decided it would ask for a license fee from certain classes of users who wanted to use gopher. Since the gopher software was being picked up so widely, the university was going to charge an annual fee. The browser, and the act of browsing, would be free, and the server software would remain free to nonprofit and educational institutions. But any other users, notably companies, would have to pay to use gopher software.
>
> This was an act of treason in the academic community and the Internet community. Even if the university never charged anyone a dime, the fact that the school had announced it was reserving the right to charge people for use of the gopher protocols meant it had crossed the line. To use the technology was too risky.
>
> Industry dropped gopher like a hot potato. Developers knew they couldn't do anything that could possibly be said to be related to the gopher protocol without asking all their lawyers first about negotiating rights... It was considered dangerous as an engineer to have even read the specification or seen any of the code, because anything that person did in the future could possibly be said to have been in some way inspired by the private gopher technology.[140]

Open architecture is a powerful, but fragile design principle.

THE IMPORTANCE OF INTERNET SERVICE PROVIDERS IN THE COMMERCIAL SUCCESS OF THE INTERNET

ISPs were the first children of the commercialization of the open network of the Internet and later the first victims of the network foreclosure strategy. ISPs were generally small operators who tied together the broader population of users. Getting 50 million households to use a new, technologically sophisticated device (the PC) to interconnect on a regular basis with a network of millions of other devices was no easy feat.[141] Domestic online service providers numbered about 400 to 500 in the late 1980s when Internet commercialization began (see Figure 5).[142] That number grew to 7,000 to 8,000 ISPs in the late 1990s.[143]

Figure 5:

ISPS, Internet Subscription And Home PC Penetration

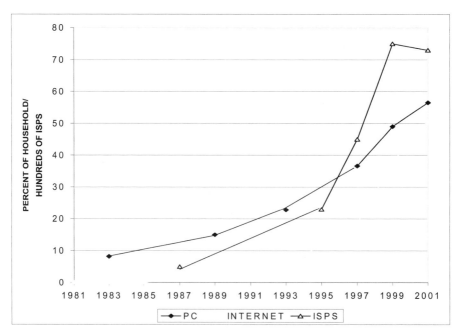

Source: Carey, John, "The First Hundred Feet for Households: Consumer Adoption Patterns," in Deborah Hurley and James H. Keller (Eds.), *The First Hundred Feet* (Cambridge: MIT Press, 1999); National Telecommunications Information Administration, *A Nation Online* (U.S. Department of Commerce, 2002). Early ISP counts are discussed in Cooper, Mark, *Expanding the Information Age for the 1990s: A Pragmatic Consumer View* (Washington, D.C.: Consumer Federation of America, American Association of Retired Persons, January 11, 1990); see also Abbate, Janet, *Inventing the Internet* (Cambridge: MIT Press, 1999) and Matos, F., *Information Service Report* (Washington, D.C.: National Telecommunications Information Administration, August 1988). Recent ISPS Counts are from *Boardwatch Magazine*, "North American ISPS,"

Buying wholesale telecommunications service from telephone companies and selling basic Internet access combined with a variety of additional applications and services to the public, they translated the complex technologies that had to be combined to use the Internet into a mass market service.[144] Once the Internet was commercialized, ISPs rapidly covered the country with dial-up access and translated a series of innovations into products and services that were accessible and useful to the public. Berners-Lee noted the critical linking role played by ISPs:

> It was already possible for anyone to download, free, all the browsers, TCP/IP, and software needed to get on the Internet and Web, but a user had to know a lot about how to configure them and make them work together, which was complicated. Neither the Internet nor the Web had initially been set up for home or individual business use; they were meant for universities, researchers and large organizations...
>
> Soon thereafter, however, many Internet service providers started to spring up – local companies that would give access to the Internet via a local telephone call. They provided all the software a subscriber required.[145]

Greenstein analyzes the activities of ISPs as "coinvention, the complementary invention that makes advances in general purpose technology valuable in particular places at particular points in time."[146] Some of the underlying innovations that the ISPs adapted and popularized had been around for a while, like the Internet protocol itself, e-mail, file transfer and sharing, and bulletin boards. Some of the innovations were very recent, like the web, the browser, instant messaging and streaming.

Greenstein argues that "[a] significant set of activities of many providers in the commercial Internet market involved 'adaptation... Adaptation does not happen on its own."[147] The process involves "one of several activities: Monitoring technical developments, distilling new information into components that are meaningful to unfamiliar users, and matching unique user needs to one of the many possible solutions."[148]

Local specificity and the importance of the linking and communications function of ISPs is strong because adaptation "depends on the users, their circumstances, their background, their capital investments, the costs of adjusting to new services, and other factors that influence the match between user needs and technological possibilities."[149] Consequently, there were few plain vanilla ISPs, offering only basic access to the Internet. Thousands of ISPs tailoring services to customer needs supported the rapid spread of Internet subscription and use. Greenstein finds that "by the summer of 1998... there were dozens of well-known national networks and scores of less-known national providers covering a wide variety of dial-up and direct access. There were also thousands of regional and local providers of Internet access that served as the link between end-users and the Internet backbone."[150]

In the view of some, the impact of "the army of ISPs" goes beyond merely spurring the adoption of Internet service on the demand side. They opened markets that were neglected by dominant ISPs and forced dominant firms to make services available that they might well have resisted had they not faced the competition. Competition at the level of service providers not only drove adoption but stimulated cross layer competition. David Mowery and Timothy Simcoe describe these impacts as follows:

> These small ISPs benefited from the distance-sensitive pricing of long distance telecommunication services that created opportunities for entry by ISPs into local markets, the focus of larger ISPs on high-density urban locations and the fact that no more than a few hundred customers were needed to provide sufficient revenues to fund a modem pool and high-speed connection. At the same time, many of the larger online services hesitated to provide unrestricted Internet access, which they saw as diluting the value of their proprietary applications. In a classic illustration of the power of network externalities, the rising number of Internet hosts and users compelled the major online service providers to offer e-mail connectivity and later, browsing, in order to keep their customers...
>
> Increased demand and entry by new service providers led to rapid investment in new capacity, particularly in major metropolitan areas, and brought telecommunications service providers into direct competition with national and regional ISPs... The PC networks that evolved from bulletin boards

into online service providers were a significant source of Internet growth and competition in the market for access.[151]

Throughout the history of the commercial narrowband Internet, the number of service providers was never less than 10 per 100,000 customers (see Figure 6). At present, and for most of the commercial history of the industry, there have been 15 or more ISPs per 100,000 subscribers on the open, dial-up Internet.

Figure 7 shows a map of the Internet based on data collected in June of 1999. That moment was probably the height of density of ISPs per subscriber. The commercial Internet was still almost entirely based on dial-up service. The small clusters in the Figure represent ISPs, which provide the connectivity to the Internet. A few of the larger ISPs are labeled,

Figure 6:

Density Of Internet Service Providers By Date

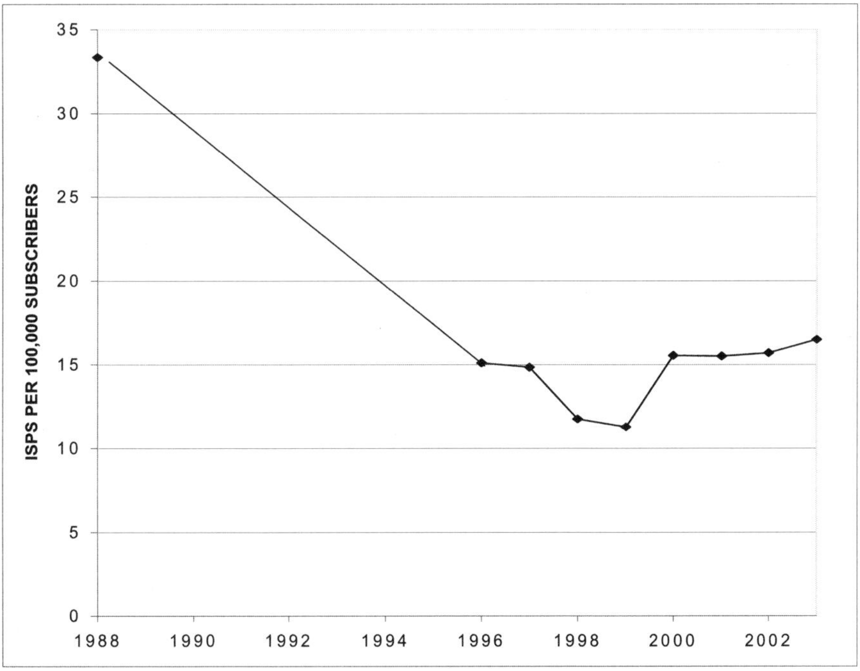

Source: Subscriber counts: Carey, John, "The First Hundred Feet for Households: Consumer Adoption Patterns," in Deborah Hurley and James H. Keller (Eds.), *The First Hundred Feet* (Cambridge: MIT Press, 1999); National Telecommunications Information Administration, *A Nation Online* (U.S. Department of Commerce, 2002). Early ISP counts are discussed in Cooper, Mark, *Expanding the Information Age for the 1990s: A Pragmatic Consumer View* (Washington, D.C.: Consumer Federation of America, American Association of Retired Persons, January 11, 1990); see also Abbate, Janet, *Inventing the Internet* (Cambridge: MIT Press, 1999 and Matos, F., *Information Service Report* (Washington, D.C.: National Telecommunications Information Administration, August 1988). Since the mid-1990s, annual counts of ISPs have been published in *Boardwatch*. Recent ISP counts are from *Boardwatch Magazine*, "North American ISPS," mid year estimates. For high speed ISPs, see Federal Communications Commission, *High-Speed Services for Internet Access*" (Washington, D.C., various issues).

but most are relatively small. The other characteristics of the network are also evident. We see hubs typified by preferential attachment and hierarchy in a decentralized and distributed architecture.

Interestingly, a close look at the data suggests that the Internet, delivering access to the World Wide Web rendered accessible by the development of web browsers, became the killer application for the PC (see Figure 8). Although the PC had enjoyed success prior to

Figure 7:

A Map Of The Internet, Mid-1999

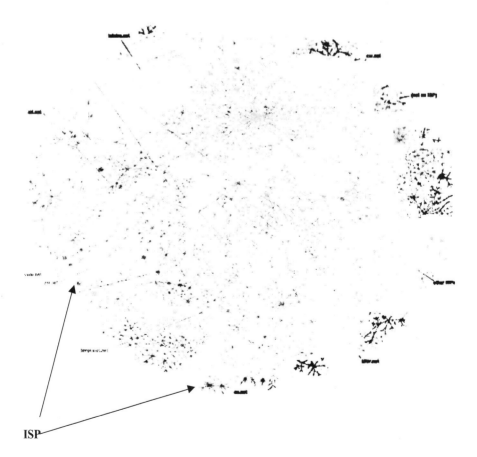

ISP

Source: Buchanan, Mark, *Nexus: Small Worlds and the Groundbreaking Theory of Networks* (New York: Norton, 2002), p. 81; Reprint of Burch/Cheswick Map of the Internet.

commercialization of the Internet, it was only after the advent of selling Internet access service to the public that PC sales exploded. PC prices played a role as well, but it can be argued that the demand stimulation created by the killer application laid the groundwork for the price reductions (see Figure 9). The initial PC price reduction of the mid-1980s sustained moderate growth of the PC for about a decade. In the mid-1990s, PC prices were stable, as Internet use escalated. In the late 1990s, PC prices came down, as demand and Internet use grew. Thus, in an important way,

Figure 8:

The Internet And The Web Were 'Killer Apps" For The PC

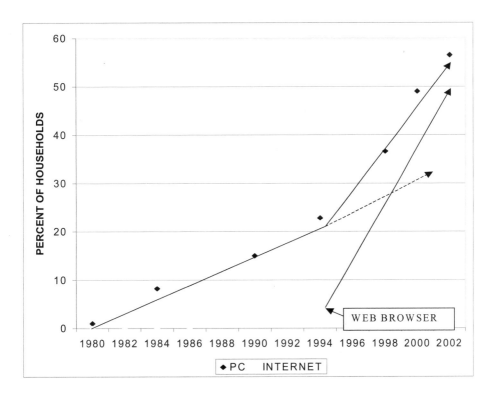

Source: Carey, John, "The First Hundred Feet for Households: Consumer Adoption Patterns," in Deborah Hurley and James H. Keller (Eds.), *The First Hundred Feet* (Cambridge: MIT Press, 1999); National Telecommunications Information Administration, *A Nation Online* (U.S. Department of Commerce, 2002). Early ISP counts are discussed in Cooper, Mark, *Expanding the Information Age for the 1990s: A Pragmatic Consumer View* (Washington, D.C.: Consumer Federation of America, American Association of Retired Persons, January 11, 1990); see also Abbate, Janet, *Inventing the Internet* (Cambridge: MIT Press, 1999) and Matos, F., *Information Service Report* (Washington, D.C.: National Telecommunications Information Administration, August 1988).

the application that triggered demand contributed to the cycle of economies of scale that is so important in the computer industry.

The competitive pressures that small ISPs brought to the Internet service market and the investment in complementary communications equipment stimulated by having nondiscriminatory access to the network represents a general pattern that can be expected to be repeated. In fact, a similar process can be seen in the development of competitive local exchange carriers (CLECs). In an effort to stimulate competition in telecommunications markets, congress mandated that the CLECs be given access to the elements that constitute the telephone network in an unbundled

Figure 9:

Average Price Of Home Personal Computers

Source: Carey, John, "The First Hundred Feet for Households: Consumer Adoption Patterns," in Deborah Hurley and James H. Keller (Eds.), *The First Hundred Feet* (Cambridge: MIT Press, 1999), p. 41.

fashion. These entities began by innovating in marketing and customer service as the ISPs had done, specializing in:

> the value added a competitor contributes through steps such as definition, marketing, sales, and support of commercialized services, all dimensions around which competitors seek to compete and innovate....In the case of UNE-P, for example, competition is keen in pricing, brandings, markets, customer service, etc... [T]hose activities constitute real competition that results in true economic efficiency.[152]

Although the marketing innovation of the new entrants is most obvious, they have also made substantial contributions to the production side of the industry. They have driven innovation in operating support and back office systems, rights of way and collocation, and the provisioning and use of fiber.

> Entrants innovated in almost every dimension of the business from use of rights-of-way, to becoming early adopters of new technology. Entrants innovated at the OSS/BSS level by working closely with new vendors that were developing modular off-the-shelf elements that would support a plug-and-play strategy. While incumbents were selling their real estate because of the miniaturization of equipment and complaining that there was not enough space for collocation, entrepreneurs created the *telehouse,* where myriad service providers could collocate and interconnect efficiently. Fiber became commercialized under a growing diversity of formats – dark or lit, by strands or lambda. While ADSL had been developed by Bellcore in the late 1980's, the CLECs were the first to push for its large-scale deployment. In all, entrants brought a new standard of innovation and efficiency to the marketplace.[153]

One of the lessons from the recent competitive era is that new entrants and competitors can be quite ingenious and innovative in tackling the challenges that they face. One of the most impressive innovations was the use of old pipelines to create a national backbone fiber network... More generally entrants have been very successful in addressing the right-of-way problem where they were at an enormous disadvantage.[154]

Thus, the introduction of competition in a middle or applications layer not only promotes efficiency in that layer, but it may provide the base for launching competition across layers, as well as stimulating investments in complementary assets.

CONCLUSION

The discussion has identified several ways in which open platforms have been ensured. Public policy played a key role in the communications network. Platform leadership played a key role in the case of the PC. A third approach, which can best be described as "philosophical," played a critical role in ensuring the World Wide Web would be open. Its developer held the firm belief (supported by the analysis presented above) that an open architecture is superior for a broad range of purposes.

Communication platforms hold a special role in the "new" economy. This Chapter argues that communications platforms should be kept open. Specifically, the physical layer of facilities (the infrastructure of communications) must remain accessible to consumers and citizens, for it is the most fundamental layer in which to ensure equitable access to the rest of the communications platform. An open communications platform promotes a dynamic space for economic innovation and a robust forum for democratic discourse. The role of regulation should be to ensure that strategically placed actors (perhaps by historical favor) cannot deter expression or innovation at any layer of the platform. This is best achieved by mandating that the core infrastructure of the communications platform remain open and accessible to all.

We are in a critical moment to reaffirm a commitment to open communications platforms because technological and institutional developments in information production are beginning to fulfill the promise of a substantial improvement in both the economy and the polity. The PC-driven Internet has been proven to be an extremely consumer-friendly, citizen-friendly environment for innovation and expression. This has resulted from a largely "open" physical layer – open in the sense of communications devices and transmission networks. The logical or code layer should be open as well, if the end-to-end principle of the Internet is to be fully realized. The end-to-end principle allows interconnection and interoperability in a manner that is particularly well-suited to the economic and political goals of our society. The transparency of the network, and its reliance on distributed intelligence, foster innovation and empower speakers at the ends of the network.

The chaos of economic experimentation and the cacophony of democratic discourse that emanates from an open communications platform model is music to our ears, but the ongoing closure of the third generation Internet has already begun to quiet the chorus.

ENDNOTES

[1] Mark Cooper, EXPANDING THE INFORMATION AGE FOR THE 1990s: A PRAGMATIC CONSUMER VIEW (January 11, 1990). This was the first in a series of reports that analyzed the effects of decentralized, open networks, prior to the dramatic commercial success of the Internet (*see* Mark Cooper, DEVELOPING THE INFORMATION AGE IN THE 1990s: A PRAGMATIC CONSUMER VIEW [June 8, 1992], "Delivering the Information Age Now, Telecom Infrastructure: 1993," TELECOMMUNICATIONS REPORTS, 1993, THE MEANING OF THE WORD INFRASTRUCTURE [June 30, 1994].)

[2] Mark Cooper, THE IMPORTANCE OF ISPs IN THE GROWTH OF THE COMMERCIAL INTERNET: WHY RELIANCE ON FACILITY-BASED COMPETITION WILL NOT PRESERVE VIBRANT COMPETITION AND DYNAMIC INNOVATION A THE HIGH-SPEED INTERNET (July 1, 2002); "Open Communications Platforms: The Physical Infrastructure as the Bedrock of Innovation and Democratic Discourse in the Internet Age," 2 J. ON TELECOMM. & HIGH TECH. L., 1 (2003).

[3] David B. Audretsch & Paul J.J. Welfens (eds.) THE NEW ECONOMY AND ECONOMIC GROWTH IN EUROPE AND THE US (2002), at 18.

[4] Janet Abbate, INVENTING THE INTERNET (1999); Lawrence Lessig, CODE AND OTHER LAWS OF CYBERSPACE (1999).

[5] Identical language is used to describe advanced telecommunications services over cable networks and telephone company advanced telecommunications networks; *see* Federal Communications Commission, *Notice of Proposed Rulemaking*, IN THE MATTER OF APPROPRIATE FRAMEWORK FOR BROADBAND ACCESS TO THE INTERNET OVER WIRELINE FACILITIES, UNIVERSAL SERVICE OBLIGATIONS OF BROADBAND PROVIDERS, COMPUTER III FURTHER REMAND PROCEEDING: BELL OPERATING COMPANY PROVISION OF ENHANCED SERVICES; 1998 BIENNIAL REGULATORY REVIEW – REVIEW OF COMPUTER III AND ONA SAFEGUARDS AND REQUIREMENTS, CC Docket No. 02-33; CC Docket Nos. 95-20, 98-10, para. 25, and Federal Communications Commission, *Declaratory Ruling and Notice of Proposed Rulemaking*, IN THE MATTER OF INQUIRY CONCERNING HIGH-SPEED ACCESS TO THE INTERNET OVER CABLE AND OTHER FACILITIES, INTERNET OVER CABLE DECLARATORY RULING, APPROPRIATE REGULATORY TREATMENT FOR BROADBAND ACCESS TO THE INTERNET OVER CABLE FACILITIES, GN Docket No. 00-185, CS Docket No. 02-52, March 15, 2002, para. 41. The cable operators were officially excused from the obligation for nondiscrimination by the declaratory ruling. The FCC excused telephone companies from many of their obligations in a third order (*see Report and Order on Remand and Further Notice of Proposed Rulemaking*, IN THE MATTER OF REVIEW OF SECTION 251 UNBUNDLING OBLIGATIONS OF INCUMBENT LOCAL EXCHANGE CARRIERS, IMPLEMENTATION OF THE LOCAL COMPETITION PROVISIONS OF THE TELECOMMUNICATIONS ACT OF 1996, DEPLOYMENT OF WIRELINE SERVICE OFFERING ADVANCED TELECOMMUNICATIONS CAPABILITY, CC Docket Nos. 01-338, 96-98, 98-147).

[6] Michael Powell, *Preserving Internet Freedom: Guiding Principles for the Industry*, the DIGITAL BROADBAND MIGRATION: TOWARD A REGULATORY REGIME FOR THE INTERNET AGE, UNIVERSITY OF COLORADO SCHOOL OF LAW, February 8, 2004.

[7] Tim Wu & Lawrence Lessig, *Ex Parte Submission* in CS DOCKET *No. 02-52,* August 22, 2003, at 7-8.

[8] Albert-Laszlo Barabasi, LINKED (2002), Mark Buchanan, NEXUS: SMALL WORLDS AND THE GROUNDBREAKING THEORY OF NETWORKS (2002); Duncan Watts, SIX DEGREES: THE SCIENCE OF A CONNECTED AGE (2003).

[9] Cooper, EXPANDING THE INFORMATION AGE, *supra* note 1, at ES-1.

[10] *Id.*, at ES-6.

[11] *Id.*, at ES-5.

[12] *Id.*, at 12.

[13] Earl W. Comstock & John Butler, *Access Denied: The FCC's Failure to Implement Open Access as Required by the Communications Act,* J. OF COMM. L. & POL. (Winter 2000).

[14] Lawrence Lessig, THE FUTURE OF IDEAS (2001), at 148, emphasizes the break with the Computer Inquiries in the approach to advanced telecommunications services.

[15] Mark A. Lemley & Lawrence Lessig, *The End of End-to-End: Preserving the Architecture of the Internet in the Broadband Era,* 48 UCLA L. REV. 925, 935 (2001) (written as a direct response to James P. Speta, *Written Ex Parte,* APPLICATION FOR CONSENT TO THE TRANSFER OF CONTROL OF LICENSES MEDIAONE GROUP, INC. TO AT&T CORP. FCC DOC. NO. 99-251 (1999)). *See also* James B. Speta, *The Vertical Dimension of Cable Open Access,* 71 U. COLO. L. REV. 975 (2000); Phil Weiser, *Paradigm Changes in Telecommunications Regulation,* 71 U. COLO. L. REV. 819 (2000) (responding to an earlier piece by Lemley & Lessig, *Written Ex Parte,* APPLICATION FOR CONSENT TO TRANSFER CONTROL OF LICENSES OF MEDIAONE GROUP INC. TO AT&T CORP., FCC DOC. NO. 99-251 (1999) *available at* http://cyber.law.harvard.edu/works/lessig/filing/lem-les.doc.html.

[16] Janet Abbate, INVENTING THE, *supra* note 4.

[17] David B. Audretsch & Paul J.J. Welfens, *Introduction*, in THE NEW ECONOMY AND ECONOMIC GROWTH IN EUROPE AND THE US (David B. Audretsch and Paul J.J. Welfens, eds., 2002).

[18] Mark Cooper, TRANSFORMING THE INFORMATION SUPER HIGHWAY INTO A PRIVATE TOLL ROAD (October, 1999), at 3. *See* also, *Reply Comments of Center for Media Education, et al.,* INQUIRY CONCERNING THE DEPLOYMENT OF ADVANCED TELECOMMUNICATIONS CAPABILITY TO AMERICA AMERICANS IN A REASONABLE AND TIMELY FASHION, AND POSSIBLE STEPS TO ACCELERATE SUCH DEPLOYMENT PURSUANT TO SECTION 706 OF THE TELECOMMUNICATIONS ACT OF 1996, Federal Communications Commission, CC Docket No. 98-146, October 10, 1998; *Petition to Deny Consumers Union, et al.,* JOINT APPLICATION OF AT&T CORPORATION AND TELE-COMMUNICATIONS INC. FOR APPROVAL OF TRANSFER OF CONTROL OF COMMISSION LICENSES AND AUTHORIZATIONS, FEDERAL COMMUNICATIONS COMMISSION, CS Docket No. 98-178, October 28, 1998.

[19] *Comments of Texas Office of Public Utility Counsel, Consumer Federation of America, Consumers Union,* IN THE MATTER OF INQUIRY CONCERNING HIGH SPEED ACCESS TO THE INTERNET OVER CABLE AND OTHER FACILITIES, Federal Communications Commission, GN Docket No. 96-262, December 12, 1999, January 12, 2000; *Comments of Consumers Union, et al.,* INQUIRY CONCERNING HIGH-SPEED ACCESS TO THE INTERNET OVER CABLE AND OTHER FACILITIES, GEN Docket No. 00-185 (filed December 1, 2001); *Comments of Texas Office of Consumer Counsel, Consumer Federation of America,* IN THE MATTER OF INQUIRY CONCERNING HIGH-SPEED ACCESS TO THE INTERNET OVER CABLE AND OTHER FACILITIES; DECLARATORY RULING; APPROPRIATE REGULATORY TREATMENT FOR BROADBAND

ACCESS TO THE INTERNET OVER CABLE FACILITIES, Federal Communications Commission, GN Dockets Nos. 00-185, CS Dockets No. 02-52, March 15, 2002.

[20] *Comments of Arizona Consumer Council, et al.*," IN THE MATTER OF APPROPRIATE FRAMEWORK FOR BROADBAND ACCESS TO THE INTERNET OVER WIRELINE FACILITIES UNIVERSAL SERVICE OBLIGATIONS OF BROADBAND PROVIDERS COMPUTER III FURTHER REMAND PROCEEDINGS: BELL OPERATING COMPANY PROVISION OF ENHANCED SERVICES; 1998 BIENNIAL REGULATORY REVIEW – REVIEW OF COMPUTER III AND ONA SAFEGUARDS AND REQUIREMENTS, Federal Communications Commission, CC Dockets Nos. 95-20, 98-10, May 3, 2002; Reply Comments, July 1,2002; *Comments and Reply Comments of The Consumer Federation of America, Texas Office of Public Utility Counsel, Consumers Union, and Center For Digital Democracy*, IN THE MATTER OF REVIEW OF THE SECTION 251 UNBUNDLING, OBLIGATIONS OF INCUMBENT LOCAL EXCHANGE CARRIERS, IMPLEMENTATION OF THE LOCAL COMPETITION PROVISIONS OF THE TELECOMMUNICATIONS ACT OF 1996, DEPLOYMENT OF WIRELINE SERVICES OFFERING ADVANCED TELECOMMUNICATIONS CAPABILITY, Federal Communications Commission, CC Dockets Nos. 01-338, 96-98, 98-147, April 5, 2002; *Reply Comments*, July 1, 2002.

[21] *Brand X Internet Services v FCC*, 9th Circ. No. o2-50518,October 6, 2003.

[22] Lessig, FUTURE, *supra* note 14, at 23 notes that Tim Berners-Lee, WEAVING THE WEB: THE ORIGINAL DESIGN AND ULTIMATE DESTINY OF THE WORLD WIDE WEB BY ITS INVENTOR (1999), at 129-30, identified four layers: transmission, computer, software and content.

[23] Carl Shapiro & Hal Varian, INFORMATION RULES: A STRATEGIC GUIDE TO THE NETWORK ECONOMY (1999), at 9-15; Richard N. Langlois, *Technology Standards, Innovation, and Essential Facilities: Toward a Schumpeterian Post-Chicago Approach*, in DYNAMIC COMPETITION & PUBLIC POLICY: TECHNOLOGY, INNOVATIONS, AND ANTITRUST ISSUES (Jerry Ellig, ed., 2001), at 193, 207 *available at* http://papers.ssrn.com/sol3/papers.cfm?abstract_id=204069 (last visited Jan. 24, 2003).

[24] Shane Greenstein, *The Evolving Structure of the Internet Market*, in UNDERSTANDING THE DIGITAL ECONOMY (Erik Brynjolfsson and Brian Kahin, eds., 2000), at 155.

[25] Id., at 155.

[26] Sara Baase, A GIFT OF FIRE: SOCIAL, LEGAL AND ETHICAL ISSUES IN COMPUTING (1997); George Gilder, TELECOMS: HOW INFINITE BANDWIDTH WILL REVOLUTIONIZE OUR WORLD (2000).

[27] Brian R. Gaines, *The Learning Curve Underlying Convergence*, TECHNOLOGICAL FORECASTING & SOC. CHANGE (Jan./Feb. 1998), at 30-31.

[28] Bruce Owen, THE INTERNET CHALLENGE TO TELEVISION (1999), at 29.

[29] Id., at 151.

[30] Shapiro & Varian, INFORMATION RULES, *supra* note 23, at 22-23.

[31] High first copy costs are an enduring quality of information that is reinforced in the industrial age by the presence of high capital costs. In the pre-industrial and (perhaps) post-industrial periods first copy costs entail high human capital costs.

[32] Gaines, *The Learning Curve, supra* note 27, at 30-31.

[33] C. Edwin Baker, MEDIA, MARKET AND DEMOCRACY (2001), at 8.

[34] Shapiro & Varian, INFORMATION RULES, *supra* note 23, at 22-23.

[35] Yochai Benkler, *Intellectual Property and the Organization of Information Production*, 22 INT'L REV. L. & ECON. 81 (2002), *available at* http://www.law.nyu.edu/benklery/IP&Organization.pdf, (last visited Jan. 24, 2003) at 5; *see also* Baker, *supra* note 33, at 8-14.

[36] John B. Taylor, ECONOMICS (1998), at 412-25.

[37] Shapiro & Varian, INFORMATION RULES, *supra* note 23, at 13-17.

[38] W. Brian Arthur, *Positive Feedbacks in the Economy*, 262 SCIENTIFIC AM., 95 (Feb. 1990); *see also* W. Brian Arthur, *Competing Technologies, Increasing Returns and Lock-in by Historical Events*, 99 ECON. J. (1989).

[39] Distinctions between classes of users might be made, but all members of the class had the same access to the element.

[40] Gaines, *The Learning Curve, supra* note 27, at 20. *See*, e.g., James Gleick, FASTER: THE ACCELERATION OF JUST ABOUT EVERYTHING (1999); Jeffrey L. Sampler, *Redefining Industry Structure for the Information Age*, ENGINEERING MGMT. REV., 68 (Summer 1999).

[41] Stephen Moore & Julian L. Simon, *The Greatest Century That Ever Was: 25 Miraculous U.S. Trends of the Past 100 Years* (Cato Inst. Policy Analysis No. 364, 1999), at 24, *available at* http://www.cato.org/pubs/pas/pa364.pdf (last visited Jan. 24, 2003).

[42] Following Lessig's paradigm of modalities of regulation as interpreted as realms of social order in Mark Cooper, *Inequality in Digital Society: Why the Digital Divide Deserves All the Attention it Gets*, 20 CARDOZO ARTS & ENTERTAINMENT L. J., 93 (2002). We can track the technological transformation affecting the economy (see BRIE-IGCC E-conomy Project, TRACKING A TRANSFORMATION: E-COMMERCE AND THE TERMS OF COMPETITION IN INDUSTRIES (2001)), the polity (*see* GOVERNANCE.COM: DEMOCRACY IN THE INFORMATION AGE (Elaine Ciulla Kamarck & Joseph S. Nye Jr. eds., 2002)) and civic institutions (*see* Jeremy Rifkin, THE AGE OF ACCESS: THE NEW CULTURE OF HYPERCAPITALISM, WHERE ALL OF LIFE IS A PAID-FOR EXPERIENCE (2000), chs. 11-12; Andrew L. Shapiro, THE CONTROL REVOLUTION: HOW THE INTERNET IS PUTTING INDIVIDUALS IN CHARGE AND CHANGING THE WORLD WE KNOW (1999), chs. 20-21).

[43] Ida Harper Simpson, *Historical Patterns of Workplace Organization: From Mechanical to Electronic Control and Beyond*, CURRENT SOC. 47 (Apr. 1999); Barry Bluestone & Bennett Harrison, GROWING PROSPERITY: THE BATTLE FOR GROWTH WITH EQUITY IN THE TWENTY-FIRST CENTURY (2001), seeking historical parallels to previous technological revolutions, ultimately acknowledge uniqueness of current transformation; George Evans, et al., *Growth Cycles*, 88 AM. ECON. REV. 495 (1998).

[44] Erik Brynjolfsson and Brian Kahin, *Introduction*, in UNDERSTANDING THE DIGITAL ECONOMY (Erik Brynjolfsson and Brian Kahin, eds., 2000), at 1.

[45] Langlois, *Technology Standards, supra* note 23, at 207.

[46] François Bar, et al., *Defending the Internet Revolution in the Broadband Era: When Doing Nothing is Doing Harm* (1999), *at* http://e-conomy.berkeley.edu/publications/ wp/ewp12.pdf.

[47] *See* Yochai Benkler, *Coase's Penguin, or Linux and the Nature of the Firm* (paper presented at the CONFERENCE ON THE PUBLIC DOMAIN, DUKE UNIVERSITY LAW SCHOOL, Nov. 9-11, 2001), *at*

http://www.law.duke.edu/pd/papers/ Coase's_Penguin.pdf (last visited Jan. 24, 2003), at 2.

[48] Manuel Castells, THE INTERNET GALAXY – REFLECTIONS ON THE INTERNET, BUSINESS, AND SOCIETY (2001), at 28.

[49] Yochai Benkler, *Property Commons and the First Amendment: Toward a Core Common Infrastructure,* BRENNAN CENTER FOR JUSTICE, NEW YORK UNIVERSITY LAW SCHOOL, March 2000.

[50] Langlois, *Technology Standards, supra* note 23.

[51] Benkler, *Coase's Penguin, supra* note 47, at 22-23.

[52] Cooper, *Inequality, supra* note 42.

[53] Marina N. Whitman, NEW WORLD, NEW RULES (1999), at 17, 32-37, 55-62.

[54] Manuel Castells, THE RISE OF NETWORK SOCIETY (1996); Richard C. Longworth, GLOBAL SQUEEZE (1998).

[55] Philip Evans & Thomas S. Wurster, BLOWN TO BITS: HOW THE NEW ECONOMICS OF INFORMATION TRANSFORMS STRATEGY (2000), at 17 (footnote omitted).

[56] National Research Council, REALIZING THE INFORMATION FUTURE, (1994), at 43.

[57] Id., at 43.

[58] Id., at 44.

[59] "Comments of the High Tech Broadband Coalition," *In the Matter of Appropriate Regulatory Treatment for Broadband Access to the Internet Over Cable Facilities*, CC Docket No. 96-45, June 17, 2002, at 7-9 (hereafter Cable Modem Proceeding); *see also* "Reply Comments of the High Tech Broadband Coalition," *In the Matter of Appropriate Framework for Broadband Access to the Internet over Wireline Facilities,* CC Docket No. 02-33, July 1, 2002.

[60] High Tech Broadband Coalition, *Id.* Cable Modem Proceeding, at 9.

[61] Lee W. McKnight, *Internet Business Models: Creative Destruction as Usual*, in CREATIVE DESTRUCTION: BUSINESS SURVIVAL STRATEGIES IN THE GLOBAL INTERNET ECONOMY (Lee W. McKnight, Paul M. Vaaler, & Raul L. Katz, eds., 2001), at 45.

[62] Buchanan, NEXUS, *supra* note 8, at 76.

[63] *Id.*, at 76-77.

[64] Joel Mokyr, *Innovation in an Historical Perspective: Tales of Technology and Evolution*, in TECHNOLOGICAL INNOVATION AND ECONOMIC PERFORMANCE (Benn Steil, David G. Victor & Richard R. Nelson, eds., 2002).

[65] *Id.*, at 42.

[66] *Id.*, at 141.

[67] *Id.*, at 42.

[68] Harold Evans, THE AMERICAN CENTURY (1998).

[69] This understanding of common carriage is quite prevalent, as an analysis prepared by Morgan Stanley Dean Witter, THE DIGITAL DECADE, April 6, 1999, at 177-178, noted in describing common carriers:

> Generally, they are involved in the sale of infrastructure services in transportation and communications. The legal principle of common carriage is used to ensure that no customer seeking service upon reasonable demand, willing and able to pay the established prices,

however, set, would be denied lawful use of the service or would otherwise be discriminated against...

Significantly, a carrier does not have to claim to be a common carrier to be treated as such under the law: a designation of common carriage depends upon a carriers actual business practices, not its charter... .

Common carriage is also thought to be an economically efficient response to reduce the market power of carriers through government regulation, preventing discrimination and/or censorship and promoting competition. It is also said to promote the basic infrastructure, reduce transaction costs from carrier to carrier, and extend some protections for First Amendment rights from the public to the private sector.

[70] Cited in James B. Speta, *A Common Carrier Approach to Internet Interconnection*, 54 FED. COMM. L.J., 254 (2002).

[71] Andrew Odlyzko, PRICING AND ARCHITECTURE OF THE INTERNET: HISTORICAL PERSPECTIVES FROM TELECOMMUNICATIONS AND TRANSPORTATION (2003), notes price discrimination between classes of goods but not in access to the network. He also notes the central role of government policy in establishing rights of access and setting rates (*see* also Hal Varian, MARKETS FOR PUBLIC GOODS [January 2003]; D. Davis, SHINE YOUR LIGHT ON ME, December 23, 2002 (http://D-squareddiest.blogpost.org/2002_12_22_d-squareddigest_archives.html#86435321)).

[72] Hockett v. State Indiana, 1886, cited Speta, *Common Carrier, supra* note 70, at 262.

[73] Cited in Alfred Kahn, THE ECONOMICS OF REGULATION: PRINCIPLES AND INSTITUTIONS (1988), at 55.

[74] Speta, *The Vertical Dimension, supra* note 15, at 975; Phil Weiser, *Paradigm Changes in Telecommunications Regulation,* 71 UNIV. COLO. L. REV., 819 (2000).

[75] Mokyr, *Innovation, supra* note 64, at 42-43.

[76] Barabasi, LINKED, *supra* note 8, at 110.

[77] *Id.*, at 110.

[78] *Id.*, at 113.

[79] *Id.*, at 232.

[80] The biological analogy is strong here, since "cells sustain a multitude of functions – i.e., multitask – thanks to a discrete modular organization... [T]he network behind the cell is fragmented into groups of diverse molecules, or modules, each module being responsible for a different cellular function." (Barabasi, LINKED, *supra* note 8, at 231).

[81] Barabasi, LINKED, *supra* note 8, at 236.

[82] Barabasi, LINKED, *supra* note 8, at 86.

[83] Watts, SIX DEGREES, *supra* note 8, at 277.

[84] WEBSTER'S THIRD NEW INTERNATIONAL DICTIONARY (1986), at 2102.

[85] *Id.*, at 277.

[86] *Id.*, at 277.

[87] *Id.*, at 277.

[88] Buchanan, NEXUS, *supra* note 8, at 58.

[89] Watts, SIX DEGREES, *supra* note 8, at 279.

[90] Buchanan, NEXUS, *supra* note 8, at 43.

[91] Watts, Six Degrees, *supra* note 8, at 286.

[92] Barabasi, Linked, *supra* note 8, at 236.

[93] Watts, Six Degrees, *supra* note 8, at 279-80.

[94] Searchability in problem solving implies another characteristic of the network, feedback. Steven Johnson, Emergence: The Connected Lives of Ants, Brains, Cities and Software (2001), at 134, frames the explanation in terms of neural networks asking, "why do these feedback loops and reverberating circuits happen?"

[95] Watts, Six Degrees, *supra* note 8, at 56.

[96] *Id.*, at 288.

[97] *Id.*, at 279.

[98] *Id.*, at 288.

[99] Barabasi. Linked, *supra* note 8, at 148.

[100] Berners-Lee, Weaving the Web, *supra* note 22, at 211.

[101] Barabasi, Linked, *supra* note 8, at 129).

[102] Watts, Six Degrees, *supra* note 8, at 244.

[103] *Id.*, at 230-231.

[104] *Id.*, at 241.

[105] *Id.*, at 287.

[106] Buchanan, Nexus, *supra* note 8, at 69.

[107] Watts, Six Degrees, *supra* note 8, at 287.

[108] Ashish Arora, Andrea Fosfuri and Alfonso Gamardella, Markets for Technology: The Economics of Innovation and Corporate Strategy (2001), at 112.

[109] *Id.,* at 106.

[110] *Id.,* at 106.

[111] *Id.,* at 103. The efficient solution emerges in a direct analogy to the biological cell. "A work cell is a small group of technical and human resources closely located and dedicated to processing a family of similar parts, products, information deliverables or services." Comparing work cells to an assembly line underscores the critical superiority of modular design. Real cells have "more flexibility in that they can produce a range of service or products within a family… [and] normally perform a broader range of tasks." They are a "hybrid that combines the focus of an assembly line with the flexibility of a job shop functional arrangement."

> [A] "real cell" links tasks and those who perform them in terms of space, time, and information.
> *Space Linkages:* Cell resources must be located closely together. Moreover proximal human and technical resources must include all the necessary skill sets and processing capabilities a product or service family will require…
> *Time Linkages:* both the physical layout of the cell and its operating routines must permit work to flow expediently from one station to the next…
> *Information Linkages:* A cell should be configured and operated such that information about the work being processed flows easily.

[112] Brown John Seely & Paul Duguid, *Mysteries of the Region: Knowledge Dynamics in Silicon Valley*, in The Silicon Valley Edge: A Habitat for Innovation and

ENTREPRENEURSHIP (Chong-Moon Lee, William F. Miller, Marguerite Gong Hancock & Henry S. Rowen, eds., 2000), at 29.

[113] *Id.*, at 31-32.

[114] *Id.*, at 32.

[115] *Id.*, at 32.

[116] Annalee Saxenian, *The Origins and Dynamics of Production Networks in Silicon Valley*, in UNDERSTANDING SILICON VALLEY (Martin Kenney, ed., 2000), at 144.

[117] Id., at 145.

[118] David B. Audretsch & Charles F. Bonser, *Regional Policy in the New Economy*, in THE NEW ECONOMY AND ECONOMIC GROWTH IN EUROPE AND THE US (David B. Audretsch & Paul J.J. Welfens, eds., 2002), at 130.

[119] Chong-Moon Lee, William F. Miller, Marguerite Gong Hancock & Henry S. Rowen, "The Silicon Valley Habitat," in THE SILICON VALLEY EDGE: A HABITAT FOR INNOVATION AND ENTREPRENEURSHIP (Chong-Moon Lee, William F. Miller, Marguerite Gong Hancock & Henry S. Rowen, eds., 2000), at 6.

[120] Von Hippel, at 642.

[121] Arora, *supra* note 108, at 112.

[122] *Id.*, at 112.

[123] *Id.*, at 113.

[124] *Id.*, at 104-105.

[125] *Id.*, at 255.

[126] David J. Teece, MANAGING INTELLECTUAL CAPITAL (2000), at 71.

[127] Werner Roger, *Structure Changes and New Economy in the EU and the US,* in THE NEW ECONOMY AND ECONOMIC GROWTH IN EUROPE AND THE US (David B. Audretsch & Paul J.J. Welfens, eds., 2002), at 18.

[128] Mark A. Carree, *The Effect of Restructuring the Organization of Production on Economic Growth*, in THE NEW ECONOMY AND ECONOMIC GROWTH IN EUROPE AND THE US (David B. Audretsch & Paul J.J. Welfens, eds., 2002), at 205… 210.

[129] Arora, *supra* note 108, at 113.

[130] *Id.*, at 263.

[131] *Id.*, at 263.

[132] *Id.*, at 263-64.

[133] Annabelle Gawer & Michael A. Cusumano, PLATFORM LEADERSHIP: HOW INTEL, MICROSOFT AND CISCO DRIVE INNOVATION (2002), at 55-56.

[134] Id., at 55.

[135] *Id.*, at 51.

[136] *Id.*, at 52.

[137] Saxenian, *The Origin and Dynamic, supra* note 115, at 148.

[138] Brown & Duguid, *Mysteries of the Region, supra* note 111, at 32.

[139] Gawer and Cusimano, PLATFORM LEADERSHIP, *supra* note 132, at 28-29.

[140] Berners-Lee, WEAVING THE WEB, *supra* note 22, at 72-73.

[141] Abbate, INVENTING THE INTERNET (1999); Lessig, FUTURE OF IDEAS, *supra* note 8, Chapters 3 and 4; Shane Greenstein, *Commercialization of the Internet: The Interaction of Public Policy and Private Choices, or Why Introducing the Market Worked so Well* (NBER, N.D.), *Building and Delivering the Virtual World: Commercializing Services*

for Internet Access (March 31, 2000); *The Evolving Structure of Commercial Internet Markets*, in Understanding the Digital Economy (Erik Brynjolfsson & Brian Kahin, eds., 2000).

[142] Frank Matos, Information Service Report (1988); Abbate, Inventing the Internet, *supra* note 134.

[143] Recent ISPS counts are from Boardwatch Magazine, *North American ISPS*. There are differences of opinion about the precise numbers. We use this source as an internally consistent set of numbers. While there are differences in details, the trends seem clear – rapid growth in the late 1990s and declines in the past couple of years.

[144] Greenstein, *Commercialization of the Internet, supra* note 134, emphasizes the range of services offered; "Comments of Earthlink, Inc," *In the matter of Appropriate Framework for Broadband Access to the Internet Over Wireline Facilities, Universal Service Obligations of Broadband Providers, Computer III Remand Proceedings: Bell Operating Company Provision of Enhanced Services; 1998 Biennial Regulatory Review – Review of Computer II and ONA Safeguards and Requirements*, Federal Communications Commission, CC Docket NO. 02-33, 95-20, 98-10, May 3, 2002, at 6, offers the following list: "ISPs offer a host of information functionalities under the rubric "Internet access" that includes, but is not limited to, email, web access, instant messaging ("IM"), chat rooms, content-based services (such as news, weather, music, stock quotes, etc.) web-hosting, access to software or games, and more."

[145] Berners-Lee, title, *supra* note 22, at 80-81.

[146] Shane Greenstein, *Building and Delivering the Virtual World: Commercializing Service for Internet Access* (March, 31, 2000), at 2.

[147] Greenstein, *Building and Delivering, supra* note 139, at 168.

[148] *Id.,* at 168.

[149] *Id.*, at 168.

[150] *Id.*, at 3.

[151] David C. Mowery & Timothy Simcoe, *The Internet*, in Technological Innovation and Economic Performance (Benn Steil, David G. Victor, & Richard R. Nelson, 2002), at 238.

[152] Allaine DeFontenay, Why Inefficient Incumbents Can Prevail in the Marketplace Over More Efficient Entrant: An Analysis of Economies of Scale and Scope, Transaction Costs and the Misuse of Data, (2003), at 27.

[153] Id., at 57.

[154] Id., at 39.

V. ANTICOMPETITIVE PROBLEMS OF CLOSED COMMUNICATIONS FACILITIES

Collective action problems and positive externalities have been identified as critical justifications for public policies that promote open communications platforms. In this Chapter I argue that the heightened potential for negative, anticompetitive actions by private parties who have a dominant position at key locations of the platform also provides the basis for policies to defend the open architecture of the platform. Antitrust authorities reviewing mergers or evaluating complaints of anticompetitive conduct and Communications Act authorities considering obligations of interconnection and universal service must consider anticompetitive conduct because dominant firms in the critical layers of the platform may have the incentive and ability to protect and promote their interests at the expense of competition and the public.

The discussion starts with a framework for economic analysis of the digital communications platform that emphasizes the potential for new and more harmful types of anticompetitive behavior in platform industries. It shows that firms that own and control key layers of the platform can undermine competition, distort the architecture of the platform and slow innovation. By describing threats to the open architecture of the digital communications platform, the paper endeavors to create a broader understanding of the nature and role of networks that will convince policymakers to reconsider the decision to allow proprietary discrimination to undermine the open architecture of the digital communications platform. After outlining the theoretical concerns, I review complaints offered by major players in the industry. The analytic framework for anticompetitive concerns in the network industries is then applied to the case of Internet Service Providers, who were impacted severely as the openness of the digital communications platform was reduced as it moves from narrowband to broadband.

THE THREAT OF MARKET POWER

The vertical nature of the digital communications platform raises new concerns about these anticompetitive behaviors. Competition within a given layer, the equivalent of traditional horizontal competition, can take place without competition across layers.[1] The type of behavior across layers is very important, both because it can promote dynamic change and because it can involve powerful anticompetitive leverage. If it is procompetitive, it can move the whole platform to a higher level of production. If it is anticompetitive, it can be very dangerous. It can pollute a competitive layer and it can undermine the best basis for introducing competition in a layer that had not hitherto been competitive.

In old economy industries, vertical leverage is exploited by business practices. Companies vertically integrate to internalize transactions. Where concerns about vertical integration have traditionally been raised, they focus on integration for critical inputs across markets. Vertically integrated companies may withdraw business from the open market, driving up the cost of inputs for competitors, or deny supply to the market.[2] If they constitute a large share of the market or refuse to buy or sell intermediate inputs (or raise the costs to rivals) the impact can be anticompetitive. By integrating across stages of production, incumbents can create barriers to entry by forcing potential competitors to enter at more than one stage, making competition much less likely due to increased capital requirements.[3] Exclusive and preferential deals for the use of facilities and products compound the problem. They "reduce the number of alternative sources for other firms at either stage, [which] can increase the costs of market or contractual exchange."[4] Integrated firms can impose higher costs on their rivals, or degrade their quality of service to gain an advantage. "[F]or example, the conduct of vertically integrated firms increase[s] risks for nonintegrated firms by exposing downstream specialists to regular or occasional price squeezes."[5] Vertical integration facilitates price squeezes and enhances price discrimination.[6]

The platform nature of digital communications creates unique new sources of vertical leverage (see Figure 1). The physical and code layers that lie at the bottleneck of the platform makes threats to the openness of the network very potent. They have great leverage because of their critical location. In a platform industry, vertical leverage can take a more insidious form, technological integration/manipulation.[7] Introduction of incompatibilities can impair or undermine the function of disfavored complements. The ability to undermine interoperability or the refusal to interoperate is an extremely powerful tool for excluding or undermining rivals and thereby short circuiting competition, as is the withholding of functionality. The mere threat of incompatibility or foreclosure through the refusal to interoperate can drive competitors away.

The dominant players in the physical and code layers have the power to readily distort the architecture of the platform to protect their market

Figure 1

**Unique Characteristics Of Communications Platforms
That Raise Special Market Power Concerns**

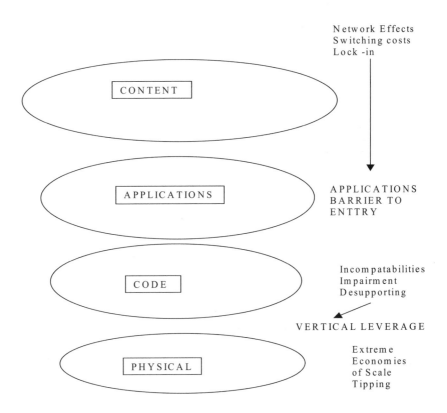

interests.[8] They have a variety of tools to create economic and entry barriers[9] such as exclusive deals,[10] retaliation,[11] manipulation of standards,[12] and strategies that freeze customers.[13] Firms can leverage their access to customers to reinforce their market dominance[14] by creating ever-larger bundles of complementary assets.[15] As the elasticity of demand declines over the course of the product life cycle, market power lodged in the physical layer results in excessive bundling[16] and overpricing of products under a variety of market conditions.[17] Control over the product cycle can impose immense costs by creating incompatibilities,[18] forcing upgrades,[19] and by spreading the cost increases across layers of the platform to extract consumer surplus.[20]

Scale and scope economies may be so strong in the critical layers of the platform that they may give rise to a unique characteristic of a market called tipping. Interacting with network effects and the ability to set standards, the market tips toward one producer. Firms seek to accomplish technological "lock-in."[21] These processes create what has been called an 'applications barrier to entry.' After capturing the first generation of customers and building a customer base, it becomes difficult, if not impossible, for later technologies to overcome this advantage.[22] Customers hesitate to abandon their investments in the dominant technology and customer acquisition costs rise for latecomers.

This creates an immense base of monopsony power for dominant players in the critical layers. I use the term monopsony broadly to refer to the ability to control demand. If a firm is a huge buyer of content or applications or can dictate which content reaches the public through control of a physical or code interface (a cable operator that buys programming or an operating system vendor who bundles applications), it can determine the fate of content and applications developers. In fact, network effects are also known as demand side economies of scale. To the extent that a large buyer or network owner controls sufficient demand to create such effects, particularly in negotiating with sellers of products, they have monopsony power.

These anti-competitive behaviors are attractive to a dominant new economy firm for static and dynamic reasons.[23] Preserving market power in the core market by erecting cross-platform incompatibilities that raise rivals' costs is a critical motivation. Preventing rivals from achieving economies of scale can preserve market power in the core product and allow monopoly rents to persist. Profits may be increased in the core product by enhanced abilities to price discriminate. Conquering neighboring markets has several advantages. By driving competitors out of neighboring markets, market power in new products may be created or the ability to preserve market power across generations of a product may be enhanced by diminishing the pool of potential competitors.

The growing concern about digital information platform industries derives from the fact that the physical and code layers do not appear to be very competitive.[24] There are not now nor are there likely to be a sufficient number of networks deployed in any given area to sustain vigorous competition. Vigorous and balanced competition between operating systems has not been sustained for long periods of time.

Most communications markets have a small number of competitors. In the high speed Internet market, there are now two main competitors and the one with the dominant market share has a substantially superior technology.[25] When or whether there will be a third, and how well it will be able to compete, is unclear. This situation is simply not sufficient to sustain a competitive outcome.

Confronted with the fact that the physical and code layers have very few competitors, defenders of closed, proprietary platforms argue that monopoly may be preferable. As the FCC put it, "[s]ome economists, most notably Schumpeter, suggest that monopoly can be more conducive to innovation than competition, since monopolists can more readily capture the benefits of innovation."[26] Thus, some argue that facility owners, exercising their property rights to exclude and dictate uses of the network, will produce a more dynamic environment than an open communications platform.[27] The hope is that a very small number of owners engaging in the rent seeking behavior of innovators will stimulate more investment, and that this enlightened self-interest will probably convince them to open their network. Notwithstanding the clear success of the open communications platform,[28] and the demonstrated unwillingness of incumbent facility owners to open their platforms when they are not required to do so,[29] monopoly proponents tell us that the next generation of the Internet cannot succeed under the same rules of open communications that were responsible for its birth.

This argument is conceptually linked to long-standing claims that "firms need protection from competition before they will bear the risks and costs of invention and innovation, and a monopoly affords an ideal platform for shooting at the rapidly and jerkily moving targets of new technology."[30] Lately this argument is extended to claims that, in the new economy, "winner take all" industries exhibit competition for the entire market, not competition within the market. As long as monopolists are booted out on a regular basis, or believe they can be, monopoly is in the public interest.[31]

In a sense, this argument is a return to the pre-Internet logic of communications platforms, in which it is assumed that the center of value creation resides in the physical layer.[32] The contrast with the demonstrated impact of freeing the code and content layers to innovate and add value, while running on top of an open physical layer, could not be more dramatic.

The theory supporting Schumpeterian rents appears to be particularly ill-suited to several layers of the digital communications platform. It breaks down if the monopoly is not transitory, a likely outcome in the physical layer. In the physical layer, with its high capital costs and other barriers to entry, monopoly is more likely to quickly lead to anticompetitive practices that leverage the monopoly power over bottleneck facilities into other layers of the platform.

The theory has also been challenged for circumstances that seem to typify the code and applications layers of the Internet platform. [33] The monopoly rent argument appears to be least applicable to industries in which rapid and raucous technological progress is taking place within the framework of an open platform, as has typified the Internet through its first two decades.[34] The "winner take all" argument was firmly rejected in the Microsoft case.[35] The Internet seems to fit the mode of atomistic competition much better than the creative monopolist rent-seeking model, as did the development and progress of its most important device, the PC.[36]

One of the most important factors in creating a positive feedback process is openness in the early stages of development of the platform.[37] In order to stimulate the complementary assets and supporting services, and to attract the necessary critical mass of customers, the technology must be open to adoption and development by both consumers and suppliers.[38] This openness captures the critical fact that demand and consumers are interrelated.[39] If the activities of firms begin to promote closed technologies,[40] this is a clear sign that motivation may have shifted.[41] While it is clear in the literature that a company's installed base is important, it is not clear that an installed base must be so large that a single firm can dominate the market. Schumpeter's observation deals with the issue of the size of the firm, so that it achieves economies of scale, not the market share of the firm. As long as platforms are open, the installed base can be fragmented and still be large.[42] In other words, a large market share is not synonymous with a large market.[43] A standard is not synonymous with a proprietary standard.[44] Open platforms and compatible products are identified as providing a basis for network effects that are at least as dynamic as closed, proprietary platforms[45] and much less prone to anti-competitive conduct.[46]

FROM THEORY TO PRACTICE

The emerging model for closed communications platforms is one in which the firm with a dominant technology at the central layers of the platform can leverage control to achieve domination of applications and content. Given the hourglass shape of the platform, the critical layers are at the waist of the platform. Proprietary control of network layers in which there is a lack of adequate alternatives allows owners to lock in consumers and squeeze competitors out of the broader market. The observable behavior of the incumbent wire owners contradicts the theoretical claims made in defense of closed platforms. The track record of competition in the physical facilities of telephony and cable certainly should not be a source of encouragement for those looking for dynamic Schumpeterian monopolists.[47] For the last several decades of the 20th century, general analysis concerning vertical integration in market structure was muted. However, a number of recent mergers in the communications industries, between increasingly larger owners of communications facilities, have elicited vigorous analysis of the abuse of vertical market power (e.g. Comcast/AT&T/MediaOne/TCI, AOL/Time Warner/Turner, SBC Communications Inc. (SBC)/Ameritech/SNET/Pacific Bell and Bell Atlantic/GTE/NYNEX).[48] As one former antitrust official put it, "[t]he increasing number of mergers in high-technology industries has raised both horizontal and vertical antitrust issues . . . the interest in and analysis of vertical issues has come to the forefront.[49]

The behavioral analysis in this section relies on a variety of analyses and complaints from participants in the sector including AT&T as a long distance carrier, before it became a cable owner, [50] AOL as an ISP, before it became a cable owner,[51] analyses prepared by experts for local[52] and long distance[53] telephone companies, when they were not effectuating mergers of their own, Wall Street analyses of the business models of dominant, vertically integrated cable firms,[54] and observations offered by independent ISPs[55] and small cable operators.[56]

Current theoretical literature provides an ample basis for concerns that the physical layer of the communications platform will not perform efficiently or in a competitive manner without a check on market power. In this layer, barriers to entry are substantial, and go far beyond simple entrepreneurial skills that need to be rewarded.[57] At the structural level, new entry into these physical markets is difficult. AOL argued that the small number of communications facilities in the physical layer can create a transmission bottleneck that would lead directly to the problem of vertical leverage or market power. "[A] vertically integrated broadband provider such as AT&T will have a strong incentive and opportunity to discriminate against unaffiliated broadband content providers."[58]

Problems caused by vertical integration are particularly troubling in communications markets because a communications provider with control over essential physical facilities can exploit its power in more than one market. For example, a local voice service provider with control over physical transmission can provide vertically integrated digital subscriber line (DSL) service, preventing competition from other Internet providers over the same network.[59] At the same time, the company can bundle its voice services with the DSL service. Cable can bundle video with other services. Consumers may be more likely to choose the communications service that can provide for all of their needs, thereby inhibiting competition in the voice market as well. Whether we call them essential facilities,[60] choke points[61] or anchor points,[62] the key leverage point of a communications network is controlling access to facilities.

> The key, after all, is the ability to use "first mile" pipeline control to deny consumers direct access to, and thus a real choice among, the content and services offered by independent providers. Open access would provide a targeted and narrow fix to this problem. AT&T simply would not be allowed to control consumer's ability to choose service providers other than those AT&T itself has chosen for them. This would create an environment where independent, competitive service providers will have access to the broadband "first mile" controlled by AT&T – the pipe into consumers' homes – in order to provide a full,

expanding range of voice, video, and data services requested by consumers. The ability to stifle Internet-based video competition and to restrict access to providers of broadband content, commerce and other new applications thus would be directly diminished.[63]

Experts for the local telephone companies, in opposing the merger of AT&T and MediaOne, made this point arguing that "the relevant geographic market is local because one can purchase broadband Internet access only from a local residence"[64] and that "a dominant market share is not a necessary condition for discrimination to be effective."[65] "[A] hypothetical monopoly supplier of broadband Internet access in a given geographic market could exercise market power without controlling the provision of broadband access in neighboring geographic markets."[66]

The essential nature of the physical communication platform was the paramount concern for AT&T long distance in determining interconnection policy for cable networks in Canada.[67] AT&T attacked the claim made by cable companies that their lack of market share indicates that they lack market power, arguing that small market share does not preclude the existence of market power because of the essential function of the access input to the production of service.[68] AT&T further argued that open access "obligations are not dependent on whether the provider is dominant. Rather they are necessary in order to prevent the abuse of market power that can be exercised over bottleneck functions of the broadband access service."[69]

AT&T maintained that the presence of a number of vertically integrated facilities owners does not solve the fundamental problem of access that nonintegrated content providers face, pointing out that since independent content providers will always outnumber integrated providers, competition could be undermined by vertical integration. In order to avoid this outcome, even multiple facilities owners must be required to provide non-discriminatory access.[70] This also applies in the ISP arena. AOL also believed that the presence of alternative facilities did not eliminate the need for open access (see Figure 2).[71]

Two or three vertically integrated facilities in the broadband arena will not be enough to ensure vigorous competition.[72] It is also important to note the consensus that cable is the dominant and preferred technology.[73]

Cable's advantages are substantial, and DSL is not likely to be able to close the gap.[74]

Content discrimination has been the focal point of concern in relation to high-speed Internet services. Content discrimination involves an integrated provider "insulating its own affiliated content from competition by blocking or degrading the quality of outside content."[75] It benefits the vertically integrated entity "by enhancing the position of its affiliated content providers in the national market by denying unaffiliated

Figure 2:

**Anti-Consumer/ Anticompetitive Elements Of The
Cable Industry Communications Platform**

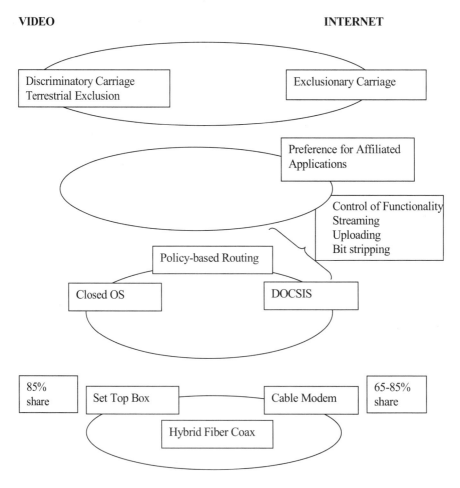

content providers critical operating scale and insulating affiliated content providers from competition."[76]

AT&T identified four forms of anticompetitive leveraging—bundling, price squeeze, service quality discrimination, and first mover advantage.[77] It describes the classic vertical leveraging tools of price squeezes and quality discrimination as content discrimination. The experts for the local telephone companies identified a similar series of tactics that a vertically integrated broadband provider could use to disadvantage competing unaffiliated content providers.

> First, it can give preference to an affiliated content provider by caching its content locally. . . Such preferential treatment ensures that affiliated content can be delivered at faster speeds than unaffiliated content.

> Second, a vertically integrated broadband provider can limit the duration of streaming videos of broadcast quality to such an extent that they can never compete against cable programming . . .Third, a vertically integrated firm such as AT&T or AOL-Time Warner could impose proprietary standards that would render unaffiliated content useless. . .Once the AT&T standard has been established, AT&T will be able to exercise market power over customers and those companies trying to reach its customers.[78]

Even after AT&T became the largest cable TV company in the U.S., its long distance division criticized local telephone companies for abusing their monopoly control over their telephone wires. AT&T complained about bottleneck facilities, vertical integration, anticompetitive bundling of services, and the distortion of competition when it opposed the entry of SBC into the long distance market in Texas.[79] These are the very same complaints AOL made about AT&T as a cable company at about the same time.[80] AOL expressed related concerns about the manipulation of technology and interfaces, complaining about "allowing a single entity to abuse its control over the development of technical solutions – particularly when it may have interests inconsistent with the successful implementation of open access… It is therefore vital to ensure that unaffiliated ISPs can gain access comparable to that the cable operators choose to afford to its cable-affiliated ISP . [81]

Long distance companies and competitive local exchange carriers have similar concerns about the merging local exchange carriers. Their experts argued in the proposed SBC-Ameritech and Bell Atlantic-GTE mergers that large size gave network owners an incentive to discriminate. "The economic logic of competitive spillovers implies that the increase in [incumbent local exchange carrier (ILEC)] footprints resulting from these proposed mergers would increase the ILECs' incentive to disadvantage rivals by degrading access services they need to compete, thereby harming competition and consumers."[82]

Wall Street analysts point out that the key to controlling the supply side is controlling essential functions through proprietary standards.[83] Independent ISPs point out that cable operators like AOL use control over functionalities to control the services available on the network.[84] Cable operators have continued to insist on quality of service restrictions by unaffiliated ISPs, which places the ISPs at a competitive disadvantage.[85] Cable operators must approve new functionalities whether or not they place any demands on the network.[86]

Price squeeze and extraction of rents are apparent in the implementation of closed platforms. Thomase Hazlett and George Bittlingmayer cite Excite@Home executive Milo Medin describing the terms on which cable operators would allow carriage of broadband Internet to AOL (before it owned a wire) as follows:

> I was sitting next to [AOL CEO] Steve Case in Congress during the open access debates. He was saying that all AOL wanted was to be treated like Excite [@]Home. If he wants to be treated like us, I'm sure he could cut a deal with [the cable networks], but they'll take their pound of flesh. We only had to give them a 75 percent equity stake in the company and board control. The cable guys aren't morons.[87]

In the high speed Internet area, conduit discrimination has received less attention than content discrimination. This is opposite to the considerable attention it receives in the cable TV video service area. Nevertheless, there are examples of conduit discrimination in the high speed Internet market.

In implementing conduit discrimination, the vertically integrated company would refuse to distribute its affiliated content over competing transmission media.[88]   In so doing, it seeks to drive consumers to its transmission media and weaken its rival. This is profitable as long as the revenue gained by attracting new subscribers exceeds the revenue lost by not making the content available to the rival. Market size is important here, to ensure adequate profits are earned on the distribution of service over the favored conduit.[89] Although some argue that "the traditional models of discrimination do not depend on the vertically integrated firm obtaining some critical level of downstream market share,"[90] in reality, the size of the vertically integrated firm does matter since "a larger downstream market share enhances the vertically integrated firm's incentive to engage in discrimination."[91]

AT&T has been accused of conduit discrimination in the high speed Internet market.[92] The AOL-Time Warner merger has also raised similar concerns. The significance of AOL's switch to cable-based broadband should not be underestimated. This switch has a powerful effect on the hoped-for competition between cable modems and DSL.[93] Although telephone companies are reluctant to admit that their technology will have trouble competing, their experts have identified the advantages that cable enjoys.[94] Fearing that once AOL became a cable owner it would abandon the DSL distribution channel, the FTC required AOL to continue to make its service available over the DSL conduit.[95]

The focal point of a leveraging strategy is bundling early in the adoption cycle to lock in customers. AOL has also described the threat of vertically integrated cable companies in the U.S.[96] Once AT&T became the largest vertically integrated cable company selling broadband access in the U.S., it set out to prevent potential competitors from offering bundles of services. Bundles could be broken up either by not allowing Internet service providers to have access to video customers, or by preventing companies with the ability to deliver telephony from having access to high-speed content. For the Wall Street analysts, bundling seems to be the central marketing strategy for broadband.[97]

AOL argued that requiring open access early in the process of market development would establish a much stronger structure for a pro-consumer, pro-competitive market.[98] Early intervention prevents the architecture of the market from blocking openness, and thus avoids the difficult task of having to reconstruct an open market at a later time.[99] AOL did not hesitate to point out the powerful anticompetitive effect that integrating video services in the communications bundle could have. AOL argued that, as a result of a vertical merger, AT&T would take an enormous next step toward its ability to deny consumers a choice among competing providers of integrated voice/video/data offerings – a communications marketplace that integrates, and transcends, an array of communications services and markets previously viewed as distinct.[100]

Wall Street saw the first mover advantage both in the general terms of the processes that affect network industries, and in the specific advantage that cable broadband services have in capturing the most attractive early adopting consumers.[101] First mover advantages have their greatest value where consumers have difficulty switching or substituting away from the dominant product.[102] Several characteristics of broadband Internet access are conducive to the first mover advantage, or "lock-in."

The local telephone companies have outlined a series of concerns about lock in.[103] High-speed access is a unique product.[104] The Department of Justice determined that the broadband Internet market is a separate and distinct market from the narrowband Internet market.[105] There are switching costs that hinder competition, including equipment (modems) purchases, learning costs, and the inability to port names and addresses. Combining a head start with significant switching costs raises the fear among the independent ISPs that consumers will be locked in. In Canada, AT&T argued that the presence of switching costs could impede the ability of consumers to change technologies, thereby impeding competition.[106]

THE MONOPOLIZATION OF THE HIGH-SPEED INTERNET

The high degree of control and foreclosure of the broadband platform was encapsulated in a term sheet offered by Time Warner to Internet Service Providers. Time Warner sought to relieve the severe pressures of a merger review before policymakers had officially abandoned the policy of nondiscrimination by offering to allow unaffiliated ISPs to compete for Internet access service over their last mile facilities. Complete foreclosure was to be replaced with severe discrimination. There in black and white are all the levers of market power and network control that stand to stifle innovation on the Internet. Time Warner demanded the following:

(1) Prequalification of ISPs to ensure a fit with the gatekeeper business model

(2) Applying ISPs must reveal sensitive commercial information as a precondition to negotiation

(3) Restriction of interconnecting companies to Internet access sales only, precluding a range of other intermediary services and functions provided by ISP to the public (e.g. no ITV [interactive TV] functionality)

(4) Restriction of service to specified appliances (retarding competition for video services)

(5) Control of quality by the network owner for potentially competing video services

(6) Right to approve new functionalities for video services

(7) A large nonrefundable deposit that would keep small ISPs off the network

(8) A minimum size requirement that would screen out niche ISPs

(9) Approval by the network owner of the unaffiliated ISP's home page

(10) Preferential location of network owner advertising on all home pages

(11) Claim by the network owner to all information generated by the ISP

(12) Demand for a huge share of both subscription and ancillary revenues

(13) Preferential bundling of services and control of cross marketing of services

(14) Applying ISP must adhere to the network operator's privacy policy.[107]

Under these conditions, the commercial space left for the unaffiliated and smaller ISPs is sparse and ever shrinking.[108] It took tremendous courage to put the Term Sheet in the public record in violation of the nondisclosure agreements that Time Warner had demanded,[109] especially in light of the threats and actions that the dominant cable operators have hurled at those who challenge their proprietary plans.[110]

At one time or another these "conditions" were written into a contract with a service provider or a consumer service agreement or were implemented in the network. In comments at the Federal Communications Commission, the High Tech Broadband Coalition noted "troubling evidence of restrictions on broadband consumers' access to content, applications and devices."[111] From the point of view of the technical design features of the Internet that unleashed the dynamic forces of innovation, the fact that these negotiations must take place at all is the truly chilling proposition.

The largest ISP, AOL, capitulated to the cable monopolists as part of the effort to untangle its holdings with AT&T, which was being acquired by Comcast. After a five-year struggle for carriage, AOL signed a three-year contract for access to less than one-half of Comcast's[112] lines under remarkably onerous conditions. [113] AOL agreed to pay $38 at wholesale for a service that sells for $40 in the cable bundle. It allowed Comcast to keep control of the customer and to determine the functionality available. It apparently agreed to a no–compete clause for video. As AOL put it, the deal turned the high-speed Internet into the equivalent of a premium cable channel, like HBO. Nothing could be farther from the Internet as it was.

Why did AOL agree? It was desperate for carriage. You cannot be a narrowband company in a broadband world, and DSL just does not cut it. The AOL-Comcast agreement punctuates a seven-year policy of exclusion. The deal with Comcast only allowed AOL to negotiate with the individual cable franchises for carriage, but AOL never reached the specific agreements that are necessary to actually deliver the service to consumers. Ultimately AOL gave up on the approach.[114]

Although telephone companies ostensibly have been required to provide access to their advanced telecommunications networks, they have made life miserable for the independent ISPs.[115] A major source of potential discrimination lies in the architecture of the network. The technical capabilities of the network controlled by the proprietor can be configured and operated to disadvantage competitors.

ISPs have identified a range of ways the dominant telephone companies impede their ability to interconnect in an efficient manner. The proprietary network owner can seriously impair the ability of competitors to deliver service by restricting their ability to interconnect efficiently and deploy or utilize key technologies that dictate the quality of service. Forcing independent ISPs to connect to the proprietary network or operate in inefficient or ineffective ways or giving affiliated ISPs preferential location and interconnection can result in substantial discrimination. Similarly, forcing competitive local exchange carriers (CLECs) to make digital to analog to digital conversions to implement cross connects raises costs. The result is a sharp increase in the cost of doing business or degradation of the quality of service.

Refusing to peer with other ISPs and causing congestion by "deliberately overloading their DSL connections by providing them with insufficient bandwidth from the phone company's central offices to the Internet"[116] creates a roadblock that forces ISPs to enter into expensive transport arrangements for traffic.[117] Refusing to guarantee quality of service to unaffiliated ISPs and imposition of speed limits[118] has the effect of restricting the products they can offer.[119] The network owners then add insult to injury by forcing ISPs to buy bundles of redundant services,[120] preventing competitors from cross connecting to one another,[121] restricting calling scopes for connection to ISPs,[122] and refusing to offer a basic service arrangement or direct connection to the network.[123] The effect is to undermine competition and restrict service offerings.[124]

The most critical architectural decisions are to impose network configurations that prevent competition for the core monopoly service, voice.[125] This bundling of competitive and noncompetitive services places competitors at a disadvantage.[126] Ironically, Cox complains that it is being discriminated against when incumbent telephone monopolists bundle voice and data, while it pursued a similar exclusionary tactic with respect to the bundling of video and data.[127] Independent ISPs have pointed out that their ability to offer voice is being frustrated by architectural decisions that deny them the ability to offer the voice/data bundle.[128] Moreover, incumbents are reserving the right to offer additional services, like video, over lines for which independent ISPs are the Internet access service provider.[129]

The price squeeze that AOL was subject to in its agreement with Comcast was similar to that imposed by both the cable modem and DSL network owners. The price for access to the network is far above costs and leaves little margin for the unaffiliated ISP.[130] The margins between the wholesale price ISPs are forced to pay and the retail price affiliated ISPs charge are as small as $1 on the telephone network.[131] For cable networks, the margins are as low as $5. In other words, independent ISPs are forced to look at margins in the single digits and never much above 20 percent. Cable and telephone company margins for these services are well in excess of 40 percent.[132]

Consumers pay a price too. With costs falling[133] and demand lagging in the midst of a recession, both cable operators and telephone companies raised prices. Cable companies imposed a severe interruption of service on their customers, which, in a highly competitive market, would have been suicidal.[134] In 2003, Comcast, the dominant high-speed modem service provider, raised the price of stand-alone cable modem service by $10 to $15 per month. In 2003, some of the Bell companies offered discounts, but the cable companies refused to respond to telephone company pricing moves. DSL service is not competitive on price on a megabit basis. Since DSL cannot compete on a quality-adjusted basis, the cable operators ignore it. Their advertising harps on their speed superiority. With the dominant technology insulated from cross-technology competition and operating a closed network, cable companies have strategically priced their digital services. This becomes quite apparent to any consumer who tries to buy the service in the marketplace. If a consumer adds a digital tier, the charge would be an additional $15 on average. If a consumer adds cable modem service, the consumer must pay $45 ($55 to $60 if basic cable is not taken). Moreover, if the consumer wants to keep an unaffiliated ISP, the charge is an additional $15. The resulting price is too high and dampens adoption.

SQUEEZING INTERNET SERVICE PROVIDERS OUT OF THE MARKET

ISPs were the first victims of the network foreclosure strategy. The results of the closure of advanced telecommunications services are becoming clear. The independent business of buying telecommunications services and selling Internet access service has been all but eliminated from the high-speed Internet market by the withholding of advanced telecommunications services. In contrast to the 15 ISPs per 100,000 customers on the dial-up Internet, on the high-speed Internet there are now less than 2 ISPs per 100,000 customers (see Figure 3). For cable modem service there is less than 1 Internet service provider per 100,000 customers. For DSL service, there are fewer than 2.5 ISPs per 100,000 customers. Viewed on a market size basis, the impact is even starker (see Figure 4).

The foreclosure of the market to independents is even more profound than these numbers indicate. Approximately 95 percent of high-speed Internet access service customers are served by ISPs affiliated with either cable companies or telephone companies.[135] This dominance is not the result of winning in a competitive market; it is the result of leveraging control of physical facilities. The fact that control over the wires is the cornerstone of this market foreclosure is demonstrated by the failure of the cable and telephone affiliated ISPs to have any success in the truly competitive narrowband Internet market. Cable companies have not sold Internet service in any product and geographic market where they do not control a monopoly wire. Telephone companies have done very poorly as ISPs in the dial-up market. Consequently, 95 percent of the customers in the dial-up market take their service from independent ISPs – treating AOL as an independent in the dial-up market. In other words, incumbent monopolists have a 95 percent market share where they can leverage their market power over their wires, and a 5 percent market share where they cannot.

Figure 3:
Density Of Dial-Up And High-Speed ISP

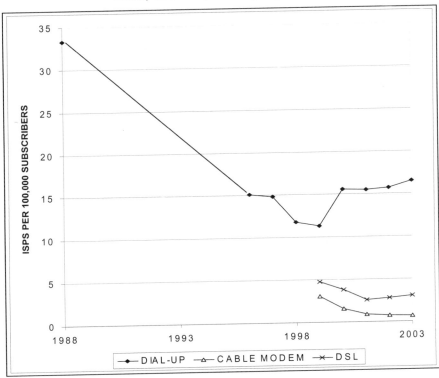

Source: Subscriber counts: Carey, John, "The First Hundred Feet for Households: Consumer Adoption Patterns," in Deborah Hurley and James H. Keller (Eds.), *The First Hundred Feet* (Cambridge: MIT Press, 1999); National Telecommunications Information Administration, *A Nation Online* (U.S. Department of Commerce, 2002). Early ISP counts are discussed in Cooper, Mark, *Expanding the Information Age for the 1990s: A Pragmatic Consumer View* (Washington, D.C.: Consumer Federation of America, American Association of Retired Persons, January 11, 1990). See also Abbate, Janet, Inventing the Internet (Cambridge: MIT Press, 1999) and Matos, F., *Information Service Report* (Washington, D.C.: National Telecommunications Information Administration, August 1988), p. x. More recent numbers are from the Bureau of Labor Statistics; 2001b. Since the mid-1990s, annual counts of ISPs have been published in *Network World*.

It may well be that the Internet service market was due for some consolidation.[136] However, the staying power of ISPs is impressive. One recent count found that after taking into account the largest 23 ISPs, all of whom had 200,000 or more users, the "other U.S. ISPs" still accounted for 57 percent of Internet users in the U.S.[137] Focusing on the dial-up market, after the largest ISPs (ten in all) were taken into account, the "other U.S.

Figure 4:
Density Of Dial-Up And High Speed ISPs By National Market Size

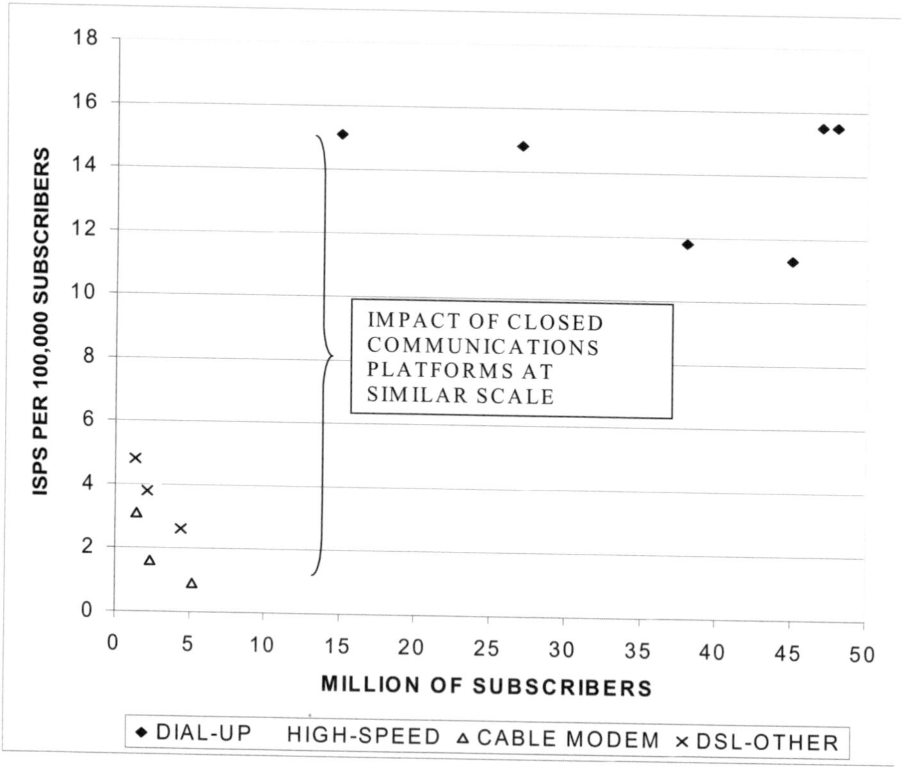

Source: Subscriber counts: Carey, John, "The First Hundred Feet for Households: Consumer Adoption Patterns," in Deborah Hurley and James H. Keller (Eds.), *The First Hundred Feet* (Cambridge: MIT Press, 1999); National Telecommunications Information Administration, *A Nation Online* (U.S. Department of Commerce, 2002). Early ISP counts are discussed in Cooper, Mark, *Expanding the Information Age for the 1990s: A Pragmatic Consumer View* (Washington, D.C.: Consumer Federation of America, American Association of Retired Persons, January 11, 1990). See also Abbate, Janet, Inventing the Internet (Cambridge: MIT Press, 1999) and Matos, F., *Information Service Report* (Washington, D.C.: National Telecommunications Information Administration, August 1988), p. x. More recent numbers are from the Bureau of Labor Statistics; 2001b. Since the mid-1990s, annual counts of ISPs have been published in *Network World*.

ISPs" accounted for over 62 percent of the total. In the high-speed Internet, there are virtually no "other U.S. ISPs."

The closing of the Internet produces a very different picture of service development and innovation than we saw on the dial-up Internet. In contrast to the dial-up Internet, which witnessed a steady flow of innovations and the growth of a large customer service sector that stimulated the adoption of Internet service by a majority of households, the broadband Internet is a wasteland. The body of potential innovators and customer care providers has shrunk. At a minimum, ISPs provided customer care, extended service throughout the country and adapted applications to customer needs. They are like the mechanics and gas stations in the automobile industry. There are now just too few ISPs on the broadband Internet.

A small number of entities dominating the sale of high-speed Internet access and dictating the nature of use is the antithesis of the environment in which the narrowband Internet was born and enjoyed such rapid growth. Changing the environment changes the nature of activity. One thing we never heard about the narrowband Internet was a complaint about the slowness of innovation. High-speed service is into its seventh year without a major innovation to drive adoption. Complaints about high prices for high-speed Internet have come earlier and louder than they did for narrowband service.

The Internet model has been turned on its head in the closed broadband space. Analysts proclaim critical mass of deployment and wait for the killer application, while they worry about how average users will be induced to adopt services.

> With close to 27 million US business and residential subscribers at the end of 2003, broadband is now clearly a mainstream service… However, the one major challenge that faces the future provisioning of broadband will come from a less tech-savvy subscriber. As broadband moves into mass adoption, newer subscribers will be less experienced with computers and the Internet. They will expect all of the benefits of the Internet, but will have less patience for dealing with its technical issues.[138]

That was exactly the function of the ISPs who have been decimated by the denial of access to customers. More importantly, Internet applications did not wait for a subscriber base, they drove demand for subscription. The potential applications that are expected to flourish have run into problems with the closed platform. "[T]he existence of a significant subscriber base opens up markets for other services that are looking to take advantage of the broadband connection, such as home entertainment/ networking, Voice over IP (VoIP) and online gaming."[139] Home networking and entertainment, as well as online gaming have been possible for several years, but have been resisted by cable operators who want to control them. VoIP, which relies more on the "always on" characteristic of the broadband platform, is still confronted with questions of proprietary restrictions.

> [A] spokesman for cable broadband provider <u>Cox Communications</u>, agreed that VoIP can be a crapshoot depending on what broadband provider you have. "People should keep in mind that VoIP from companies not offering their own broadband is only a 'best effort' service."

> Cox offers a VoIP service over its own broadband network. According to Amirshahi, the company goes to great pains to ensure its own VoIP customers' traffic stays on its own network, where problems can be acted on very quickly.[140]

Thus, the hoped for uplift in services and adoption is still hampered by the obstacles that the open Internet architecture/open communications platform had solved over a decade ago. The process we observe on the high-speed Internet is like strangulation through the exercise of market power. By cutting off access to advanced telecommunications service – the oxygen of the Internet market – facility-owners have eliminated competition at the level of applications and services. The threat of withholding functionality or banning applications chills innovation.

CONCLUSION

After repeated efforts by telecommunications facility owners to assert control over access to the Internet, it is hard to imagine they will willingly adopt an open architecture. The leverage they enjoy in a blocking technology and the interest they have in related product markets disposes them to maximize profits by maximizing proprietary control over the network. In so doing, they can reduce the competitive threat to their core franchise services and gain advantages in new product markets.[141] "One strategy, which is profitable for a dominant firm but wrecks the benefits of the net, is, for instance, to take advantage of network externalities to 'balkanize' the Internet by reducing connectivity."[142] Facility owners demand a level of vertical control that creates uncertainty about future discrimination, whose mere existence is sufficient to chill innovation.

Faced with the long history of openness and the obvious power of discriminatory access to the communications networks to strangle competition, the defenders of discrimination run through a series of defenses. The owners will voluntarily abandon their proprietary standard and pursue an open architecture. Competition between proprietary standards promotes technological progress and the costs of the proprietary monopoly are smaller than the benefits. Small numbers competition in physical facilities will control rent collection and anti-competitive, antisocial behavior.

These arguments ignore the history and incentives of owners of the physical facilities and they misunderstand the value and role of the digital communications platform. It has the unique characteristic of being both a bearer service that affects the ability of many industries to function, as all transportation and communications technologies do, and a general purpose, cumulative, systemic, enabling technology that alters the fundamental way in which numerous industries conduct their business and create technological progress. It is electricity, the railroads and the telephone rolled into one.

Closure of the information platform at a key choke point alters the nature of the environment. Discrimination in access diminishes the value of the network. The positive externalities of connectivity are reduced. The claim that we should focus on the physical infrastructure because that is where the value creation lies should be rejected. The true value in the network arises from the creative exploitation of functionalities at the higher levels of the platform, which is exactly what the monopolist or oligopolist cannot see. Even oligopolistic competition for a critical infrastructure industry will leave far too much rent and control in the hands of the network owners.

Adding another last mile facility competitor will help a little if the network is proprietary and closed, but it will help a great deal if it is open, because applications will flock there. The lesson of the long history of layering of communications facilities, all subject to an obligation to provide nondiscriminatory access, converges with the lesson of network theory. The layering of open communications networks is an evolving process that has carried multiscale connectivity to ever higher levels. The greater the multiscale connectivity, the more conducive the network is for commerce, communication and innovation.

What is clear, then, is that maintaining an open communications platform for advanced services is the public policy that will ensure a vibrant, high-speed, next generation of the Internet. That policy choice is what will drive innovation, provide a greater flow of information and have a positive impact on the economy and society.

ENDNOTES

[1] Michael L. Katz & Carl Shapiro, *System Competition and Network Effects*, 8 J. ECON. PERSPECTIVES 93, 105-6 (1994), argue that competition between incompatible systems is possible, depending on consumer heterogeneity. Paul Belleflamme, *Stable Coalition Structures with Open Membership and Asymmetric Firms*, 30 GAMES & ECON. BEHAVIOR 1, 1-3 (2000), and Berd Woeckener, *The Competition of User Networks: Ergodicity, Lock-ins, and Metastability*, 41 J. ECON. BEHAVIOR & ORG. 85, 86-7 (2000), reach a similar conclusion in a different theoretic framework. Timothy F. Bresnahan & Shane Greenstein, *Technological Competition and the Structure of the Computer Industry*, 47 J. INDUSTRIAL ECON. 1, 5-8 (1999), envision a great deal of competition within the layers of a platform and across layers in relatively short periods of time. The description of IBM's mainframe platform provided by Franklin M. Fisher, *The IBM and Microsoft Cases: What's the Difference?*, 90 AM. ECON. REV. 180, 183 (1999), stresses both these points. See also Daniel L. Rubinfeld, *Antitrust Enforcement in Dynamic Network Industries,* 43 ANTITRUST BULL. 859, 873-75 (1998); Willow A. Sheremata, *New Issues in Competition Policy Raised by Information Technology Industries*, 43 ANTITRUST BULL. 547, 573-74 (1998); Timothy Bresnahan, *The Economics of the Microsoft Case* (available from the author); Steven C. Salop and R. Craig Romaine, *Preserving Monopoly: Economic Analysis, Legal Standards, and Microsoft*, GEO. MASON L. REV. (1999).

[2] William G. Shepherd, THE ECONOMICS OF INDUSTRIAL ORGANIZATION (3d ed., 1990), at 289-90.

[3] *See* Martin K. Perry, *Vertical Integration: Determinants and Effects*, in HANDBOOK OF INDUSTRIAL ORGANIZATION (Richard Schmalensee & Robert D. Willigs, eds., 1989), at 183, 247; F. Michael Scherer & David Ross, INDUSTRIAL MARKET STRUCTURE AND ECONOMIC PERFORMANCE (1990), at 526.

[4] Martin K. Perry, *Vertical Integration: Determinants and Effects*, in HANDBOOK OF INDUSTRIAL ORGANIZATION (Richard Schmalensee & Robert D. Willigs, eds., 1989), at 246; *see* also WILLIAM G. SHEPHERD, THE ECONOMICS OF INDUSTRIAL ORGANIZATION (3d ed. 1990), at 294.

[5] Scherer & Ross, INDUSTRIAL MARKET STRUCTURE, *supra* note 3, at 526.

[6] Other behavior effects may occur, for example, collusion, mutual forbearance and reciprocity may exist where the small number of interrelated entities in the industry recognize and honor each others' spheres of influence. The final behavioral effect is to trigger a rush to integrate and concentrate. Being a small independent entity at any stage renders the company extremely vulnerable to a variety of attacks. *See* Shepherd, ECONOMICS, *supra* note 4, at 290.

[7] Richard N. Langlois, *Technology Standards, Innovation, and Essential Facilities: Toward a Schumpeterian Post-Chicago Approach*, in DYNAMIC COMPETITION & PUB. POLICY: TECHNOLOGY, INNOVATIONS, AND ANTITRUST ISSUES (Jerry Ellig, ed., 2001), *available at http://papers.ssrn.com/sol3/papers.cfm?abstract_id=204069* (last visited Jan. 24, 2003) at 52, "The owner of a dominant standard may thus want to manipulate the standard in ways that close off the possibilities for a competitor to achieve compatibility. This has a tendency to retard the generational advance of the system."

[8] *See id. See* also Franklin M. Fisher, *Innovation and Monopoly Leveraging,* in DYNAMIC COMPETITION AND PUBLIC POLICY: TECHNOLOGY, INNOVATION, AND ANTITRUST ISSUES 138 (Jerry Ellig, ed., 2001).

[9] *See* Joseph Farrell & Garth Saloner, *Installed Base and Compatibility: Innovation, Product Preannouncements, and Predation,* 76 AM. ECON. REV. 940, 948-51 (1986); Michael L. Katz & Carl Shapiro, *Product Introduction with Network Externalities,* 40 J. INDUS. ECON. 55, 73 (1992); Richard Makadok, *Can First-Mover and Early-Mover Advantages Be Sustained in an Industry with Low Barriers to Entry/Imitation?,* 19 STRATEGIC MGMT. J. 683, 685-86 (1998); Ulrich Witt, *"Lock-in" vs. "Critical Masses"– Industrial Change Under Network Externalities,* 15 INT'L J. INDUS. ORG. 753, 768-69 (1997); Robin Mansell, *Strategies for Maintaining Market Power in the Face of Rapidly Changing Technologies,* 31 J. ECON. ISSUES 969, 970 (1997).

[10] *See* Melissa A. Schilling, *Technological Lockout: An Integrative Model of the Economic and Strategic Factors Driving Technology Success and Failure,* 23 ACAD. MGMT. REV. 267, 276 (1998).

[11] *See* Willow A. Sheremata, *"New" Issues in Competition Policy Raised by Information Technology Industries,* 43 ANTITRUST BULL. 547, 573-74 (1998); Glenn A. Woroch et al., *Exclusionary Behavior in the Market for Operating System Software: The Case of Microsoft,* in OPENING NETWORKS TO COMPETITION: THE REGULATION AND PRICING OF ACCESS 221 (David Gabel & David F. Weiman, eds., 1998).

[12] Sheremata, *"New" Issues in Competition Policy, supra* note 11, at 560-61; *see* also Charles H. Ferguson, HIGH ST@KES, NO PRISONERS: A WINNER'S TALE OF GREED AND GLORY IN THE INTERNET WARS (1999), at 307; Mark A. Lemley & David McGowan, *Could Java Change Everything? The Competitive Propriety of a Proprietary Standard,* ANTITRUST BULL., 43 (1998), at 715, 732-33; Joseph P. Guiltinan, *The Price Bundling of Services: A Normative Framework,* J. MKTG. 74 (April 1987); Lester Telser, *A Theory of Monopoly of Complementary Goods,* 52 J. BUS. 211 (1979); Richard Schmalensee, *Gaussian Demand and Commodity Bundling,* 57 J. BUS. 211 (1984).

[13] Joseph Farrell & Michael L. Katz, *The Effects of Antitrust and Intellectual Property Law on Compatibility and Innovation,* 43 ANTITRUST BULL. 609, 643-50, (1998); Sheremata, *"New" Issues in Competition Policy, supra* note 11, at 547, 573-74.

[14] Makadok, *First-Mover and Early-Mover Advantages, supra* note 9, at 685.

[15] David B. Yoffie, *CHESS and Competing in the Age of Digital Convergence,* in COMPETING IN THE AGE OF DIGITAL CONVERGENCE (David B. Yoffie, ed., 1997), at 1, 27; *see* also Robert E. Dansby & Cecilia Conrad, *Commodity Bundling,* 74 AM. ECON. REV. 377 (1984).

[16] Carmen Matutes & Pierre Regibeau, *Compatibility and Bundling of Complementary Goods in a Duopoly,* 40 J. INDUS. ECON. 37 (1992).

[17] *See id.; see* also Joseph P. Guiltinan, *The Price Bundling of Services: A Normative Framework,* J. MKTG. 74 (April 1987); Lester Telser, *A Theory of Monopoly of Complementary Goods,* 52 J. BUS. 211 (1979); Richard Schmalensee, *Gaussian Demand and Commodity Bundling,* 57 J. BUS. 211 (1984).

[18] Jay Pil Choi, *Network Externality, Compatibility Choice, and Planned Obsolescence,* 42 J. INDUS. ECON. 167, 171-73 (1994).

[19] Glenn Ellison & Drew Fudenberg, *The Neo-Luddite's Lament: Excessive Upgrades in the Software Industry*, 31 RAND J. ECON. 253 (2000); Drew Fudenberg & Jean Tirole, *Upgrades, Trade-ins, and Buybacks*, 29 RAND J. ECON. 235, 235-36 (1998).

[20] *See* K. Sridhar Moorthy, *Market Segmentation, Self Selection, and Product Lines Design*, 3 MKTG. SCI. 256 (1985); Marcel Thum, *Network Externalities, Technological Progress, and the Competition of Market Contract*, 12 INT. J. INDUS. ORG. 269 (1994).

[21] Schilling, *Technological Lockout, supra* note 10, at 267, 268, 270; Willow A. Sheremata, *Barriers to Innovation: A Monopoly, Network Externalities, and the Speed of* Innovation, 42 ANTITRUST BULL. 937, 941, 964, 967 (1997); Robin Cowan, *Tortoises and Hares: Choice Among Technologies of Unknown Merit*, 101 ECON. J. 807, 808 (1991); Dominique Foray, *The Dynamic Implications of Increasing Returns: Technological Change and Path Dependent Efficiency*, 15 INT. J. INDUSTRIAL ORG. 733, 748-49 (1997); Joseph Farrel & Garth Saloner, *Standardization, Compatibility, and Innovation*, 16 RAND J. ECON. 70-83 (1986).

[22] Jeffrey Church & Neil Gandal, *Complementary Network Externalities and Technological Adoption*, 11 INT'L J. INDUS. ORG. 239, 241 (1993); Chou Chien-fu & Oz Shy, *Network Effects Without Network Externalities*, 8 INT'L J. INDUS. ORG. 259, 260 (1990).

[23] See Michael Katz & Carl Shapiro, *Antitrust and Software Markets*, in COMPETITION, INNOVATION AND THE MICROSOFT MONOPOLY: ANTITRUST AND THE DIGITAL MARKETPLACE, (Jeffrey A. Eisenach & Thomas M. Lenard, eds., 1999), at 70-80; Lansuz A. Ordover & Robert D. Willig, *Access and Bundling in High Technology Markets*, in COMPETITION, INNOVATION AND THE MICROSOFT MONOPOLY: ANTITRUST AND THE DIGITAL MARKETPLACE (Jeffrey A. Eisenach & Thomas M. Lenard, eds., 1999); Rubinfeld, *Antitrust Enforcement, supra* note 1, at 877-81; Steven C. Salop, *Using Leverage to Preserve Monopoly*, in COMPETITION, INNOVATION AND THE MICROSOFT MONOPOLY: ANTITRUST AND THE DIGITAL MARKETPLACE (Jeffrey A. Eisenach & Thomas M. Lenard, eds., 1999).

[24] Daniel L. Rubinfeld & John Hoven, *Innovation and Antitrust Enforcement*, in DYNAMIC COMPETITION AND PUBLIC POLICY: TECHNOLOGY, INNOVATION, AND ANTITRUST ISSUES (Jerry Ellig, ed., 2001), at 65, 75-76. T. Randolph Beard, George S. Ford & Lawrence J. Spiwak, *Why ADCo? Why Now: An Economic Exploration into the Future of Industry Structure for the "Last Mile" in Local Telecommunications Markets (*Phoenix Center, November 2001); Computer Science and Telecommunications Board, National Research Council, BROADBAND, BRINGING HOME THE BITS (2002), at 23; 152-154; Anupam Banerjee & Marvin Sirvu, "Towards Technologically and Competitively Neutral Fiber to the Home (FTTH) Infrastructure," paper presented at *Telecommunications Policy Research Conference, 2003; Stagg Newman, "Broadband Access Platforms for the Mass Market,* paper presented at *Telecommunications Policy Research Conference, 2003.*

[25] National Research Council, BROADBAND, *supra* note 24.

[26] Implementation of Section 11 of the Cable Television Consumer Protection and Competition Act of 1992, *Further Notice of Proposed Rulemaking,* 16 F.C.C.R. 17,312, ¶ 36 (2001) (citation omitted). *See also* 47 C.F.R. §§ 21, 73 & 76 (2001).

[27] *See* Phil Weiser, *Networks Unplugged: Toward a Model of Compatibility Regulation Between Communications Platforms* (paper presented at *Telecommunications Policy Research Conference*, Oct. 27, 2001), *at* http://www.arxiv.org/html/cs/

_0109070_ (last visited Jan. 24, 2003) stating "in markets where more than one network standard battle it out in the marketplace, users can benefit from a greater degree of dynamism."

[28] Lawrence Lessig, THE FUTURE OF IDEAS (2001), Ch. 8.

[29] _Id.,_ at Ch. 10.

[30] Scherer & Ross, INDUSTRIAL MARKET STRUCTURE, _supra_ note 3, at 31.

[31] _See_ Stan J. Liebowitz & Stephen E. Margolis, WINNERS, LOSERS & MICROSOFT: COMPETITION AND ANTITRUST IN HIGH TECHNOLOGY (2001), using the term 'serial monopoly' (as do a bevy of other Microsoft supported experts); Mark Cooper, _Antitrust as Consumer Protection in the New Economy: Lessons from the Microsoft Case_, 52 HASTINGS L.J. 813 (2001) pointing out that there is nothing serial in Microsoft's monopolies. Rather, Microsoft conquers market after market using leverage and anticompetitive tactics, never relinquishing any of its previous monopolies.

[32] Weiser, _Networks Unplugged:_, _supra_ note 27, at 29:

> ISPs cannot compete on the core value proposition in a broadband world unless they are offering a facilities-based service that enables them to compete on price and quality with a cable provider of Internet service. To the extent that a cable provider desires to find new marketing channels, it may well strike arrangements with ISPs to assist on that score, but the ISPs are not competing on the core product.
>
> At best, the ISPs are able to offer differentiated content on the portal screen, added security features, more reliable privacy policies and the like.

[33] Scherer & Ross, INDUSTRIAL MARKET STRUCTURE, _supra_ note 3, at 660:

> Viewed in their entirety, the theory and evidence [in support of monopoly power] suggest a threshold concept of the most favorable climate for rapid technological change. A bit of monopoly power in the form of structural concentration is conducive to innovation, particularly _when advances in the relevant knowledge base occur slowly_. But very high concentration has a positive effect only in rare cases, and more often it is apt to retard progress by restricting the number of independent sources of initiative and by dampening firms' incentive to gain market position through accelerated R&D. Likewise, given the important role that technically audacious newcomers play in making radical innovations, it seems important that barriers to new entry be kept at modest levels. Schumpeter was right in asserting that perfect competition has no title to being established as the model of dynamic efficiency. But his less cautious followers were wrong when they implied that powerful monopolies and tightly knit cartels had any strong claim to that title. What is needed for rapid technical progress is a subtle blend of competition and monopoly, with more emphasis in general on the former than the latter, and with the role of monopolistic elements diminishing when rich technological opportunities exist.

[34] Daniel L. Rubinfeld & John Hoven, *Innovation and Antitrust Enforcement,* in DYNAMIC COMPETITION AND PUBLIC POLICY: TECHNOLOGY, INNOVATION, AND ANTITRUST ISSUES 65, 75-76 (Jerry Ellig, ed., 2001).

> One policy implication for antitrust is the need to preserve a larger number of firms in industries where the best innovation strategy is unpredictable. . . . Another implication is . . . that "Technical progress thrives best in an environment that nurtures a diversity of sizes and, perhaps especially, that keeps barriers to entry by technologically innovative newcomers low." . . . A third implication is the awareness that dominant firms may have an incentive to act so as to deter innovative activities that threaten the dominant position.

[35] United States v. Microsoft, 253 F.3d 34, 103 (D.C. Cir. 2001) (*per curiam*); Mark Cooper, *Antitrust as Consumer Protection in the New Economy: Lessons from the Microsoft Case,* 52 HASTINGS L.J. 815-25 (2001).

[36] Langlois, Technology Standards, supra note 7. In the case of the personal computer, the rise of a single dominant – but largely open and nonproprietary – standard focused innovation in modular directions. [I]t is the ensuing rapid improvement in components, including not only the chips but various peripheral devices like hard disks and modems, as well as the proliferation of applications software, that has led to the rapid fall in the quality-adjusted price of the total personal computer system.

[37] Yoffie, *CHESS and Competing,* supra note 15, at 21; *see* also Bresnahan & Greenstein, *Technological Competition,* supra note 1, at 36-37; Katz & Shapiro, *System Competition,* supra note 1, at 103.

[38] Schilling, *Technological Lockout, supra* note 10, at 280-81.

[39] Katz & Shapiro, *Antitrust and Software Markets, supra* note 23, at 424.

[40] *See* generally id.; Jay Pil Choi, *Network Externalities, Compatibility Choice and Planned Obsolescence,* 42 J. INDUS. ECON. 167 (1994).

[41] Robin Mansell, *Strategies for Maintaining Market Power in the Face of Rapidly Changing Technologies,* 31 J. ECON. ISSUES 969, 970 (1997).

[42] Schilling, *Technological Lockout, supra* note 10, at 274.

[43] Sheremata, *Barriers to Innovation,* supra note 21, at 965.

[44] Carl Shapiro & Hal R. Varian, INFORMATION RULES: A STRATEGIC GUIDE TO THE NETWORK ECONOMY (1999), at 22-23.

[45] Bresnahan & Greenstein, *Technological Competition,* supra note 1, at 36-37; Joseph Farrell & Michael L. Katz, *The Effect of Antitrust and Intellectual Property Law on Compatibility and Innovation,* 43 ANTITRUST BULL. 645, 650 (1998); Katz & Shapiro, *System Competition, supra* note 1, at 109-12; Carmen Matutes & Pierre Regibeau, *Mix and Match: Product Compatibility Without Network Externalities,* 19 RAND J. OF ECON. 221-233 (1988).

[46] Lemley & McGowan, *Could Java Change Everything?supra* note 12, at 715; Mark A. Lemley & David McGowan, *Legal Implications of Network Effects,* 86 CAL. L. REV. 479, 516-18 (1998).

[47] *See* Weiser, *Networks Unplugged, supra* note 27, at n.136 (suggesting that we "ask whether, 18 years after the rollout of this technology, will consumers benefit from

a number of alternative providers. . ." He then answers the question by looking at the wrong industry (cellular, instead of cable)).

[48] Time Warner Inc., 123 F.T.C. 171 (1997) [hereinafter *Time Warner/Turner/TCI*]. In the Time Warner/Turner/TCI merger analysis, the FTC found that entry into the distribution market was difficult in part because of vertical leverage.

[49] Daniel L. Rubinfeld & Hal. J. Singer, *Open Access to Broadband Networks: A Case Study of the AOL/Time Warner Merger*, 16 BERKELEY TECH. L.J. 631 (2001).

[50] AT&T in Canada before it became the nation's largest cable company. S*ee* AT&T Canada Long Distance Services, *Comments of AT&T Canada Long Distance Services Company*, REGULATION OF CERTAIN TELECOMMUNICATIONS SERVICE OFFERED BY BROADCAST CARRIERS, the Canadian Radio-television and Telecommunications Commission, Telecom Public Notice CRTC 96-36: (1997). The AT&T policy on open access after it became a cable company was first offered in a Letter from David N. Baker, Vice President, Legal & Regulatory Affairs, Mindspring Enterprises, Inc., James W. Cicconi, General Council and Executive Vice President, AT&T Corp., and Kenneth S. Fellman, Esq., Chairman, FCC Local & State Government Advisory Committee, to William E. Kennard, Chairman of FCC (Dec. 6, 1999), *available at* http://www.fcc.gov/mb/attmindspringletter.txt. Virtually no commercial activity took place as a result of the letter, which was roundly criticized. Subsequently their activities were described in Peter S. Goodman, *AT&T Puts Open Access to a Test: Competitors Take Issue with Firm's Coveted First-Screen Presence,* WASH. POST, Nov. 23, 2000, at E1. AT&T in the U.S. in situations where it does not possess an advantage of owning wires, *see AT&T Corp., Reply Comments*, DEPLOYMENT OF WIRELINE SERVS. OFFERING ADVANCED TELECOMMS. CAPABILITY CC Docket No. 98-147 (1998); *see AT&T Corp., Reply comments,* OPPOSITION TO SOUTHWESTERN BELL TEL. CO. SECTION 271 APPLICATION FOR TEX., APPLICATION OF SBC COMMUNICATIONS INC., SOUTHWESTERN BELL TEL. CO., & SOUTHWESTERN BELL COMMUNICATIONS SERVS., INC. D/B/A SOUTHWESTERN BELL LONG DISTANCE FOR PROVISION OF IN-REGION INTERLATA SERVICES. IN TEXAS (2000), *at* http://gullfoss2.fcc.gov/ prod/ecfs/ comsrch_v2.cgi.

[51] *See America Online, Inc., Comments*, TRANSFER OF CONTROL OF FCC LICENSES OF MEDIAONE GROUP INC., TO AT&T CORP*.,* CS Docket 99-251 (filed Aug. 23, 1999) (providing, at the federal level, AOL's most explicit analysis of the need for open access); America Online Inc., *Open Access Comments of America Online, Inc.*, before the DEPARTMENT OF TELECOMMUNICATIONS AND INFORMATION SERVICES, SAN FRANCISCO, October 27, 1999 (on file with author).

[52] Jerry A. Hausman, et al., *Residential Demand for Broadband Telecommunications and Consumer Access to Unaffiliated Internet Content Providers,* 18 YALE J. ON REG. (2001).

[53] John B. Hayes, Jith Jayaratne, and Michael L. Katz, *An Empirical Analysis of the Footprint Effects of Mergers Between Large ILECS*, citing "Declaration of Michael L. Katz and Steven C. Salop," submitted as an attachment to PETITION TO DENY OF SPRING COMMUNICATIONS COMPANY L.P, IN AMERITECH CORP. & SBC COMMUNICATIONS, INC., FOR CONSENT TO TRANSFER OF CONTROL, CC Dkt. No. 98-141 (filed Oct. 15, 1998) and PETITION TO DENY OF SPRING COMMUNICATIONS COMPANY L.P, IN GTE CORPORATION AND BELL

ATLANTIC CORP. FOR CONSENT TO TRANSFER OF CONTROL, CC Docket. No. 98-184 (filed Nov. 23, 1998) (on file with author).

[54] Sanford C. Bernstein and McKinsey and Company, *Broadband!*, January, 2000 (on file with author); Merrill Lynch, AOL *Time Warner*, February 23, 2000; Paine Webber, *AOL Time Warner: Among the World's Most Valuable Brands*, March 1, 2000; Goldman Sachs, *America Online/Time Warner: Perfect Time-ing*, March 10, 2000 (on file with author).

[55] Earthlink, the first ISP to enter into negotiations with cable owners for access, has essentially given up and is vigorously seeking an open access obligation. *See* Notice of Ex Parte, Presentation Regarding the Applications of America Online, Inc. & Time Warner Inc. for Transfers of Control CS Docket No 00-30 (filed Oct. 18, 2000), *available at* http://gullfoss2.fcc.gov/prod/ecfs/comsrch_v2.cgi; NorthNet, Inc., An Open Access Business Model For Cable Systems: Promoting Competition & Preserving Internet Innovation On A Shared, Broadband Communications Network, Ex Parte, *Application of America Online Inc. & Time Warner, Inc. for Transfers of Control*, F.C.C., CS-Docket No. 0030, October 16, 2000.

[56] *See American Cable Association, Comments*, IN RE IMPLEMENTATION OF THE CABLE TELEVISION CONSUMER PROTECTION & COMPETITION ACT OF 1992, DEVELOPMENT OF COMPETITION IN VIDEO PROGRAMMING DISTRIBUTION: SECTION 628(C)(5) OF THE COMMUNICATIONS ACT: SUNSET OF EXCLUSIVE CONTRACT PROHIBITION, CS Docket No. 01-290 (filed Dec. 3, 2001) *available at* http://gullfoss2.fcc.gov/prod/ecfs/comsrch_v2.cgi.

[57] *See* Legal Rights Satellite Org., *Communications Convergence of Broadcasting and Telecommunications Services* (arguing that there were barriers to entry into physical facilities), at http://www.legal-rights.org/Laws/convergence.html (last visited Jan. 17, 2003):

> In the opinion of AT&T Canada LDS, the supply conditions in broadband access markets are extremely limited. There are significant barriers to entry in these markets including lengthy construction periods, high investment requirements and sunk costs, extensive licensing approval requirement (including the requirements to obtain municipal rights-of-way) . . . Under these circumstances, the ability for new entrants or existing facilities-based service providers to respond to non-transitory price increases would be significantly limited, not to mention severely protracted.

[58] Hausman, et al., *Residential Demand for* Broadband, *supra* note 52, at 129, 134.

[59] Mark Cooper, *The Importance of ISPs in The Growth of The Commercial Internet: Why Reliance on Facility-Based Competition Will Not Preserve Vibrant Competition and Dynamic Innovation on the High-Speed Internet*, Attachment A to Comments of the Texas Office of People's Council, et al., APPROPRIATE FRAMEWORK FOR BROADBAND ACCESS TO THE INTERNET OVER WIRELINE FACILITIES UNIVERSAL SERVICE OBLIGATIONS OF BROADBAND PROVIDERS COMPUTER III FURTHER REMAND PROCEEDINGS: BELL OPERATING COMPANY PROVISION OF ENHANCED SERVICES; 1998 BIENNIAL REGULATORY REVIEW – REVIEW OF COMPUTER III AND ONA SAFEGUARDS AND REQUIREMENTS, Federal Communications Commission, CC Dockets Nos. 02-33, 98-10. 95-20 (July 1, 2002), at 135.

[60] *See* Langlois, *Technology Standards, supra* note 7, at 195.

[61] *See* Mark Cooper, *Open Access to the Broadband Internet: Technical and Economic Discrimination in Closed, Proprietary Networks*, 71 U. COLO. L. REV. 1013 (2000).

[62] Bernstein, *Broadband!, supra* note 54, at 18, 21.

> [T]he current set of alternatives for reaching customers with broadband connections is inadequate. At least for the time being, cable is closed, meaning that much of the value is, in effect, ceded to the platform rather than captured by the content/applications providers
> [B]roadband access platforms are the anchor points for much of the value at stake and vehicles for accessing new revenue streams. Furthermore, access is currently a bottleneck, and access winners have the potential to leverage their privilege positioned to ensure long-term value creation.

[63] That is exactly what AOL said about AT&T, when AOL was a nonaffiliated ISP. *See AOL, Transfer of Control, supra* note 51, at 13.

[64] Hausman, et al., *Residential Demand for Broadband, supra* note 52, at 135.

[65] *Id.* at 156.

[66] *Id.* at 135.

[67] *AT&T Canada, Comments of AT&T Canada, supra* note 50, at 12.

> Each of these pronouncements made by regulators, policy makers and individual members of the industry reflects the strongly held view that access to the underlying facilities is not only necessary because of the bottleneck nature of the facilities in question, but also because it is critical for the development of competition in the provision of broadband services. AT&T Canada LDS shares this view and considers the control exercised by broadcast carriers over these essential inputs is an important factor contributing to the dominance of broadcast carriers in the market for access services.

[68] *Id.* at 8-9.

> By contrast, the telephone companies have just begun to establish a presence in the broadband access market and it will likely take a number of years before they have extensive networks in place. This lack of significant market share, however, is overshadowed by their monopoly position in the provision of local telephony services

Id. at 8.

> [I]n any event, even if it could be argued that the telephone companies are not dominant in the market for broadband access services because they only occupy a small share of the market, there are a number of compelling reasons to suggest that measures of market share are not overly helpful when assessing the dominance of telecommunications carriers in the *access* market.

Id. at 9 (emphasis in original).

[69] *Id.* at 24.

[70] *Id.* at 12.

Because there are and will be many more providers of content in the broadband market than there are providers of carriage, there always will be more service providers than access providers in the market. Indeed, even if all of the access providers in the market integrated themselves vertically with as many service providers as practically feasible, there would still be a number of service providers remaining which will require access to the underlying broadband facilities of broadcast carriers.

[71] AOL, *Comments, Transfer of Control, supra* note 51, at 14.

[A]n open access requirement] would allow ISPs to choose between the first-mile facilities of telephone and cable operators based on their relative price, performance, and features. This would spur the loop-to-loop, facilities-based competition contemplated by the Telecommunications Act of 1996, thereby offering consumers more widespread availability of Internet access; increasing affordability due to downward pressures on prices; and a menu of service options varying in price, speed, reliability, content and customer service.

Another indication that the availability of alternative facilities does not eliminate the need for open access policy can be found in AOL's conclusion that the policy should apply to both business and residential customers. If ever there was a segment in which the presence of two facilities competing might alleviate the need for open access requirement, the business segment is it. AOL rejected the idea.

Id. at 1-2.

[72] *See* Mark Cooper, "Breaking the Rules," attached to Petition to Deny of Consumers Union, Consumer Federation of America and Media Access Project, Applications for Consent to Transfer of Control of Licenses, MediaOne Group, Inc. Transferor to AT&T Corp., Transferee, CS 99-251 (filed August 23, 1999) (on file with author).

[73] *See* Bernstein, *Broadband!, supra* note 54, at 30, 33, 50-51.

[74] *See id.* at 7; Merrill Lynch, AOL *Time Warner, supra* note 54, at 33.

[75] Hausman et al., *Residential Demand for Broadband, supra* note 52, at 158.

[76] *Id.* at 159.

[77] *AT&T Canada, Comments of AT&T Canada, supra* note 50.

[78] Hausman et al., *Residential Demand for Broadband, supra* note 52, at 160-62.

[79] *AT&T SBC, supra* note 50.

[80] *AT&T Canada, Comments of AT&T Canada, supra* note 50, at 15-16.

The dominant and vertically integrated position of cable broadcast carriers requires a number of safeguards to protect against anticompetitive behaviour. These carriers have considerable advantages in the market, particularly with respect to their ability to make use of their underlying network facilities for the delivery of new services. To grant these carriers unconditional forbearance would provide them with the opportunity to leverage their existing networks to the detriment of other potential service providers. In particular, unconditional forbearance of the broadband access services provided by cable broadcast carriers would create both the incentive and opportunity for these carriers to lessen competition and choice in the provision of broadband service that could be made available to the end customer . . .

The telephone companies also have sources of market power that warrant maintaining safeguards against anticompetitive behaviour. For example, telephone companies are still overwhelmingly dominant in the local telephony market and, until this dominance is diminished, it would not be appropriate to forebear unconditionally from rate regulation of broadband access services.

[81] *AOL, Open Access Comments, supra* note 51, at 8.

[82] Hayes, et al., *Empirical Analysis, supra* note 53, at 1.

[83] *See* Bernstein, *Broadband!, supra* note 54, at 57.

Thus, the real game in standards is to reach critical mass for your platform without giving up too much control. This requires a careful balance between openness (to attract others to your platform) and control over standards development (to ensure an advantaged value-capture position). Of course, the lessons of Microsoft, Cisco, and others are not lost on market participants, and these days no player will willingly cede a major standards-based advantage to a competitor. Therefore, in emerging sectors such as broadband, creating a standards-based edge will likely require an ongoing structural advantage, whether via regulatory discontinuities, incumbent status, or the ability to influence customer behavior.

[84] *See* Hausman et al., *Residential Demand for Broadband, supra* note 52, at 133.

Video streaming has received an immense amount of attention not only because it might compete directly with the cable TV product, but also because it embodies the qualitative leap in functionality and quantum jump in speed that broadband Internet provides.

Video streaming is foreclosed as a threat to Time Warner's services. By singling out current cable TV customers for an extremely high floor price for independent ISP broadband Internet service, Time Warner is leveraging its monopoly position in cable into the broadband Internet market.

Time Warner asserts complete control over video streaming by controlling the economic terms on which Quality of Service is offered. Time Warner goes on to build a wall around the video market with pricing policy that dissuades ISPs from competing for the Internet business of cable TV customers. Time Warner buttresses that wall with a marketing barrier and a service quality barrier that can further dissuade ISPs from competing for TV customers.

Northnet, An Open Access Business Model, supra note 55, at 6-7.

[85] Time Warner's Term Sheet and AT&T public statements about how it will negotiate commercial access after its technical trial give a clear picture of the threat to dynamic innovation on the Internet. The companies' own access policies reveal the levers of

market power and network control that stand to stifle innovation on the Internet. Under the imposed conditions, the commercial space available for unaffiliated and smaller ISPs (where much innovation takes place) is sparse and ever shrinking.

[86] The AT&T preference is illustrated as follows:

> Radio GoGaGa [is] a music radio network that transmits over the Internet [and] depends on word-of-mouth and bumper stickers to attract users. . . . [Radio GoGaGa f]ounder Joe Pezzillo worries that the competitive gap could widen as broadband brings new business models.
>
> He envisions AT&T making deals with major music labels to deliver its own Internet radio, with AT&T providing the fastest connections to its partners and slower connections to sites like his. "Someone's not going to wait for our page to load when they can get a competitor's page instantly," Pezzillo said.
>
> AT&T says it has yet to formulate business models with partners, but the software the company has designed for the Boulder trial – demonstrated at its headquarters in Englewood, Colo[rado] last week – clearly includes a menu that will allow customers to link directly to its partners. Company officials acknowledge that AT&T's network already has the ability to prioritize the flow of traffic just as Pezzillo fears.
>
> "We could turn the switches in a matter of days to be able to accommodate that kind of environment," said Patrick McGrew, an AT&T manager working on the technical details of the Boulder trial. Though the Boulder trial is focused on technical issues alone, AT&T will study the way customers navigate the system as it negotiates with ISPs seeking to use its network.

Goodman, *supra* note 156.

[87] Thomas W. Hazlett & George Bittlingmayer, *The Political Economy of Cable "Open Access,* (AEI-Brookings Joint Center for Regulatory Studies, Working Paper No. 01-06, 2001), *available at* http://www.aei.brookings.org/publications/working/working_01_06.pdf., at 17 n.47 (quoting Jason Krause & Elizabeth Wasserman, *Switching Teams on Open Access?*, THE INDUSTRY STANDARD, Jan. 24, 2000, *available at* http://www.thestandard.com/article/display/1,1153,8903,00.html).

[88] *See* Hausman et al., *Residential Demand for Broadband*, *supra* note 52, at 159.

> [A] cable broadband provider will engage in conduit discrimination if the gain from additional access revenues from broadband users offsets the loss in content revenues from narrower distribution. . .
>
> To capture the gains from such discrimination, the vertically integrated cable provider must have a cable footprint in which to distribute its broadband portal service, either through direct ownership or through an arrangement to share the benefits of foreclosure with other cable providers.

[89] *See* Rubinfeld & Singer, *Open Access*, *supra* note 49, at 657.

Hence, a cable broadband provider will engage in conduit discrimination if the gain for additional access revenues from broadband users offsets the loss in content revenues form narrower distribution. What determines whether conduit discrimination will be profitable? Simply put, if a cable broadband transport provider that controls particular content only has a small fraction of the national cable broadband transport market, then that provider would have little incentive to discriminate against rival broadband transport providers *outside of its cable footprint.* The intuition is straightforward: out-of-franchise conduit discrimination would inflict a loss on the cable provider's content division, while out-of-region cable providers would be the primary beneficiaries of harm done to non-cable competitors.

[90] Hausman et al., *Residential Demand for Broadband, supra* note 52, at 156 (footnote omitted). The ACA provides the calculation for cable operators:

The major MSOs will be the clear winners in these transactions. MSOs granted exclusive distribution rights will have an opportunity to attract DBS subscribers with exclusive programming, resulting in increased subscriber revenues (a minimum of $40-$50 per subscriber) and increased system values (at least $3,500-$5,000 per subscriber)....

Where do ACA members fit into these transactions? Nowhere. ACA members operate locally, not regionally or nationally. In situations involving regional or national exclusive distribution rights, there is little incentive to carve out exceptions for smaller cable systems. For each small system subscriber lost under exclusivity, the vertically integrated program provider will likely lose revenue between $0.10 and $0.75 per month, depending on the service. In contrast, for each former DBS subscriber gained through regional or national exclusive program offerings, the MSO with exclusive distribution rights will gain all monthly revenue from that subscriber, plus increased system value. In economic terms, an external cost of this gain will be the cost to small cable companies and consumers of reduced program diversity.

ACA, Comments, supra note 56, at 13-14.

[91] Hausman et al., *Residential Demand for Broadband, supra* note 52, at 156 (footnote omitted).

[92] *See* Comments of the Competitive Broadband Coalition, *Implementation of the Cable Television Consumer Protection & Competition Act of 1992,* Cable Services Bureau Dkt. No. 01-290, at 10-11 (Dec. 3, 2001).

CTCN [CT Communications Network Inc.], a registered and franchised cable operator, has been unable to purchase the affiliated HITS transport service from AT&T Broadband, the nation's largest cable operator, despite repeated attempts to do so. . . . Based on its own experience and conversations with other companies who have experienced similar problems, CTCN believes that AT&T is refusing to sell HITS to any company using DSL technology to deliver video services over existing phone lines because such companies would directly compete with AT&T's entry into the local telephone market using both its own cable systems and the cable plant of unaffiliated cable operators. AT&T simply does not want any terrestrial based competition by other broadband networks capable of providing bundled video, voice and data services.

[93] Bernstein, *Broadband!*, *supra* note 54, at 12-14; Merrill Lynch, AOL *Time Warner,* *supra* note 54, at 33.

[94] *See* Hausman et al., *Residential Demand for Broadband*, *supra* note 52, at 149. It is possible that at some point in the future new technologies will emerge, or existing technologies will be refined, in such a way that they will compete effectively with cable-based Internet services. . . . [W]ithin the relevant two-year time horizon, neither DSL nor satellite-based Internet service will be able to offer close substitutes for cable-based Internet service. Hence, neither will be able to provide the price-disciplining constraint needed to protect consumer welfare.

[95] *See* Am. Online, Inc., No. C-3989, at 12 (Fed. Trade Comm'n Apr. 17, 2001), *available at* http://www.ftc.gov/os/2001/04/aoltwdo.pdf.

[96] AOL has argued:

At every key link in the broadband distribution chain for video/voice/ data services, AT&T would possess the ability and the incentive to limit consumer choice. Whether through its exclusive control of the EPG or browser that serve as consumers' interface; its integration of favored Microsoft operating systems in set-top boxes; its control of the cable broadband pipe itself; its exclusive dealing with its own proprietary cable ISPs; or the required use of its own "backbone" long distance facilities; AT&T could block or choke off consumers' ability to choose among the access, Internet services, and integrated services of their choice. Eliminating customer choice will diminish innovation, increase prices, and chill consumer demand, thereby slowing the roll-out of integrated service.

AOL, *Comments, Transfer of Control*, *supra* note 51, at 11.

[97] *See Goldman Sachs, America Online/Time Warner, supra* note 54, at 14, 17. AOL Time Warner is uniquely positioned against its competitors from both technology and media perspectives to make the interactive opportunity a reality. This multiplatform scale is particularly important from a pricing perspective, since it will permit the new company to offer more compelling and cost effective pricing bundles and options than its competitors. Furthermore, AOL Time Warner will benefit from a wider global footprint than its competitors" ". . .[W]e believe the real value by consumers en masse will be not in the "broadband connection" per se, but rather an attractively packaged, priced, and easy-to-use service that will bundle broadband content as an integral part of the service.

[98] AOL, *Comments, Transfer of Control*, *supra* note 51.

[99] *See* Jonathan Krim, *FCC Rules Seek High-Speed Shift; Phone Firms Would Keep Cable Rights*, WASH. POST, Feb. 15, 2002, at E1 (on the higher cost of addressing problems *ex post*).

[100] AOL, *Comments, Transfer of Control, supra* note 51, at 9-10.

[101] *See* Merrill Lynch, AOL *Time Warner, supra* note 54, at 38 ("If the technology market has a communications aspect to it, moreover, in which information must be shared [spreadsheets, instant messaging, enterprise software applications], the network effect is even more powerful."); Bernstein, *Broadband!, supra* note 54, at 26: "Thus, if the MSOs can execute as they begin to deploy cable modem services in upgraded areas, they have a significant opportunity to seize many of the most attractive customers in the coming broadband land grab. These customers are important both because they represent a disproportionate share of the value and because they are bell weathers for mass-market users."

[102] Shapiro & Varian, INFORMATION RULES, *supra* note 44.

[103] *See* Hausman, et al., *Residential Demand for Broadband, supra* note 52, at 164. "Due to the nature of network industries in general, the early leader in any broadband Internet access may enjoy a "lock-in" of customers and content providers – that is, given the high switching costs for consumers associated with changing broadband provider (for example, the cost of a DSL modem and installation costs), an existing customer would be less sensitive to an increase in price than would a prospective customer."

[104] *See* generally Hausman, et al., *Residential Demand for Broadband, supra* note 52, at 136-48; Bernstein, *Broadband!, supra* note 54, at 8; *AT&T Canada, supra* note 156, at 12. "AT&T Canada notes that narrowband access facilities are not an adequate service substitute for broadband access facilities. The low bandwidth associated with these facilities can substantially degrade the quality of service that is provided to the end customer to the point where transmission reception of services is no longer possible."

[105] Amended Complaint of the Dep't of Justice at 6, U.S. v. AT&T Corp., 2000 WL 1752108 (D.C. Cir. 2000) (No. 1:00CV01176), *available at* http://www.usdoj.gov/atr/cases/indx4468.htm.

[106] *AT&T Canada, Comments of AT&T Canada, supra* note 50, at 12.

> The cost of switching suppliers is another important factor which is used to assess demand conditions in the relevant market. In the case of the broadband access market, the cost of switching suppliers could be significant, particularly if there is a need to adopt different technical interfaces or to purchase new terminal equipment for the home or office. Given the fact that many of the technologies involved in the provision of broadband access services are still in the early stages of development, it is unlikely that we will see customer switching seamlessly form one service provider to another in the near-term.

[107] *Northnet, An Open Access Business Model, supra* note 55.

[108] David Clark and Rosemary Blumenthal, *Rethinking the Design of the Internet: The End-to-End Argument vs. The Brave New World*, TELECOM. POLICY, August 10, 2000, at 24.

[109] While Earthlink pointed out that the "nondisclosure provisions have an adverse impact on the ability of the market to operate freely and on the ability of government agencies to evaluate the competitiveness of the market," it was others who actually released the agreement.

[110] AT&T has sued and threatened to sue every local jurisdiction that required open access and withheld investment in those areas. Time Warner pulled the plug on Disney and threatened to extract full subscriber value from Disney for every customer it lost when Disney offered to give satellite dishes to the public. AOL threatened to sue Prodigy for the economic harm it caused AOL when Prodigy hacked into AOL's instant messaging service.

[111] High Tech Broadband Coalition, Cable Modem Proceeding.

[112] The agreement was reached with AT&T shortly before the Comcast AT&T merger closed.

[113] *A New Model for AOL May Influence Cable's Future,* NEW YORK TIMES, August 26, 2002, at C.1; Dan Gilmore, *AOL Capitulates, Gives Up Struggle for 'Open Access',* SAN JOSE MERCURY NEWS, September 1, 2002.

[114] Jim Hu, *AOL's Unrequited Cable Love,* CNET NEWS.COM, January 26, 2004.

[115] The Federal Communications Commission has been presented with a mountain of specific evidence of anticompetitive behavior by wire owners. Notwithstanding the grant of entry into long distance, many of these problems still afflict the provision of DSL service, as recent testimony in Texas (the second state in which an incumbent RBOC was granted entry) attest; see *Response of Onramp,* TEN QUESTIONS TO BEGIN THE COMMITTEE'S INQUIRY INTO STATE BROADBAND POLICY, Committee on State Affairs, April 3, 2002 (Hereafter Onramp); *Response of Cbeyond, Inc.,"* TEN QUESTIONS TO BEGIN THE COMMITTEE'S INQUIRY INTO STATE BROADBAND POLICY, Committee on State Affairs, April 3, 2002 (hereafter, Cbeyond); *Response of IP Communications,* TEN QUESTIONS TO BEGIN THE COMMITTEE'S INQUIRY INTO STATE BROADBAND POLICY, Committee on State Affairs, April 3, 2002 (hereafter IP Communications); *Response of Hometown Communications,* TEN QUESTIONS TO BEGIN THE COMMITTEE'S INQUIRY INTO STATE BROADBAND POLICY, Committee on State Affairs, April 3, 2002 (hereafter Hometown); *Response of Texas CLEC Coalition,* TEN QUESTIONS TO BEGIN THE COMMITTEE'S INQUIRY INTO STATE BROADBAND POLICY, Committee on State Affairs, April 3, 2002 (hereafter TxCLEC); *Reply Comments of the California ISP Association, Inc., FURTHER NOTICE OF PROPOSED RULEMAKING IN THE MATTER OF THE COMPUTER III REMAND PROCEEDINGS: BELL OPERATING COMPANY PROVISION OF ENHANCED SERVICES; 1998 BIENNIAL REGULATORY REVIEW – REVIEW OF COMPUTER II AND ONA SAFEGUARDS AND REQUIREMENTS*, Federal Communications Commission, CC Docket NO. 95-20, 98-10, April 30, 2000 (hereafter, CISPA, 2001b); *Reply Comments of the Texas Internet Service Providers Association, .*FURTHER NOTICE OF PROPOSED RULEMAKING IN THE MATTER OF THE COMPUTER III REMAND PROCEEDINGS: BELL OPERATING COMPANY PROVISION OF ENHANCED SERVICES; 1998 BIENNIAL REGULATORY REVIEW – REVIEW OF COMPUTER II AND ONA SAFEGUARDS AND REQUIREMENTS*, Federal Communications Commission, CC Docket NO. 95-20, 98-10, April 30, 2000 (hereafter, TISPA, 2001a); *Reply Comments of the Commercial Internet Exchange Association, .FURTHER NOTICE OF PROPOSED RULEMAKING IN THE MATTER OF THE COMPUTER III REMAND PROCEEDINGS: BELL OPERATING COMPANY PROVISION OF ENHANCED SERVICES; 1998 BIENNIAL*

REGULATORY REVIEW – REVIEW OF COMPUTER II AND ONA SAFEGUARDS AND REQUIREMENTS, FEDERAL COMMUNICATIONS COMMISSION, CC DOCKET NO. 95-20, 98-10, APRIL 30, 2000 (hereafter, CIX, 2001a); *Comments of the Information Technology Association of America, IN THE MATTER OF REVIEW OF REGULATORY REQUIREMENTS FOR INCUMBENT LEC BROADBAND TELECOMMUNICATIONS SERVICES*, Federal Communications Commission, CC Docket No. 01-337, March 1, 2002 (hereafter ITAA, 2002).; *Comments of the IP Communications Corporation, IN THE MATTER OF REVIEW OF REGULATORY REQUIREMENTS FOR INCUMBENT LEC BROADBAND TELECOMMUNICATIONS SERVICES*, Federal Communications Commission, CC Docket No. 01-337, March 1, 2002 (hereafter IPCommunications, 2002); *Comments of the Public Service Commission of the State of Missouri, IN THE MATTER OF REVIEW OF REGULATORY REQUIREMENTS FOR INCUMBENT LEC BROADBAND TELECOMMUNICATIONS SERVICES*, Federal Communications Commission, CC Docket No. 01-337, March 1, 2002 (hereafter MOPSC, 2002); *Joint Comments of NASUCA, et al., IN THE MATTER OF REVIEW OF REGULATORY REQUIREMENTS FOR INCUMBENT LEC BROADBAND TELECOMMUNICATIONS SERVICES*, Federal Communications Commission, CC Docket No. 01-337, March 1, 2002 (hereafter NASUCA, 2002); *Comments of Ad Hoc Telecommunications Users Committee, IN THE MATTER OF REVIEW OF REGULATORY REQUIREMENTS FOR INCUMBENT LEC BROADBAND TELECOMMUNICATIONS SERVICES*, Federal Communications Commission, CC Docket No. 01-337, March 1, 2002 (hereafter Ad Hoc, 2002); *Comments of the New Mexico Information Professionals Association of America, IN THE MATTER OF REVIEW OF REGULATORY REQUIREMENTS FOR INCUMBENT LEC BROADBAND TELECOMMUNICATIONS SERVICES*, Federal Communications Commission, CC Docket No. 01-337, March 1, 2002 (hereafter NMIPA, 2002); *Comments of Cox Communications, Inc., IN THE MATTER OF APPROPRIATE FRAMEWORK FOR BROADBAND ACCESS TO THE INTERNET OVER WIRELINE FACILITIES, UNIVERSAL SERVICE OBLIGATIONS OF BROADBAND PROVIDERS, COMPUTER III REMAND PROCEEDINGS: BELL OPERATING COMPANY PROVISION OF ENHANCED SERVICES; 1998 BIENNIAL REGULATORY REVIEW – REVIEW OF COMPUTER II AND ONA SAFEGUARDS AND REQUIREMENTS*, Federal Communications Commission, CC Docket NO. 02-33, 95-20, 98-10, May 3, 2002 (Hereafter Cox, 2002); *Comments of BrandX., IN THE MATTER OF APPROPRIATE FRAMEWORK FOR BROADBAND ACCESS TO THE INTERNET OVER WIRELINE FACILITIES, UNIVERSAL SERVICE OBLIGATIONS OF BROADBAND PROVIDERS, COMPUTER III REMAND PROCEEDINGS: BELL OPERATING COMPANY PROVISION OF ENHANCED SERVICES; 1998 BIENNIAL REGULATORY REVIEW – REVIEW OF COMPUTER II AND ONA SAFEGUARDS AND REQUIREMENTS*, Federal Communications Commission, CC Docket NO. 02-33, 95-20, 98-10, May 3, 2002 (Hereafter BrandX, 2002); *Comments of the New Hampshire ISP Association, IN THE MATTER OF APPROPRIATE FRAMEWORK FOR BROADBAND ACCESS TO THE INTERNET OVER WIRELINE FACILITIES, UNIVERSAL SERVICE OBLIGATIONS OF BROADBAND PROVIDERS, COMPUTER III REMAND PROCEEDINGS: BELL OPERATING COMPANY PROVISION OF ENHANCED SERVICES; 1998 BIENNIAL REGULATORY REVIEW – REVIEW OF COMPUTER II AND ONA SAFEGUARDS AND REQUIREMENTS*, Federal Communications Commission, CC Docket NO. 02-33, 95-20, 98-10, May 3, 2002 (Hereafter NHISP, 2002); *Comments of Ruby Ranch Cooperative Association, IN THE MATTER OF APPROPRIATE FRAMEWORK FOR BROADBAND ACCESS TO THE INTERNET OVER WIRELINE FACILITIES, UNIVERSAL SERVICE OBLIGATIONS OF BROADBAND PROVIDERS, COMPUTER III REMAND PROCEEDINGS: BELL OPERATING COMPANY PROVISION OF ENHANCED SERVICES; 1998 BIENNIAL REGULATORY REVIEW*

– REVIEW OF COMPUTER II AND ONA SAFEGUARDS AND REQUIREMENTS, Federal Communications Commission, CC Docket NO. 02-33, 95-20, 98-10, May 3, 2002 (Hereafter Ruby Ranch, 2002); *Comments of Earthlink, Inc.*, IN THE MATTER OF APPROPRIATE FRAMEWORK FOR BROADBAND ACCESS TO THE INTERNET OVER WIRELINE FACILITIES, UNIVERSAL SERVICE OBLIGATIONS OF BROADBAND PROVIDERS, COMPUTER III REMAND PROCEEDINGS: BELL OPERATING COMPANY PROVISION OF ENHANCED SERVICES; 1998 BIENNIAL REGULATORY REVIEW – REVIEW OF COMPUTER II AND ONA SAFEGUARDS AND REQUIREMENTS, Federal Communications Commission, CC Docket NO. 02-33, 95-20, 98-10, May 3, 2002 (Hereafter Earhtlink, 2002); *Comments of U.S. LEC Corp.*, IN THE MATTER OF APPROPRIATE FRAMEWORK FOR BROADBAND ACCESS TO THE INTERNET OVER WIRELINE FACILITIES, UNIVERSAL SERVICE OBLIGATIONS OF BROADBAND PROVIDERS, COMPUTER III REMAND PROCEEDINGS: BELL OPERATING COMPANY PROVISION OF ENHANCED SERVICES; 1998 BIENNIAL REGULATORY REVIEW – REVIEW OF COMPUTER II AND ONA SAFEGUARDS AND REQUIREMENTS, Federal Communications Commission, CC Docket NO. 02-33, 95-20, 98-10, May 3, 2002 (Hereafter US LEC, 2002); *Comments of Big Planet, Inc.,* IN THE MATTER OF APPROPRIATE FRAMEWORK FOR BROADBAND ACCESS TO THE INTERNET OVER WIRELINE FACILITIES, UNIVERSAL SERVICE OBLIGATIONS OF BROADBAND PROVIDERS, COMPUTER III REMAND PROCEEDINGS: BELL OPERATING COMPANY PROVISION OF ENHANCED SERVICES; 1998 BIENNIAL REGULATORY REVIEW – REVIEW OF COMPUTER II AND ONA SAFEGUARDS AND REQUIREMENTS, Federal Communications Commission, CC Docket NO. 02-33, 95-20, 98-10, May 3, 2002 (Hereafter Big Planet, 2002); *Joint Comments of Cbeyond and Nuvox*, IN THE MATTER OF REVIEW OF REGULATORY REQUIREMENTS FOR INCUMBENT LEC BROADBAND TELECOMMUNICATIONS SERVICES, Federal Communications Commission, CC Docket No. 01-337, March 1, 2002 (hereafter CBeyond, 2002).

[116] Steven J. Vaughn-Nichols, *DSL Spells Trouble for Many ISPs*, SMART RESELLER, February 24, 1999.

[117] Onramp, *supra* note 115, at 16-17.

[118] ITAA, *supra* note 115, at 11; DirecTV, *supra* note 115, at 8-10.

[119] Onramp, *supra* note 115, at 5-6; NMIPA, *supra* note 115 at 5.

[120] TISPA, *supra* note 115, at 18.

[121] IURC, *supra* note 115, at 14; Utah ISP, *supra* note 115,at 8, 9; ISPC, *supra* note 115,at 7; IAC, *supra* note 115,at 9; AOL, *supra* note 115,at 6, 8; AdHoc, *supra* note 115,at 26; ITAA, *supra* note 115,at 13, 15.

[122] TISPA, *supra* note 115,at 27.

[123] TISPA, *supra* note 115, at 33.

[124] Onramp, *supra* note 115, at 14.

[125] ITAA, *supra* note 115, at 10-11; CISPA, *supra* note 115, 2001a, at 27-28.

[126] TISPA, *supra* note 115, at 17.

[127] Cox, *supra* note 115, at 6.

[128] IURC, *supra* note 115, at 5; TXPUC, *supra* note 115, at 14; NYDPS, *supra* note 115, at 7; Utah ISP, *supra* note 115, at 13, 15; ISPC, *supra* note 115, at 11; IAC, *supra* note 115, at 9; AdHoc, *supra* note 115, at 27; ITAA, *supra* note 115, at 16.

[129] CISPA, Reply, *supra* note 115, at 7.

[130] Onramp, *supra* note 115, at 3.

[131] TISPA, *supra* note 115, at 21, New Edge, *supra* note 115, at 6; Brand X, *supra* note 115, at 2, DirectTV, *supra* note 115, at 8; CIX, *supra* note 115, at 8.

[132] Telephone companies achieve the margin difference by offering high volume ISPs massive volume discounts that aggregate business across state lines, without any cost justification for such a discount (see TISPA, *supra* note 115, at 37; MPIPA, *supra* note 115, at 5; ITAA, *supra* note 115, at 21; DirectTV, *supra* note 115, at 9, CSIPA, *supra* note 115, at 16).

[133]   Onramp, at 3, citing CFO Stephenson.

[134] Todd Spangler, *Crossing the Broadband Divide*, PC MAGAZINE, February 12, 2002 (noting pricing and service quality problems); Brian Ploskina, and Dana Coffield, "Regional Bells Ringing Up Higher DSL Rates," *Interactive Week,* February 18, 2001; Yale Braunstein, MARKET POWER AND PRICE INCREASES IN THE DSL MARKET (July 2001).

[135] Press accounts give detailed estimates of major ISPs. The number of subscribers to independent ISPs is put at 500,000 to 600,000 in a market that is in the range of 10,000,000 to 12,000,000, see Forrester.com/ER/Press/Release/0,1769,655,00.html; ISP-Planet.

[136] Greenstein, *Building and Delivering, supra* note 139.

[137] Patricia Fusco, *Top U.S. ISPs by Subscriber: Q1 2002*, ISP-PLANET, May 29, 2002.

[138] Techweb News, *Broadband Boom,* INFORMATION WEEK, May 12, 2004.

[139] Id., see also Scott Pruitt, *ISPs Missing the Broadband Boom,* PC WORLD, November 14, 2003.

[140] Techweb News, *supra* note 138.

[141] Arora, et al., Ashish Arora, Andrea Fosfuri and Alfonso Gamardella, MARKETS FOR TECHNOLOGY: THE ECONOMICS OF INNOVATION AND CORPORATE STRATEGY (2001), at 231-232, frame this issue in terms of a trade off between "licensing revenues (the revenue effect)" and "the lower profits that the increased competition (the rent dissipation effect) from the licensee implies." Their discussion suggests the two fundamental issue that have been raised in the cable modem context are operative. The first is cable's desire to prevent high-speed Internet service from creating competitors for video services ("firms with a large market share in the product market (and by implications, possessing the required complementary assets) are better off exploiting the technology in –house)." The second is the desire to dominate the high-speed Internet market, which drives cable to undermine competition from established Internet Service Providers ("licensing is more attractive when the licensee operating in a different market and is unlikely to be a strong competitor").

[142] Jorn Kleinert & Danial Piazolo, *Governing the Cyber Space*, in THE NEW ECONOMY AND ECONOMIC GROWTH IN EUROPE AND THE US (David B. Audretsch & Paul J.J. Welfens, eds., 2002), at 283; *see also* J. Cremer, P. Rey & J. Tirole, *Connectivity in the Commercial Internet*, 84 J. INDUS. ECON. 4 (2000).

VI. NETWORK NEUTRALITY, BROADBAND DISCRIMINATION

INTRODUCTION

Communications regulators over the next decade will spend increasing time on conflicts between the private interests of broadband providers and the public's interest in a competitive innovation environment centered on the Internet. As the policy questions this conflict raises are basic to communications policy, they are likely to reappear in many different forms. So far, the first major appearance has come in the "open access" (or "multiple access") debate, over the desirability of allowing vertical integration between Internet Service Providers and cable operators.[1] Proponents of open access see it as a structural remedy to guard against an erosion of the "neutrality" of the network as between competing content and applications. Critics, meanwhile, have taken open-access regulation as unnecessary and likely to slow the pace of broadband deployment.

This paper takes a more general perspective. The questions raised in discussions of open access and network neutrality are basic to both telecommunications and innovation policy. The promotion of network neutrality is no different than the challenge of promoting fair evolutionary competition in any privately owned environment, whether a telephone network, operating system, or even a retail store. Government regulation in such contexts invariably tries to help ensure that the short-term interests of the owner do not prevent the best products or applications becoming available to end-users. The same interest animates the promotion of network neutrality: preserving a Darwinian competition among every conceivable use of the Internet so that the only the best survive.

Given the likely recurrence of these kinds of questions, this paper compares three general approaches to the regulation of broadband providers: structural remedies, a non-discrimination regime, and self- or non-regulation. It questions, first, the merits of structural remedies like open access as a means for promoting network innovation in favor of less intrusive models. While structural restrictions like open access may serve other interests, as a remedy to promote the neutrality of the network they are potentially counterproductive. Proponents of open access have generally overlooked the fact that, to the extent an open access rule inhibits vertical relationships, it can help maintain the Internet's greatest deviation from network neutrality. That deviation is favoritism of data applications, as a class, over latency-sensitive applications involving voice or video. There is also reason to believe that open access alone can be an insufficient remedy for many of the likely instances of network discrimination.

The preferable framework for ensuring network neutrality, I argue, forgoes structural remedies for a direct scrutiny of broadband discrimination. The link between anti-discrimination regulations and network innovation are as old as the *Hush-a-Phone*[2] and *Carterfone*[3] decisions, which controlled AT&T's efforts to destroy innovative network attachments. The basic principle behind a network anti-discrimination regime is to give *users* the right to use non-harmful network attachments or applications, and give innovators the corresponding freedom to supply them. Such a regime avoids some of the costs of structural regulation by allowing for efficient vertical integration so long as the rights granted to the users of the network are not compromised.

But might network neutrality be accomplished without any regulation at all? Basic economic theory suggests that operators have a long-term interest coincident with the public: both should want a neutral platform that supports the emergence of the very best applications. However the evidence suggests the operators may have paid less attention to their long-term interests than might be ideal. A 2002 survey of operator practices conducted for this paper suggests a tendency to favor short-term results.[4] In that year, evidence of a discrimination problem became clear from several sources, including consumer complaints about operators who ban classes of applications or equipment, like servers, Virtual Private Networks, or WiFi devices,[5] and in filings at the Federal Communications Commission by application developers.[6] The survey in this paper shows that operators indeed had implemented significant contractual and architectural limits on certain classes of applications. Operators showed an unfortunate tendency to want to ban new or emerging applications or network attachments, like WiFi devices or Virtual Private Networks, perhaps out of suspicion or an (often futile) interest in price-discrimination. On the whole the evidence suggests that the operators were often pursuing legitimate goals, such as price discrimination and bandwidth management. The problem was the use of methods, like bans on certain forms of applications, which are likely to distort the market and the future of application development. In short, the recent historical record gives good reason to question the efficacy of self-regulation in this area.

I don't want to suggest that operators are somehow incapable of understanding their long-term interests. Yet, when we return to the open access debate, one account of the utility of the debate is that it played an important informational role—the debate itself helped cable operators evaluate their long-term self-interests, and many have chosen to allow rival ISPs access to their networks, for a variety of reasons.[7] Even strong believers in deregulation and the advantages of vertical integration recognize that incumbents may occasionally become set in their ways.[8] In this respect, one of the functions of raising issues of broadband discrimination is to challenge broadband operators to ask whether applications restrictions are a good long-term policy. Indeed many of the improvements in operator behavior in the year 2003 may be linked to the Federal Communications Commission's increased oversight of this area.

This paper encompasses a mixture of empirical and theoretical sections. The first part of five is an effort to explain the relationship between several related concepts in this area: open access, broadband discrimination, and network neutrality. Network neutrality, as shorthand for a system of belief about innovation policy, is the end, while open access and broadband discrimination are the means. I suggest that open access regulation, as a structural remedy to ensure network neutrality, is not ideally suited to that task. A direct analysis premised on normative principle of network neutrality may provide a better means to discuss the harm in question.

The second part develops the theoretical framework for a broadband discrimination regime. It asks whether we can differentiate between justified and unjustified restrictions on user behavior, with particular reference to the restrictions seen in the survey in the third part. The use of restrictions on classes of application to pursue bandwidth management and price discrimination is troubling when those restrictions might be pursued through less restrictive means. The section also asks whether self-regulation is likely, and concludes that the threat of regulation might serve a useful purpose.

The third part is a survey of the degree to which broadband operators restrict certain applications and favor others. The study surveys the nation's 10 largest cable operators and six largest DSL providers. The results are mixed. First, cable operators tend to employ far more contractual restrictions than do DSL operators. The contractual restrictions and network designs tend to favor, as a class, one-to-many applications development. Second, there is a tendency to use restrictions on application classes to pursue goals such as price discrimination and bandwidth management.

The fourth part shows what a workable principle of network neutrality would look like and what it would mean for the conduct of broadband providers. It suggests that operators should have the freedom to "police what they own," or act reasonably to control the local broadband network. On the other hand, it suggests that the Internet community (and, at some point, regulators) should view with suspicion restrictions premised on inter-network criteria. A sample text of an anti-discrimination law is included to show how such a principle could be implemented. Finally, the fifth and final part of this paper addresses several possible counterarguments to the network neutrality regime discussed in this article.

NETWORK NEUTRALITY & OPEN ACCESS

The relationship between concepts like open-access, network neutrality, and broadband discrimination may be unclear to the reader. It is best to understand network neutrality as an end, and open access and broadband discrimination as different means to that end. In this section we will examine both why network neutrality might be an attractive goal, and, how an open-access and broadband discrimination regime differ as means toward that end.

THE CASE FOR NETWORK NEUTRALITY

So what is attractive about a neutral network—that is, an Internet that does not favor one application (say, the world wide web), over others (say, email)? Who cares if the Internet is better for some things than others?[9]

The argument for network neutrality must be understood as a concrete expression of a system of belief about innovation, one that has gained significant popularity over last two decades. The belief system goes by many names.[10] Here we can refer to it generally as the evolutionary model.[11] Speaking very generally, adherents view the innovation process as a survival-of-the-fittest competition among developers of new technologies. They are suspicious of models of development that might vest control in any initial prospect-holder, private or public, who is expected to direct the optimal path of innovation, minimizing the excesses of innovative competition.[12] The suspicion arises from the belief that the most promising path of development is difficult to predict in advance, and the argument that any single prospect holder will suffer from cognitive biases (such as a predisposition to continue with current ways of doing business) that make it unlikely to come to the right decisions, despite best intentions.

This account is simplistic; of interest is what the theory says for network design. A communications network like the Internet can be seen as a platform for a competition among application developers. Email, the web, and streaming applications are in a battle for the attention and interest of end-users. It is therefore important that the platform be neutral to ensure the competition remains meritocratic.

For these reasons, Internet Darwinians argue that their innovation theory is embodied in the "end-to-end" design argument, which in essence suggests that networks should be neutral as among applications.[13] As network theorist Jerome Saltzer puts it: "The End-to-End argument says 'don't force any service, feature, or restriction on the customer; his application knows best what features it needs, and whether or not to provide those features itself.'"[14] The Internet Protocol suite (IP) was designed to follow the end-to-end principle, and is famously indifferent both to the physical communications medium "below" it, and the applications running "above" it.[15] Packets on the Internet run over glass and copper, ATM and Ethernet, carrying .mp3 files, bits of web pages, and snippets of chat. Backers of an evolutionary approach to innovation take the Internet, the fastest growing communications network in history, as evidence of the superiority of a network designed along evolutionary principles.[16]

There is much to this debate, and I do not want to suggest that the discussion about the general merits of evolutionary innovation models are settled, nor are the debates over whether a neutral platform best stimulates competition among applications.[17] But sentiments like those I have just expressed have come to enjoy a broad normative following. From this we can understand why preserving a neutral network might be taken as a suitable goal of Internet communications policy.

THE OPEN ACCESS REMEDY AND ITS LIMITATIONS

Taking network neutrality as the goal, we can understand open access as one kind of remedy. The term open-access is used in many different ways; it generally refers to a structural requirement that would prevent broadband operators from bundling broadband service with Internet access from in-house Internet service providers.[18] Certain proponents, like Jerome Saltzer, Larry Lessig and Mark Lemley, make the logical link between open-access regulation and the preservation of a neutral Internet. They argue that if cable operators are allowed to bundle ISP services with cable services, cable operators would be in a position to destroy the neutrality of the network by foreclosing competition among Internet applications. As Lemley and Lessig put it,

> [T]here is, in principle, no limit to what a cable company could bundle into its control of the network. As ISPs expand beyond the functions they have traditionally performed, AT&T or Time Warner might be in a position to foreclose all competition in an increasing range of services provided over broadband lines. The services available to broadband cable users would then be determined by the captive ISPs owned by each local cable company. This design would contradict the principle that the network should remain neutral and empower users. It further could constitute the first step in a return to the failed architecture of the old AT&T monopoly.[19]

Critics of this argument, like Phil Weiser, Jim Speta, and Glen Robinson, have, in the main, cast doubt on the claim that regulation is needed to prevent cable operators from foreclosing competition when it would be efficient, or ask whether network neutrality is an appropriate goal.[20] But I want to raise a slightly different question. If we agree with the normative goal of network neutrality, to what degree does the structural remedy of open-access actually serve its interest? Might we do better by targeting network neutrality directly with questions of broadband discrimination?

I believe there are several reasons to question the fit between open-access remedies and network neutrality. First, the concept of network neutrality is not as simple as some IP partisans have suggested. Neutrality, as a concept, is finicky, and depends entirely on what set of subjects you choose to be neutral among.[21] A policy that appears neutral in a certain time period, like "all men may vote", may lose its neutrality in a later time period, when the range of subjects is enlarged.

This problem afflicts the network neutrality embodied in the IP protocols. As the universe of applications has grown, the original conception of IP neutrality has dated: for IP was only neutral among *data* applications. Internet networks tend to favor, as a class, applications insensitive to latency (delay) or jitter (signal distortion). Consider that it doesn't matter whether an email arrives now or a few milliseconds later. But it certainly matters for applications that want to carry voice or video. In a universe of applications, that includes both latency-sensitive and insensitive applications, it is difficult to regard the IP suite as truly neutral as among all applications.

This point is closely linked to questions of structural separation. The technical reason IP favors data applications is as implemented, vendors have not implemented uniform mechanisms for offering quality of service (QoS) guarantees for the internet.[22] It doesn't insist that data arrive at any time or place. Instead, IP generally adopts a "best-effort" approach: it says, deliver the packets as fast as you can, which over a typical end-to-end connection may range from a basic 56K connection at the ends, to the precisely timed gigabits of bandwidth available on backbone SONET links. IP doesn't care: it runs over everything. But as a consequence, it implicitly disfavors applications that do care.

Network design is an exercise in tradeoffs, and IP's designers would point out that the approach of avoiding QoS had important advantages. Primarily, it helped IP be "downwardly" neutral as to the underlying physical media. But this requires us to be more circumspect in our discussions of network neutrality. IP's neutrality is actually a tradeoff between upward (application) and downward (connection) neutrality. If it is upward, or application neutrality that consumers care about, principles of downward neutrality may be a necessary sacrifice.

This returns us to the question of structural separation. We have a public network that is indeed a great creative commons for data applications, but it is less so for any application that requires a minimum quality of service. True application neutrality may, in fact, sometimes require a close vertical relationship between a broadband operator and Internet service provider. The reason is that the operator is ultimately the gatekeeper of quality of service for a given user, because only the broadband operator is in a position to offer service guarantees that extend to the end-user's computer (or network). Delivering the full possible range of applications either requires an impracticable upgrade of the entire network, or some tolerance of close vertical relationships.

This point indicts a strict open-access requirement. To the extent open access regulation prevents broadband operators from architectural cooperation with ISPs for the purpose of providing QoS dependent applications, it could hurt the cause of network neutrality.[23] By threatening the vertical relationship required for certain application types, it could maintain IP's discrimination in favor of data applications. More broadly, this argument shows that the concept of network neutrality cannot be taken as counsel against all vertical integration.[24]

A second, and simpler, problem with open access from a neutrality perspective is that the structural remedy may also be an underinclusive means of ensuring network neutrality. Competition among ISPs does not necessarily mean that broadband operators will simply retreat to acting as passive carriers in the last mile. As the survey in this study shows, operators continue to have reasons to want to control usage of the Internet based on their status as broadband operators, regardless of ISP competition. Hence, open-access does not end the debate over whether broadband operators are capable of engaging in undesirable behavior from the perspective of the public network.

For these reasons, this paper seeks to see if we might do better to address questions of network neutrality directly, through the remedial concept of "broadband discrimination," rather than through structural solutions like open-access.

THE CONCEPT OF BROADBAND DISCRIMINATION

The question of controlling what people do with their network services is hardly new to communications regulation. It is as least as old as *Hush-A-Phone*, and the D.C. Circuit's interpretation of the 1934 Communications Act to find that the subscriber has a "right reasonably to use his telephone in ways which are privately beneficial without being publicly detrimental."[25]

Nor is the prevention of discrimination a new topic in communications regulation. Over the history of communications regulation, the Government has employed both common carriage requirements (similar to the neutrality regime discussed here) and limits on vertical integration as means of preventing unwanted discrimination. The goal of this section is to further explain how a common carriage or anti-discrimination model might be better developed to address the current Internet environment.

Why might thinking in discrimination terms be useful? Only because it borrows from what is familiar to achieve new goals. What is critical to the study of discrimination regimes is the existence of both justified and suspect bases of discrimination. For example, in the employment context, where discrimination norms are most developed, employers are generally permitted to fire or refuse to hire individuals for a range of reasons, such as education-level, intelligence, and demeanor.[26] The law implicitly recognizes that it is essential that the employer retain the freedom to fire incompetents and hire only those with necessary skills. On the other hand, criteria such as race, sex, or national origin are suspect criteria of discrimination, but can only be justified by a bona fide rationale.[27]

While discrimination among Internet applications is a different context, the framework of analysis can be usefully retained. As the proposal in Part IV develops, it is possible to distinguish between classes of restrictions that should generally be allowable, and those that might raise suspicion. Overall, there is a need to strike a balance between legitimate interests in discriminating against certain uses, and reasons that are suspect either due to irrationality or because of costs not internalized by the broadband operator.

To get a better feeling for what a discrimination approach entails, it is helpful to map out some of the extremes of clearly permissible and clearly troublesome discrimination in the broadband context. At one extreme, many of the usage or application bans surveyed are clearly justified. For example, operators usually ban users from using applications or conduct that are meant to hurt the network or other users, like network viruses.[28] It is true that this is a departure from network neutrality, because it disfavors a class of applications—those that are disruptive to the network. Yet, it is clear that the operator has acted to solve a problem of a negative externality—the costs imposed by one user on others. Few could or would argue that this is a bad thing.

At the opposite extreme, the harm from totally unjustified discrimination is equally clear. Leaving aside whether operators would actually act in this way, imagine that the nation's broadband operators came to feel that IP "chat" programs were just a waste of time, and were able to use their control over the last mile to ban their use.[29] Such discrimination has both a direct harm as well as several negative externalities. The direct harm is obvious: existing broadband consumers who like chat programs lose the opportunity to use a valued application, while creators of chat programs lose whatever revenue opportunity chat programs create. But the more interesting costs are the various losses of positive externalities. Three stand out. First, if chat programs have positive externalities for other network applications—say, if the chat program is middle-ware for a file-exchange program, as in the case of Aimster—dependent applications are hurt as well. Second, to the degree other applications depend on a critical mass of high-bandwidth users, they are hurt by potential subscribers who at the margin are not willing to pay for broadband without the chat programs. Finally, to the extent chat programs have positive social externalities, like helping people to plan meetings or meet new boyfriends, the public suffers too.[30] Thus, there are considerable potential costs from an irrational or unjustified ban on certain application types.

These are the easy cases. We next consider whether reasons like price discrimination and bandwidth management should justify discrimination among applications.

PRICE DISCRIMINATION & RESTRICTIONS ON COMMERCIAL USE

As detailed in the survey below, nearly every operator places limits on "commercial" use, sometimes including limits on Virtual Private Networks, as well as limits on acting as a server.[31] Why might an operator put such a restriction on usage? Doing so obviously makes the service less attractive to consumers who might want to act in a commercial way, even in a fairly casual manner.[32]

The simple answer is price discrimination. That this is the case is not just intuition, but can be confirmed by company policy. As evidence we can consider Comcast's reply in 2001 to a user who had complained about the ban on VPN usage on Comcast's network:

Thank you for your message.

High traffic telecommuting while utilizing a VPN can adversely affect the condition of the network while disrupting the connection of our regular residential subscribers.

To accommodate the needs of our customers who do choose to operate VPN, Comcast offers the Comcast @Home Professional product. @Home Pro is designed to meet the needs of the ever growing population of small office/home office customers and telecommuters that need to take advantage of protocols such as VPN. This product will cost $95 per month, and afford you with standards which differ from the standard residential product.

If you're interested in upgrading . . . .[33]

As the letter shows, Cable and DSL operators typically offer commercial packages at a considerable markup from basic broadband service. For example, phone companies like Verizon or BellSouth offer T-1 lines at prices far higher than basic DSL or cable service.[34] The goal is to exact a premium price from the customers who most desire the commercial service. Allowing subscribers to basic service to operate hosting services might erode such profits.

It is true that mainstream antitrust analysis has come to see price discrimination as generally uncontentious, or at least ambiguous.[35] As between consumers and producers, it hurts some consumers and helps others, while raising the producers' profits. Yet this analysis can, and should, change as in the broadband context, because the practice of price discrimination may have external effects on the process of innovation and competition among applications. That is to say, while price discrimination among applications may not be troubling from a static perspective (as between existing consumers and producers), it may have dynamic consequences, for the competitive development of new applications.

We can see this in the present example of a ban on commercial operations. The goal, as we've seen, is to maintain a customary markup on business services. But the restrictions on the market for what can be termed commercial applications used on home connections come at a cost.

The direct effect of a ban on hosting is to make the connection slightly less valuable to the basic consumer, which presumably the operator takes into account in her pricing scheme. But there are other costs that the operator may not internalize. The bans on commercial use or acting as a server constrain the competitive development of applications that might rely on such a function. In the Comcast letter example the problem was VPN applications, which typically can rely on end-users functioning both as clients and servers, and which can be classified as a commercial use.[36] And it is also the case that hosting services may have positive social externalities not taken into account by the operator's decision. For example, VPNs may facilitate greater productivity among employees, a benefit that may be lost in their prohibition.

Another major restriction that interests broadband operators is barring users from providing content to the public or running servers. Why do broadband operators act in this way, if, again, it might lower the value of its service to its users? One reason may be the price discrimination rationale discussed above. Yet from the reports of cable operators themselves, a major goal is bandwidth management.[37] The restrictions appear to be efforts to manage how users consume bandwidth by discriminating against types of usage. As the survey showed, such restrictions are more common on cable networks, which operate shared connections and tend to lack technological means for restricting individual bandwidth consumption.[38] Hence, the restrictions, for example, on running "game" or "ftp" programs are most likely efforts to eliminate a potential source of bandwidth consumption.

The goal of bandwidth management poses an even more difficult question than does price discrimination. The goal of bandwidth management is, at a general level, aligned with network neutrality. As discussed above, certain classes of applications will never function properly unless bandwidth and quality of service are guaranteed. Hence, the absence of bandwidth management can interfere with application development and competition.

There are good reasons to question whether price-discrimination, without more, should be permissible grounds for allowing discrimination among applications. As we have seen, such usage restrictions may harm consumer welfare without offering a public benefit. This is particularly the case when there are less-restrictive means for engaging in price discrimination. Selling different tiers of service (low, medium, and high bandwidth) does not favor or discriminate against particular application types. In the presence of a means for differentiating among customers in a way that does not distort the process of competitive innovation, we should view discrimination on the basis of application with suspicion.

Similarly, while managing bandwidth is a laudable goal, its achievement through restricting certain application types is an unfortunate solution. The result is obviously a selective disadvantage for certain application markets. The less restrictive means is, as above, the technological management of bandwidth. Application-restrictions should, at best, be a stopgap solution to the problem of competing bandwidth demands.

SELF-REGULATION AND THE EDUCATIONAL PROPERTIES OF REGULATION

The previous sections show that broadband operators may want to discriminate amongst the uses of its network for various reasons. We have also seen that there are a variety of justifications—some good and some not—for such restrictions. Even if the goal itself is legitimate, the method of achieving that goal may be suspect. The question, then, is whether cable operators will self-regulate and come up with the best policies on their own, or whether regulation may be necessary.

In this section I argue that while cable operators may come to understand that broadband discrimination is not in their best interest, both the threat of, or actual implementation of, anti-discrimination regulation may otherwise serve a useful informational or educational function. Like anti-discrimination legislation in other contexts, it may serve an educational function, forcing operators to ask whether the restrictions they draft are actually serving their interest in maximizing the value of their services.

As a baseline, the attractiveness of broadband service is a function of the applications it offers the consumer. Hence, any restriction on use will lower the value of the service, and consequently either the price the operator can charge or the number of customers who will sign up (assuming a negative demand curve). To make this clear: if an operator operated a service that screened all uses except web-access alone it might be worth $30 to the average consumer, while a service that offered access to every kind of Internet application—including, say, the opportunity to get copyrighted music for free—might be worth $50. The difference in the value to the consumer will affect the price the operator can charge.

This basic point is captured by Joseph Farell and Philip Weiser's argument that a "platform monopolist has a powerful incentive to be a good steward of the applications sector for its platform."[39] The point reflects, as the authors stress, classic arguments from antitrust. A monopolist may still want competition in its input markets, to maximize profit in the monopoly market.

But it is easy for a steward to recognize that the platform should support as many applications as possible. The more difficult challenge has always been the dynamic aspect: recognizing that serving a tangible goal—like controlling bandwidth usage—may affect the intangible status of the Internet as an application development platform. Some of the restrictions, such as those on running various types of server, are applications that are now likely to be used by only a small minority of broadband users. Their sacrifice may appear like a good cost-saving measure.

More generally, the idea that discrimination may not always be rational is a well-understood phenomenon. In the employment context, the various discrimination laws have an explicitly educational function. For example, an express purpose of age discrimination legislation is to force employers to reconsider stereotyped perceptions of the competency of the elderly in the workforce.[40] Broadband operators may simply disfavor certain uses of their network for irrational reasons, such as hypothetic security concerns or exaggerated fears of legal liability. Additionally, a restriction may become obsolete: adopted at a certain time for a certain reason that no long matters. Practical experience suggests that such things happen.

For these reasons, anti-discrimination regulation or the threat thereof can also serve a useful educational function. It can force broadband operators to consider whether their restrictions are in their long-term best interests. And in the absence of law it can establish norms around discrimination that may preserve network neutrality over the long term.

The events of the year 2003 provide evidence to support the utility of a regulatory threat in promoting desirable conduct. Both Comcast and Cox Communications openly disavowed their old practices of placing bans on Virtual Private Networks, and filed documents with the FCC to that effect.[41] The cable industry has furthermore begun to publicly insist that it wants to avoid broadband discrimination in the future, stating, for example, that "Cable Believes in Open Connectivity for the Internet."[42]

There is the possibility that the current regulatory process has forced cable operators to rethink their practices and conclude that discrimination is not in their long term self-interest. The process demonstrates the continuing utility of communications regulators in remaining appraised on potential problems of anti-competitive practices.

A SURVEY OF BROADBAND USAGE RESTRICTIONS

Have broadband operators tended to favor certain uses of the Internet? To what extent? The goal of this section is to answer these questions, to the extent possible, for broadband networks during the year 2002.[43]

The study divides measures of favoritism and discrimination into two categories: contractual and architectural. The study surveyed the network designs (to the extent that the information was available) and usage restrictions in subscriber agreements and incorporated acceptable use policies from the 10 largest cable operators (AT&T,[44] Time Warner, Comcast, Cox Communications, Adelphia, Mediacom, Charter Communications, CableOne, Insight, and Cablevision), and 6 major DSL operators (Verizon, SBC, Qwest, BellSouth, Sprint and WorldCom). A chart containing full results can be found in the appendix.

The survey showed the following general results. On the whole, broadband operators' networks and usage restrictions favored the applications of the late 1990s (primarily the World Wide Web and other client-server applications), and disfavored more recent applications and usage, like home networking, peer-to-peer applications, and home telecommuting.

There are differences between cable and DSL operators. On the contractual side, cable operators tended to impose far more restrictions on usage than DSL operators. Major differences exist with respect to the extent of restrictions on home networking, operation of servers, commercial use, and overuse of bandwidth.

An illustrative example is the difference in attitudes toward home networking.[45] At the extremes, then-Cable operator AT&T Broadband defined home networking as "theft of services" and threatened subscribers with civil and criminal penalties.[46] In contrast, DSL provider Verizon made it clear in its service contract that home networking is permissible, as did Sprint.[47]

There existed variation between individual cable operators and DSL operators on some of the restrictions. On the cable side, AT&T Broadband and Comcast (later combined to form the nation's largest cable operator), stood out for having the strictest usage restrictions. AOL Time-Warner, Charter Communications and smaller operators CableOne and Insight Broadband had the fewest restrictions. Among DSL operators, BellSouth stood out with the most restrictions, similar in extent to a cable operator. Overall, perhaps the most "liberal" broadband provider was DSL provider Sprint. Sprint had very few usage restrictions, told subscribers in FAQs that they may run home networks, web servers, and promises users that they "will have complete unrestricted access to all content available on the Internet."[48]

On the architectural side, the outstanding deviation from neutrality in broadband networks today is the asymmetric bandwidth common across networks. Other, future controls may include application specific controls, as the survey of equipment vendors' offerings shows.

CONTRACTUAL RESTRICTIONS

We first consider the individual types of restrictions found in usage agreements, focusing attention on restrictions that are likely to influence the development of certain application-types. The following chart shows the 13 main types of restrictions along with the percentage of major cable operators and DSL operators who stated such restrictions.

The appendix indicates which operators in the survey implemented the restrictions above. The following pages provide further details on the language of the most controversial restrictions: (1) providing information to the public or operating a server, (2) commercial uses, (3) Home Networking, and (4) WiFi network operation.

Table 1.
Major Usage Restrictions

RESTRICTION	CABLE	DDSL
Using a Virtual Private Network	10%	0%
Attaching WiFi Equipment	10%	0%
Making the Connection a Network End Point	10%	0%
Using Home Networking	40%	0%
Misusing IP Addresses	60%	0%
Any Commercial or Business Use	100%	33%
Operating a Server or Providing Public Information	100%	33%
Overusing Bandwidth	100%	33%
Reselling Bandwidth or Acting as an ISP	100%	33%
Conducting Spam or Consumer Fraud	100%	100%
Hacking or Causing Security Breaches	100%	100%
Any Unlawful Purpose	100%	100%
Any Offensive or Immoral Purpose	100%	100%

Restrictions on Providing Content

Nearly every cable operator and one third of DSL operators restricted operating a server and/or providing content to the public.[49] This restriction has the greatest potential significance because it affects the broadest class of applications—those where the end-user shares content, as opposed to simply downloading content. The potential breadth of server restriction can be seen from AT&T Broadband's acceptable use agreement:"[Subscriber may not] run programs, equipment or servers from the Premises which provide network content or any other services to anyone outside of the your home . . . . Examples of prohibited programs and equipment include, but are not limited to, mail, ftp, http, file sharing, game, newsgroup, proxy, IRC servers, multi-user interactive forums and Wi-Fi devices."[50]

Again, this restriction can be understood as favoring a "one-to-many" or vertical model of application over a "many-to-many" or "horizontal" model. In application design terms, the restriction favors client-server applications over peer-to-peer designs.[51] If taken seriously, the inability to provide content or act as a server would serve to restrict a major class of network applications.

Not all the restrictions are as broad as AT&T Broadband's. More typical is a simple ban on servers, as seen in this example from Cox Systems: "**Servers** You may not operate, or allow others to operate, servers of any type or any other device, equipment, and/or software providing server-like functionality in connection with the Service, unless expressly authorized by Cox."[52] Others, like Charter Communications, name banned applications: "Customer will not use, nor allow others to use, Customer's home computer as a web server, FTP server, file server or game server or to run any other server applications."[53] The narrowest form of server restriction is seen in the Verizon terms of service agreement: "You may not use the Service to host a dedicated or commercial server."[54] Finally, contrary to others, DSL provider Sprint suggests that consumers may, in fact, run a web server, based on the following excerpt from Sprint's FAQ site:

Q: Can I run a web server?

A: Yes it is possible to set-up a web server using your Sprint FastConnect DSL service.[55]

Bans on Commercial Use

A second restriction with potential implications for application development is a limit on "commercial" or "enterprise" use of residential broadband connections. Every cable operator and most DSL operators surveyed had some ban on using a basic residential broadband connection for commercial use.

The broadest and most controversial of such restrictions barred home users from using "Virtual Private Network" (VPN) services, which are used by telecommuters to connect to their work network through a secure connection. Cox Systems provides an example of a ban on Virtual Private Networks: "You agree not to use the Service for operation as an Internet service provider, or for any other business enterprise, including, without limitation, virtual private network usage, IP address translation, or similar facilities intended to provide additional access."[56] More typical bans on commercial use came in the following form, as seen in the Time Warner Subscriber Conduct provision in its acceptable use agreement:

The ISP Service as offered and provided under this Agreement is a residential service offered for personal, non-commercial use only. Subscrber will not resell or redistribute (whether for a fee or otherwise) the ISP Service, or any portion thereof, or otherwise charge others to use the ISP Service, or any portion thereof. Subscriber agrees not to use the ISP Service for operation as an internet service provider, for the hosting of websites (other than as expressly permitted as part of the ISP Service) or for any enterprise purpose whether or not the enterprise is directed toward making a profit.[57]

Again, the limitations found in DSL restrictions were far less extensive. For example, the BellSouth subscriber agreement mixed the restrictions on providing content and acting commercially as follows: "Subscribers may not provide public or commercial information over such [residential DSL] connections."[58]

Home Networking

When home networking first became widespread in 2002, four of ten of the nation's largest cable operators contractually limited the deployment of home networks.[59] They did so by stating restrictions on the number of computers that could be attached to a single connection. The strongest example of such a usage restriction in 2002 came from AT&T Broadband:

THEFT OF SERVICE. Customer shall not connect the Service or any AT&T Broadband Equipment to more computers, either on or outside of the Premises, than are reflected in Customer's account with AT&T Broadband. Customer acknowledges that any unauthorized receipt of the Service constitutes theft of service, which is a violation of federal law and can result in both civil and criminal penalties. In addition, if the violations are willful and for commercial advantage or private financial gain, the penalties may be increased.[60]

A milder approach was taken by Aldelphia's online FAQ:

Can I network more than one computer?

Yes. Please check with a reputable computer electronics retailer for home networking solutions that are right for you. Adelphia will support a cable modem that is connected to a hub or router to the gateway or host computer. Adelphia does not install or support the network. Adelphia Power Link may not be connected to a broadcast server of any kind.[61]

In contrast, some DSL operators in their agreements explicitly acknowledged that multiple computers could be connected to the DSL connection. As Verizon's agreement stated: "You may connect multiple computers/devices within a single home or office location to your DSL modem and/or router to access the Service, but only through a single DSL account and a single IP address obtained from Verizon Online."[62] Other DSL providers were vague. For example, in BellSouth's terms of service: "Unless otherwise specified in the BellSouth Internet Service subscriber's pricing plan agreement, sharing of accounts and/or connections on unlimited usage plans with anyone other than immediate family members in the same dwelling is strictly prohibited."[63]

Restrictions on Wireless (WiFi) Networks

In addition to restrictions on home networking, several cable operators signaled a particular interest in controlling the deployment of home wireless networks. This is clearest with AT&T Broadband: They explicitly banned the connection of "Wi-Fi" equipment.[64] The provider also made it a breach of the subscriber's agreement to maintain a WiFi service that is available to outsiders. "[It is a breach of the agreement to] resell the Service or otherwise make available to anyone outside the Premises the ability to use the Service (i.e. WiFi, or other methods of networking)."[65]

Architectural Controls, Present & Future: Present

Today, the principal deviation from network neutrality through architecture is, and continues to be, asymmetric bandwidth: that is, the practice of designing networks to provide more "downstream" bandwidth than "upstream." It is difficult to obtain a full set of data on the extent of asymmetry, because many cable operators do not make public the maximum bandwidth permitted by their networks. However, from the few sources of data that are available, we find that there is greater asymmetry in cable networks than DSL—though the shared architecture of cable networks makes the significance of this fact unclear. Published DSL rates included residential bandwidth with as low as 1:1 ratios, while the modal ratio is 6:1 ratios.[66] The few cable networks with public data promised maximum bandwidth ratios ranging from 5.3:1 (Time Warner / Earthlink) to as much as 12:1 (Cox Communications).[67]

As others have recognized, allowing more downstream than upstream bandwidth obviously favors the development of applications that are one-to-many, or client-server in design. Applications that would demand residential accounts to deliver content as quickly as they receive it will do less well under conditions of asymmetric bandwidth.

Future – Better Bandwidth Management or Application Layer Controls?

It is difficult to predict what application controls broadband operators might implement in the future. Yet future possibilities can be gleaned from the marketing efforts of equipment vendors who target the cable and DSL market. Two trends can be briefly noted, though the full topic is well beyond the scope of this paper.

First, over the last several years, several companies have begun to market equipment described to facilitate application-based screening and control for broadband networks. Two prominent examples are Allot Communications and Packeteer Communications. The former markets a product named "NetEnforcer" to cable and DSL operators,[68] promising to control problems from both peer-to-peer traffic and unauthorized WiFi connections.[69] Allot's competitor, Packeteer, markets a similar product, named "PacketShaper," described as "an application intelligent traffic management appliance providing visibility into and control over network utilization and application performance."[70] The company claims that the product is used on hundreds of University campuses, primarily to control peer-to-peer traffic.[71] When this survey was conducted, despite the marketing efforts of both companies, there was no evidence of deployment by cable or DSL operators. It is therefore impossible to conclude whether broadband operators will begin using technological means to facilitate restrictions on usage.

Second, vendors of cable data equipment promise improved bandwidth management capabilities as between individual customers on cable networks.[72] This is the promise of the DOCSIS[73] 1.1 and 2.0 standards, which are an update to the current DOCSIS 1.0 standard in use today.[74] As the new equipment is not yet widely deployed, these claims or their impact cannot be verified.

Conclusions & Evidence of Enforcement

What, generally, can be concluded from this survey? On the one hand, there is no broad effort to ban everything that might be said to threaten the interests of cable and DSL operators. For example, cable operators have not now barred streaming video, despite the potential to compete with cable television, and despite Dan Somers' famous comment that "AT&T didn't spend $56 billion to get into the cable business to have the blood sucked out of [its] veins."[75] This conclusion is reinforced by the general perception that broadband access is not substantially limited.

To what degree are these usage restrictions enforced? While there is little formal data on enforcement patterns, there exists anecdotal evidence of enforcement on websites like DSL Reports,[76] which are dedicated to users complaining about broadband service and usage restrictions. Some examples of enforcement include the enforcement of monthly or daily bandwidth limits through threatening to terminate or restrict the accounts of users who use too much bandwidth in a single month. For example, Cox Cable in November 2002 sent letters to users who downloaded more than 2 gigabytes of bandwidth per day, or 30 gigabytes of bandwidth per month.[77] Other cable operators, though no DSL providers, have suggested similar policies may be on their way.[78] In addition, broadband consumers have complained of efforts to enforce specific bans on applications, such as threats to enforce contractual limits on VPN operations[79] and users who run file-sharing applications.[80]

APPENDIX
SURVEY OF BROADBAND USAGE RESTRICTIONS

CABLE OPERATORS:

RESTRICTION	AT&T BB	TW	CMCST	CHAR TR	Cox	Adphia	CABLE V	MEDIAC M	INSIGH T	CABL E1	FREQ
Virtual Private Network					R						10%
Attachment of WiFi Eqpt.	R										10%
Being Network End Point		R									10%
Home Networking	R		R			R		R			40%
Misuse of IP Addresses	R	R	R		R	R	R				60%
Commercial / Business Use Info	R	R	R	R	R	R	R	R	R	R	100%
Overuse of Bandwidth	R	R	R	R	R	R	R	R	R	R	100%
ISP	R	R	R	R	R	R	R	R	R	R	100%
Spam / Consumer Fraud	R	R	R	R	R	R	R	R	R	R	100%
Hacking/Security Breaches	R	R	R	R	R	R	R	R	R	R	100%
Any Unlawful Purpose	R	R	R	R	R	R	R	R	R	R	100%

DSL OPERATORS:

RESTRICTION	VERIZON	SBC	QWEST	BELLS	SPRNT	WLDCM	FREQ
Home Networking	OK	OK			OK		0%
Operating a Server	R			R	OK		40%
Use	R			R			40%
Overuse of Bandwidth	R			R			40%
Resell Bandwidth	R			R			40%
Spam / Consumer Fraud	R	R	R	R	R	R	100%
Hacking / Security Breaches	R	R	R	R	R	R	100%
Any Offensive or Immoral Purpose	R	R	R	R	R	R	100%

Legen :

R = Contractually Restricted
OK = Explicitly Permitted
CmCst = ComCast
Communications
Cox = Cox Communications
CableV = CableVision, Inc.
Insight = Insight
Communications
BellS = BellSouth

AT&T BB = AT&T Broadband
TW = Time Warner
Chartr = Charter
Communications
Adphia = Adelphia
Communications
MediaCM = MediaCom
Cable1 = CableOne
Sprnt = Sprint

UPSTREAM / DOWNSTREAM BANDWIDTH RATIOS

Provider Name	Bandwidth Down (k)	Bandwidth Up (k)	Ratio
Qwest	256	256	1:01
	640	256	2.5:1
Sprint	256	96	2.66:1
	512	128	4:01
Verizon	1.5M	256	6:01
	768	128	6:01
	1.5M	128	12:01
SBC	384	128	3:01
BellSouth	1.5M	256	6:01
WorldCom	1.5M	256	6:01
	384	128	3:01
AT&T BB	1.5M	256	6:01
	3M	384	8:01
Time Warner	2	384	5.33:1
Cox	3M	256	12:01

ENDNOTES

[1.] See generally Joseph Farrell & Philip J. Weiser, Modularity, Vertical Integration, and Open Access Policies: Towards a Convergence of Antitrust and Regulation in the Internet Age, 17 HARV. J.L. & TECH. (forthcoming 2003), available at http://repositories. cdlib.org/iber/cpc/CPC02-035 (last visited Sept. 24, 2003); Glenn A. Woroch, Open Access Rules and the Broadband Race, 2002 L. REV. MICH. ST. U. DET. C.L. 719 (2002); Glen O. Robinson, On Refusing to Deal with Rivals, 87 CORNELL L. REV. 1177, 1224-27 (2002); Mark A. Lemley & Lawrence Lessig, The End of End-to-End: Preserving the Architecture of the Internet in the Broadband Era, 48 UCLA L. REV. 925 (2001); Phil Weiser, Paradigm Changes in Telecommunications Regulation, 71 U. COLO. L. REV. 819 (2000); James B. Speta, Handicapping the Race for the Last Mile? A Critique of Open Access Rules for Broadband Platforms, 17 YALE. J. ON REG. 39, 77-90 (2000).

[2] Hush-A-Phone Corp. v. United States, 238 F.2d 266 (D.C. Cir. 1956).

[3] Use of the Carterfone Device in Message Toll Tel. Serv., 31 F.C.C.2d 420 (1968).

[4] See infra Appendix.

[5] Complaints about restrictions on broadband applications like filesharing applications or VPNs are common on discussion forums like DSL Reports. See, e.g., BROADBAND REPORTS, at http://www.dslreports.com/forum/ remark,3775421;mode=flat;root=sware (July, 2002).

[6] See Comments of the High Tech Broadband Coalition, In re: Inquiry Concerning High-Speed Access to the Internet Over Cable and Other Facilities (filed June 18, 2002), available at http://www.itic.org/policy/fcc_020618.pdf; see also FCC Ex Parte Letter, Aug. 22 2003, available at http://faculty.virginia.edu/timwu/wu_lessig_fcc.pdf.

[7] For example, AT&T Broadband has recently begun to open parts of its network to ISP competition. See Peter J. Howe, Earthlink Debuts On AT&T Networks Offers High-Speed Internet Service, BOSTON GLOBE, Oct. 17, 2002, at C4.

[8] See, e.g., Farrell & Weiser, supra note 1, at 33-36.

[9] More general arguments in favor of a network neutrality regime can be found in Lawrence Lessig & Tim Wu, FCC Ex Parte Letter, Aug. 22, 2003, available at http:// faculty.virginia.edu/timwu/wu_lessig_fcc.pdf.

[10] A full treatment of the names given to evolutionary theories of innovation is beyond the scope of this paper. Some adherents would ascribe such theories to economist Joseph Schumpeter, while in recent legal work the argument is stated as an argument over what should be owned and what should be free. See generally LAWRENCE LESSIG, THE FUTURE OF IDEAS 3-17 (2001).

[11] See, e.g., John Ziman, Evolutionary Models for Technological Change, in TECHNOLOGICAL INNOVATION AS AN EVOLUTIONARY PROCESS 3 (John Ziman ed., 2000); RICHARD NELSON, UNDERSTANDING TECHNICAL CHANGE AS AN EVOLUTIONARY PROCESS (1987).

[12] In the legal field, Edmund W. Kitch's The Nature and Function of the Patent System, 20 J.L. & ECON. 265 (1977) is often taken to exemplify this approach.

[13] See J.H. Saltzer et al., End-to-End Arguments in System Design, 2 ACM TRANSACTIONS COMPUTER SYS. 277 (1984), available at http://web.mit.edu/Saltzer/www/ publications/endtoend/endtoend.pdf (last visited Oct. 9, 2003).

[14] Id. at 3.

[15] The metaphors of "above" and "below" come from the fact that in a layered model of the Internet's design, the application layers are "above" the TCP/IP layers, while the physical layers are "below." *See* Andrew S. Tanenbaum, Computer Networks 39 (4th ed. 2002).

[16] Lessig, *supra* note 10, at 14 ("No modern phenomenon better demonstrates the importance of free resources to innovation and creativity than the internet.").

[17] For a recent work doubting the merits of open platform designs under some circumstances, *see, e.g.*, Douglas Lichtman, *Property Rights In Emerging Platform Technologies*, 29 J. Legal Stud. 615 (2000).

[18] The FCC, for example, has outlined three forms of open access remedy in ongoing open access rulemaking. *See* Inquiry Concerning High-Speed Access to the Internet Over Cable and Other Facilities, *Declaratory Ruling and Notice of Proposed Rule Making*, 17 F.C.C.R.. 4798, ¶ 74 (2002) (discussing various models of open access regulation).

[19] *See* Lemley & Lessig, *supra* note 1, at 942-43.

[20] *See* Speta, *supra* note 1, at 76; Farrell & Weiser, *supra* note 1, at 4-6; Robinson, *supra* note 1, at 1216-17.

[21] *Cf.* Lamb's Chapel v. Ctr. Moriches Union Free Sch. Dist., 508 U.S. 384, 397-400 (1993) (Scalia, J., concurring) (on the meaning of neutrality in the context of church and state).

[22] Efforts to add quality of service functionality to the Internet protocol, such as the IETF's DiffServ and IntServ's approaches, have never been implemented to provide end-to-end quality of service on an IP network.

[23] This might happen, for example, if an open-access regulation slowed the development of vertically integrated layer 2 / layer 3 architectures.

[24] Ultimately, this line of argument echoes the economists' point that efficiencies exist from vertical integration. The point here is to show that principles of network neutrality lead to the same conclusion.

[25] Hush-A-Phone Corp. v. United States, 238 F.2d 266, 269 (D.C. Cir. 1956).

[26]. *See, e.g.,* 42 U.S.C. § 2000e *et seq.* (2002) (codification of Title VII of the Civil Rights Act of 1964).

[27] *See id.*

[28] An example from the Cox Acceptable Use Policy: "You are prohibited from posting, transmitting or disseminating any information or software that contains a virus, Trojan horse, worm or other harmful program or that generates levels of traffic sufficient to impede others' ability to send or retrieve information. Prohibited conduct of this type includes denial of service attacks or similarly disruptive transmissions, as well as transmissions containing other harmful or malicious features."

Cox Communications Policies, *Acceptable Use Policy*, Cox Communications, Inc., *at* http://support.cox.net/custsup/policies/acceptableuse.shtml (revised Feb. 3, 2003).

[29] For example, by screening chat program activity by TCP port number. Such a restriction could be avoided, but it suffices for the example.

[30] Conversely, as we will see in a second, if chat programs have negative externalities because they actually do waste everyone's time, the operators may have done the world a big favor.

[31]   *See, e.g., Cable Modem Service Subscription Agreement*, Time Warner Cable, *at* http://help.twcable.com/html/twc_sub_agreement.html (last visited Mar. 12, 2003) [hereinafter *Time Warner Usage Agreement*].

[32]   Network design already discourages hosting activity, because most broadband services give asymmetric bandwidth (more downstream than upstream) and a dynamic, as opposed to fixed, IP address. These design features preclude serious commercial website operation, but leave room for casual hosting operations, such as participating in a peer-to-peer network.

[33]   *See Comcast VPN letter*, Practically Networked, *at* http://www.practically networked.com/news/comcast.htm (last visited Mar. 12, 2003).

[34]   A T-1 line, providing 1.5 mbps of symmetric data, is usually priced at over $1000 per month.

[35]   *See, e.g.*, RICHARD POSNER, ANTITRUST LAW 203-06 (2d ed. 2001).

[36]   "Servents" in Gnutella terminology.

[37]   *See*, e.g., JUSTIN PEARSE, *UK shrugs off American broadband troubles*, ZDNET NEWS.COM, *at* http://news.zdnet.co.uk/story/0,,t269-s2077792,00.html (Mar. 20, 2000).

[38]   More recent incarnations of the DOCSIS protocol attempt to add better QoS functionality, but implementation at this date seems to be scarce. *See Cable Modem/ DOCSIS^{TM}*, CABLELABS, *at* http://www.cablemodem.com/faq (last visited Mar. 13, 2003) [hereinafter *CABLELABS, DOCSIS*].

[39]   Farell & Weiser, *supra* note 1, at 21. This they describe as the "internalization of complementary efficiencies, or ICE."

[40]   *See* Gilmer v. Interstate/Johnson Lane Corp., 500 U.S. 20, 27 (1991) ("the ADEA is designed not only to address individual grievances, but also to further important social policies").

[41]   See Comcast Corp., FCC Ex Parte Letter, May 9, 2002 ("the 'VPN restriction' about which certain parties have complained has been eliminated from and is no longer part of Comcast's subscriber agreements and terms of service for its high-speed Internet customers."); Cox Enterprises Inc., FCC Ex Parte Letter, May 1, 2003 ("Cox hereby informs the Commission that the language of that [VPN] provision has been changed. . .").

[42]   NTCA, *Cable Believes in Open Connectivity for the Internet*, *at* http:// www.ncta.com/legislative/legAffairs.cfm?legRegID=20; *see also* NTCA, Ex Parte Letter, Sept. 8, 2003 (arguing that network neutrality legislation is unnecessary because of cable's commitment to non-discrimination.).

[43]   Unfortunately, nearly any feature of network design or policy can be described as a deviation from a "purely" neutral design. Something as innocuous as the length of the IP packet header could, potentially, help or hurt certain applications. To avoid an exercise in the esoteric, the goal of this section is to study major, intentional deviations from neutrality that clearly favor certain application types over others.

[44]   At the time the survey was conducted, AT&T and Comcast were still operating independently.

[45]   Home networking refers to the practice of sharing a broadband connection amongst all of the computers in a home, as opposed to the single computer attached to the cable modem. This usually requires the purchase of additional equipment, such as a home router.

[46] *AT&T Broadband Internet Subscriber Agreement*, § 6(g), *available at* http://help.broadband.att.com/listfaqs.jsp?category_id=973&category-id=34 (last revised Dec. 5, 2001).

[47] Verizon Online Internet Access, *Terms of Service, available at* http://www.verizon.net/policies/internetaa.asp (2003).

[48] Sprint FastConnect DSL, *Frequently Asked Questions, available at* http://csb.sprint.com/home/local/dslhelp/faq.html#gen16 (2003).

[49] The exception is Time Warner. *See infra* Appendix.

[50] *AT&T Broadband Internet Acceptable Use Policy,* ¶ xiv, *available at* http://help.broadband.att.com/faq.jsp?content_id=1107&category_id=34 (revised July 25, 2002).

[51] The Internet's most popular application of the early 1990s—the world wide web—followed a client-server design, where a single specialized, centralized server provides services to a large number of clients. However, today an increasing number of applications use fully or partially decentralized designs. Email was always partially decentralized, for example, and the many popular "chat" programs embody a design that technically requires the user to act as a server as well as a client. Similarly, users who want to access a home computer from work (using, for example, rlogin) need to set up the home computer to act as a server. Peer-to-peer application designs also ask home users to act both as a client and server.

[52] Cox Systems, *Acceptable Use Policy* § 6, *available at* http://www.cox.com/iNetIncludes/policy/acceptable.asp (updated Apr. 28, 2003). *See also AT&T Broadband Internet Acceptable Use Policy*, *supra* note 50.

[53] Charter Communications Pipeline, *Acceptable Use Policy* § 1(A), *available at* http://www.chartercom.com/site/rules.asp#aup (last checked Oct. 8, 2003).

[54] Verizon Online Internet Access, *Terms of Service*, *supra* note 47, at § 2.4(C).

[55] Sprint FastConnect DSL, *Questions & Answers, available at* http://csb.sprint.com/servlet/Faq/faq_category?category=DSLGenQuestions (2003).

[56] Cox Systems, *Acceptable Use Policy*, *supra* note 52, at § 5.

[57] Time Warner, *Cable Modem Service Subscription Agreement* § 5(a), *available at* http://help.twcable.com/html/twc_sub_agreement.html (last visited Oct. 8, 2003).

[58] BellSouth Internet Service, *Acceptable Use Policies, available at* http://home.bellsouth.net/csbellsouth/s/editorial.dll?fromspage=cg/legal/legal_homepage.htm&categoryid=&bfromind=354&eeid=376138&eetype=article&render=y5ck= (last visited Oct. 8, 2003).

[59] MediaOne, Comcast, AT&T and Adelphia. Due to enforcement difficulties and the ongoing regulatory proceedings at the Federal Communications Commission, most of these restrictions have been rescinded.

[60] *AT&T Broadband Internet Subscriber Agreement*, § 6(g), *at* http://www.attbi.com/general-info/bb_terms.html (last visited Mar. 13, 2003).

[61] *Adelphia FAQ, Home Networking, at* http://www.adelphia.com/high_speed_internet/faqs.cfm (last visited Mar. 13, 2003).

[62] *Verizon Online's Terms of Service*, § 2.5B, *at* http://www.verizon.net/ policies/internetaa.asp.

[63] *See* BellSouth, *Acceptable Use Policies*, *supra* note 58.

[64] *AT&T Broadband Internet Acceptable Use Agreement, supra* note 50, at ¶ 14 ("Examples of prohibited . . . equipment include . . . Wi-Fi.").

[65] *Id.* at ¶ ix. Cox Systems, *Acceptable Use Policy, supra* note 52, at 17, has a similar restriction.

[66] *See infra* Appendix.

[67] *Id.*

[68] Allot Communications Netenforcer® Data Sheet, *at* http://www.allot.com/html/products_netenforcer_sp.shtml (last visited Mar. 13, 2003).

[69] Jim Barthold*, Allot looks to help servers with bandwidth congestion problems*, TELEPHONY.ONLINE.COM, *available at* http://telephonyonline.com/ar/telecom_allot_looks_help/index.htm (Dec. 3, 2002).

[70] Packeteer, *at* http://www.packeteer.com/products/packetshaper.com (last visited Mar. 13, 2003).

[71] Gwendolyn Mariano, *Schools declare file-swapping truce*, CNET NEWS.COM, *at* http://news.com.com/2100-1023-859705.html?tag=rn (Mar. 14, 2002).

[72] *See, e.g.*, http://www.cisco.com/warp/public/779/servpro/solutions/cable (last visited Mar. 13, 2003).

[73] DOCSIS stands for Data Over Cable Service Interface Specifications. *See Seven Cable Modem Manufacturers Seek DOCSIS Certification*, CABLELABS, *at* http://www.cablelabs.com/news/newsletter/SPECS/specnewsaug/news/pgs/story2.html (last visited Mar. 13, 2003).

[74] For an explication of the claims of DOCSIS 1.1 and 2.0, *see CABLELABS, DOCSIS, supra* note 38.

[75] *See* David Lieberman, *Media Giants' Net Change Establish Strong Foothold Online*, USA TODAY, Dec. 14, 1999, at B3 (Dan Somers was CEO of AT&T Broadband at the time the comment was reported).

[76] *See* BROADBAND REPORTS.COM, *at* http://www.dslreports.com (Mar. 2002).

[77] *See* Karl Bode, *Defining Gluttony: Cox Cable Gets Specific*, *at* http://www.dslreports.com/shownews/23465 (Nov. 12, 2002).

[78] John Borland, *ISP download caps to slow swapping?* CNET NEWS.COM, *at* http://news.com.com/2100-1023-975320.html (Nov. 26, 2002).

[79] Practically Networked Earthweb, VPN Comcast Letter, *at* http://www.practicallynetworked.com/news/comcast.htm. (last visited Mar. 10, 2003).

[80] Many users have accused cable operators of blocking specific file-sharing applications like KaZaa, through port blocking, though the reports are unverified. *See, e.g., RoadRunner Blocking kaZaA,* ZEROPAID.COM, *at* http://www.zeropaid.com/news/articles/auto/07142002a (July 13, 2002).

[81] *See, e.g.*, High Tech Broadband Coalition Ex Parte Letter, June 17, 2002; Coalition of Broadband Users and Innovators Ex Parte Letter, Nov. 18, 2002.

[82] *See, e.g.*, National Cable & Telecommunications Association Ex Parte Letter, Feb. 21, 2003.

[83] Of course, it is inevitable that by its design the internet or any communications network will invariably create some favoritism for certain uses. Pure neutrality is more of an aspiration than a fully achievable design principle. The point of the argument is the minimization of bias, not the total elimination of all conceivable forms. Cf. Lamb's

Chapel v. Center Moriches Union Free Sch. Dist., 113 S. Ct. 2141, 2149-50 (1993) (Scalia, J., concurring) (on the meaning of neutrality in the context of church and state).

[84] FCC Statement of Broadband Policy, available at http://www.fcc.gov/broadband/.

[85] *See* Tam Harbert, *Broadband Penetration in U.S. Continues,* ELECTRONIC BUSINESS, July 1, 2003, at 26 (citing American Electronics Association study placing number of broadband Internet users in U.S at 16.2 million as of June 2002).

[86] *See* Tim Wu, *Network Neutrality, Broadband Discrimination,* 2 COLO. J. TELECOMM. & HIGH TECH. L. 11—12, 20—21 (forthcoming 2003).

[87] *See, e.g.,* Cox Communications Ex Parte Letter, April 7, 2003; Comcast Corporation Ex Parte Notice, May 15, 2003.

[88] *See generally,* Clay Christiansen, The Innovators Dilemma (1997) (suggesting that large firms, focused on consumers' present needs, will be unlikely to develop the products of the future).

[89] FCC Statement of Broadband Policy, available at http://www.fcc.gov/broadband/.

[90] *Appropriate Framework for Broadband Access to the Internet over Wireline Facilities, Universal Service Obligations of Broadband Providers,* CC Docket No. 02-33, Notice of Proposed Rulemaking (*"Wireline Broadband NPRM"*) ¶ 4 (rel. Feb. 15, 2002).

[91] *See, e.g.,* John Ziman, *Evolutionary Models for Technological Change,* in TECHNOLOGICAL INNOVATION AS AN EVOLUTIONARY PROCESS 3 (John Ziman ed., 2000); Richard Nelson, UNDERSTANDING TECHNICAL CHANGE AS AN EVOLUTIONARY PROCESS (1987).

[92] These ideas are also discussed in the legal literature. *See, e.g.,* Richard Posner, THE ECONOMIC STRUCTURE OF INTELLECTUAL PROPERTY LAW 364 (forthcoming, on file with author). *See also* Edmund W. Kitch, *The Nature and Function of the Patent System,* 20 J.L. & ECON. 265 (1977).

[93] *See* Clay Christiansen, The Innovators Dilemma (1997) (explaining that firms that pay too much attention to current customer needs often fail to reach the highest levels of innovation).

[94] *See, e.g., Console Wars: Video Games Grow Up,* The Economist, June 22, 2002.

[95] *See* Jerome H. Saltzer et al., *End to End Arguments in System Design,* in INNOVATIONS IN INTERNETWORKING 195 (Craig Partridge ed., 1988) (available at http://web.mit.edu/saltzer/www/publications/endtoend/endtoend.pdf).

[96] These arguments are described in greater depth in Written Ex Parte of Professor Mark A. Lemley and Professor Lawrence Lessig, In re Application for Consent to the Transfer of Control of Licenses MediaOne Group, Inc. to AT&T Corp. (FCC Dec. 15, 1999) (No. 99-251).

[97] *Wireline Broadband NPRM, supra* note 9, ¶ 4.

[98] *Inquiry Concerning High-Speed Access to the Internet over Cable and Other Facilities, Internet Over Cable Declaratory Ruling, Appropriate Regulatory Treatment for Broadband Access to the Internet over Cable Facilities,* CS Docket No. 02-52, Declaratory Notice and Notice of Proposed Rulemaking, ¶ 6 (rel. Mar. 15, 2002).

[99] Robert Sachs, Remarks to NARUC/NECA Summit on Broadband Deployment II (Apr. 28, 2003) (available at http://www.ncta.com/pdf_files/RJS_NARUC_04-28-03.pdf).

[100] *See, e.g.*, National Cable & Telecommunications Association Ex Parte Letter, Dec. 10, 2002. One particular oddity in this respect is the NCTA's claim that the development of the Data Over Cable Service Interface Specifications (DOCSIS) standard in some way demonstrates that the cable networks are "open." While it is true that DOCSIS is itself a neutral standard, the existence of DOCSIS itself does nothing to prevent cable operators from placing other forms of technical limitations on cable service, or enforcing contractual restrictions on usage of the network.

[101] *See* Verizon Service Agreement ¶ 3.6(B), http://www.verizon.net/policies/internetaa.asp.

[102] This language was in the December, 2002, AT&T Broadband Acceptable Internet Use Agreement, then available at
http://help.broadband.att.com/faq.jsp?content_id=1107&category_id=34. It has since been replaced by the present Comcast Acceptable Use policy and subscriber agreements, available at http://www.comcast.net/terms. As for home networking, the current subscriber agreement policy says that users may not use their cable service as "as an end-point on a non-Comcast local area network." See http://www.comcast.net/terms/subscriber.jsp. Whether this is meant to allow home networking or not is unclear.

[103] *See* 2 The New Palgrave: A Dictionary of Economics 263, 263-65 (John Eatwell et al. eds., 1987).

[104] *See, e.g.*, National Cable & Telecommunications Association Ex Parte Letter, Dec. 10, 2003.

[105] *See, e.g.*, Angela J. Campbell, *Publish or Carriage: Approaches to Analyzing the First Amendment Rights of Telephone Companies*, 70 N.C. L. Rev. 1071, 1097 (1992); Geoffrey Stone et al., Constitutional Law 1004 (2001).

[106] 476 U.S. 488, 494 (1986). *See also FCC v. Midwest Video Corp.*, 440 U.S. 689, 707 (1979).

[107] 391 U.S. 367 (1968).

[108] 530 U.S. 640 (2000)

[109] 491 U.S. 781 (1989); *see also* United States Civil Serv. Comm'n v. National Ass'n of Letter Carriers, 413 U.S. 548 (1973) (upholding content neutral restrictions on the speech of federal employees).

[110] *See Turner Broadcasting System, Inc. v. FCC (Turner I)*, 512 U.S. 622 (1994); *Turner Broadcasting System, Inc. v. F.C.C. (Turner II)*, 520 U.S. 180 (1997).

[111] "[L]aws that confer benefits or impose burdens on speech without reference to the ideas or views expressed are in most instances content neutral." *Turner I*, 512 U.S. at 643.

[112] *Turner I*, 512 U.S. at 662; see also *Associated Press v. United States*, 326 U.S. 1, 20 (1945) (First Amendment "rests on the assumption that the widest possible dissemination of information from diverse and antagonistic sources is essential to the welfare of the public, that a free press is a condition of a free society.").

[113] *Id.* at 664. This philosophy did not originate with the *Turner* litigation – its origins are much deeper. As Justice Black stated in *Associated Press v. United States*, 326 U.S. 1, 20 (1945):

> It would be strange indeed however if the grave concern for freedom of the press which prompted adoption of the First Amendment should be read as a command that the government was without power to protect that freedom. The First Amendment...provides powerful reasons to the contrary. That Amendment rests on the assumption that the widest possible dissemination of information from diverse and antagonistic sources is essential to the welfare of the public, that a free press is a condition of a free society. Surely a command that the government itself shall not impede the free flow of ideas does not afford non-governmental combinations a refuge if they impose restraints upon that constitutionally guaranteed freedom.

[114] 491 U.S. at 791 (content neutral restrictions must "leave open ample alternative channels for communication of the information.").

[115] *See, e.g.*, Amazon.com Ex Parte Letter, Appendix B, Dec. 10, 2002.

[116] Hush-A-Phone v. United States, 238 F.2d 266, 268 (D.C. Cir. 1956).

[117] Hush-A-Phone Corp. v. AT&T, 22 FCC 112, 114 (1957).

[118] 13 F.C.C.2d 420 (1968)

[119] See 47 CFR §68 *et seq.*

[120] Also commonly referred to as "Massively Multiple Online Games," or MMOGs.

[121] For an explanation of how a broadband carrier would do so, *see, e.g.*, *The Cisco Content Delivery Network Solution for the Enterprise*, Cisco White Paper (Apr. 2002), *available at* http://www.cisco.com/warp/public/cc/so/neso/ienesv/cxne/cdnen_wp.htm; *See also* Cosine Communications., *Digital Subscriber Lines and Managed Network-based Services: A Perfect—and Profitable—Marriage*, White Paper, *available at* http://cnscenter.future.co.kr/ resource/rsc-center/vendor-wp/cosine/dslwp.pdf.

[122] Hush-A-Phone Corp. v. AT&T, 22 FCC 112, 114 (1957). This led in turn to the broader *Carterfone* decision, 13 F.C.C.2d 420 (1968), and finally Part 68, which adopted a protective circuitry approach to protecting the telephone network, *see* 47 CFR §68 *et seq.*

[123] *Cf.* ANDREW TANENBAUM, COMPUTER NETWORKS 10-18 (4th ed. 2002).

[124] Described in IETF RFC 826, *available at* http://www.ietf.org/rfc/rfc1027.txt.

[125] In today's environment, the scarcity of IPv4 addresses does appear to justify a form of discrimination: charging more for static addresses, than dynamic addresses. This forms a good example of "permissible" discrimination.

[126] *See, e.g.*, Kevin Werbach, *A Layered Model for Telecommunications Policy*, 1 COLO. J. TELECOMM. & HIGH TECH. L. (2002); Lawrence Solum & Minn Chung, *The Layers Principle: Internet Architecture and the Law*, Loyola-LA Public Law Research Paper No. 15 (2003) (available at http://ssrn.com/abstract=416263).

PART III:
POLICY AND LEGAL FRAMEWORK FOR PRESERVING OPEN ARCHITECTURE

VII. BROADBAND POLICY

A BROADBAND POLICY USER'S GUIDE

INTRODUCTION[1]

The history of communications technology in the 20th century is largely a story of revolutions and their consequences. As we enter the 21st, a rough policy consensus centered on the 1990s internet has fractured, setting off a heated debate over the future of broadband policy and the network itself.

In the euphoric years of the internet revolution, communications policy was easier. Nearly everyone could agree that the internet was successful, indeed revolutionary, and that its growth should not be impended by unnecessary government regulation. But the success of the network hid very strong differences in opinion. The revolution, like many revolutions, turned out to mean different things to different people. We are today in the 1790s of internet communications policy. While not quite the divide between Jefferson and Hamilton, the field is nonetheless today bitterly divided, caught in a struggle over broadband policy that many fear may only be resolved by the next Telecommunications Act. The purpose of this article is to explore both the differences and common grounds that may make reconciliation possible.

What follows is a basic guide to the policy divisions that have emerged and some suggested areas of reconciliation. It is informed by many sources, often informal, including the academic literature, the thoughts of the broadband industry based on its whitepapers and industry conferences, and D.C. telecommunications chatter. Of particular significance are the series of Silicon Flatirons conferences held at the University of Colorado in Boulder where these debates take place.

The paper reflects several necessary simplifications. First, I boil things down to two sides: a debate between advocates of an "open" communications policy and advocates of a "deregulated" communications policy. This is an oversimplification, for the sides are not precise opposites, and various parties have taken nuanced positions that do not map exactly to what is here. Second, I have tried to avoid too much economic and technological jargon, which sometimes means less analytic precision.

The summary is critical. I fault the openists for being too prone to favor regulation without making clear the connection between ends and means. For example, too few openists have asked the degree to which the structural "open access" remedies pushed by independent service providers actually promote the openists' vision.[2] Meanwhile, I fault the deregulationists for two reasons. First, the deregulationists have overlooked the fact that limiting government, as they desire, sometimes *requires* government action. Remedies like network neutrality, for reasons I suggest, may be as important for control of government as it is of industry. I also fault the deregulationists for an exaggerated faith in industry decision-making. I suggest that some deregulationists have failed to familiarize themselves with the processes of industry decision-making before demanding deference to it. This is a particularly serious problem given an industry with a recent track record of terrible judgment and even outright fraud. One example is the demand by some deregulationists that deference is due to a so-called "smart pipe" vision, without analysis of whether that vision has any independent merit.

The paper, finally, seeks to reconcile the two sides of the broadband debate and defends the network neutrality principle as a starting point. Deregulationists and openists, while divided along many lines, share a common faith in innovation as the basis of economic growth. Both sides, in short, worship Joseph Schumpeter and his ideas of competitive, capitalistic innovation. Fidelity to this shared faith should mean mutual surrender of idealized models of either government or powerful private entities, respectively, in exchange for a shared cynicism. We should recognize that both government and the private sector have an unhappy record of blocking the new in favor of the old, and that such tendencies are likely to continue.

The deregulationist and openist should reconcile by remembering their common dedication to the principle of free and unmediated market entry, symbolized by the rubber-cup of Hush-A-Phone.[3] It is by returning to such points of consensus that the reconciliation of communications policy can begin.

I argue that neither deregulationists nor openists should have reason to oppose Network Neutrality rules that create rights in users to use the applications or equipment of their choice. What both sides should want in an inevitable regulatory framework for broadband are rules that pre-commit both industry and government to open market entry. It must be remembered that rules creating rights in users also guarantee the right of operators to enter the application market, free of government hindrance. For these and other reasons discussed below, limited network neutrality rules should on reflection be attractive to both sides.

This paper first describes the emergent divide in the visions of the future that underlie today's policy divisions. It explains some of what unites and divides in the economics of the deregulationists and argues for broadband reconciliation premised on user rights to access the content, applications and equipment of their choice. It suggests that operators should have the freedom to "police what they own," or act reasonably to control the local broadband network. On the other hand, it suggests that the internet community (and, at some point, regulators) should view with suspicion restrictions premised on inter-network criteria. A sample text of an anti-discrimination law is included to show how such a principle could be implemented. Finally, the paper addresses several possible counterarguments to the network neutrality regime discussed in this article.

VISIONS OF THE FUTURE

Communications theorists, like everyone else, have their visions of an ideal future that drive more of their arguments than they would like to admit. While the theorist's utopia has much less sand and sunshine than the average person's, its importance is nonetheless axiomatic.

THE OPENISTS

In the communications world some technologies attract what you might call a high chatter to deployment ratio. That means the volume of talk about the technology exceeds, by an absurd ratio, the actual number of deployments. "Videophones" are a great historical example, as is "Video-on-Demand" and, of course, the glacial version six of the internet protocol (IPv6). In the 1990s, the technology named Voice over IP (VoIP) was a starring member of this suspect class. The technology promises carriage of voice signals using internet technology, an attractive idea, and in the 1990s and the early 2000s it was discussed endlessly despite minimal deployment.

The discussion usually centered on the following question: when would broadband carriers deploy VoIP? And the answer was always, not quite yet. There were reasons. Many within the industry argued that VoIP was not a viable technology without substantial network improvements. Engineers said that the internet Protocol was too inconsistent to guarantee voice service of a quality that any customer would buy. Industry regulatory strategists, meanwhile, were concerned that voice service would attract federal regulation like honey attracts bees. As for the Bell companies, the main DSL providers, there was always the problem of providing a service that might cannibalize the industry's most profitable service, the plain old telephone.

But everyone was watching the wrong companies, for where broadband operators were timid; a company named Vonage was brave. In late 2003 Vonage leapfrogged the broadband operators and began selling VoIP directly to large volumes of customers. Vonage did so not by cooperating with broadband operators but avoiding them. It sold a plug-in device: an actual telephone that connected directly into the network and provided phone service for a fraction of the normal cost. It is true that the quality of the Vonage connection was not, to a telecommunications engineer, strictly of the same quality as that available on a traditional phone network. Yet Vonage's quality was fine to an American people schooled by cell phones; its many users claim they cannot tell the difference. Vonage, by offering what many said no one would buy, has become the internet's success story of 2004.[4]

The Vonage story captures much of the openist's vision of what the internet revolution has meant for communications policy. Without Vonage, VoIP would have arrived on the carrier's schedule: later or perhaps never. Vonage shows why openists say the nation's communications network is important, first and foremost, as an *innovation commons* — a resource of innovators of all origins to draw upon.[5] The openist credo is to care about the nation's communications infrastructure, not so much of itself, but for how it catalyzes the nation's economic and creative potential. Vonage was free to enter the market with a new way of selling voice service only because the network is open, its standards "free as the air to common use."

The openist's innovations commons can be broken down into three prescriptive principles.

The first is the *Infrastructure* principle. It is an insistence that the most important purpose of a communications networks is as public infrastructure, with particular meaning attached to that concept. It means that the principal value of the network is indirect: it as a source of positive spillovers, or externalities, that enable the work of others. It suggests that the highest potential of the network will be achieved not by the accomplishments of network *owners* but by what creative users and developers can do with a fast and reliable connection between every human on earth.

One way of understanding this vision of the network as "infrastructure" is to contrast it directly with its foil, the idea that a network is a "service" or "product" sold by a company. The *product / infrastructure* distinction is explained in personal terms by Mark Cooper, from the Consumer Federation of America:

> The proprietary platform folks [deregulationists] are talking about a BETA Max, an Atari and an Xbox, I am talking a general purpose technology, a cumulative, systemic technology, like the railroad, electricity or the telephone. For them the end-to-end principle is an obscure garden-variety interface, for me it is a fundamental design principle of an enabling technology. When they analyze the proprietary standards wars, there are few if any externalities. When I analyze a bearer service like the digital communications platform, externalities dominate.[6]

The second principle is the *Neutrality* principle. It holds that to reach its highest potential, a communications infrastructure must not discriminate as between uses, users, or content. As Federal Communications Commission (FCC) Commissioner Michael Copps puts it: "From its inception, the internet was designed, as those present during the course of its creation will tell you, to prevent government or a corporation or anyone else from controlling it. It was designed to defeat discrimination against users, ideas and technologies."[7]

The third principle is the *End-to-End* ("e2e") principle. Whatever its meaning elsewhere,[8] in broadband policy e2e stands for a theory of innovation. It rejects centralized, planned innovation and holds that the greatest rate of technological development is driven by delegating decisional authority to the decentralized "ends" of any network. The reason is fairly simple: the "ends" of the network are numerous, or nearly unlimited, and delegating authority to the ends opens the door to more approaches to a given technological challenge. The e2e principle assumes that innovation is an evolutionary process, driven by contests between competing approaches to a problem. For openists, the e2e principle puts as many players in the contest as possible to ensure the true champion emerges.

Openists believe these three principles are what made the internet different than other communications networks; they hold the embedding of these ideas in the internet is the essence of the revolution. The founder's story rejects technological determinism: the idea that the internet was destined to occur. They instead see the founding engineers, men like Paul Baran, Vint Cerf and Robert Kahn, as heroic figures and communications revolutionaries.[9] Fidelity to the vision of these founders, openists believe, requires constant vigilance.

The openist vision just described can seem abstract to regulators and policy-makers. For that reason, in recent years openists have advanced a more concrete regulatory model to explain what neutrality would entail. That model suggests that the internet will continue its success if we come to understand it as a more humble but nonetheless highly successful innovation enhancing network, the nation's electric grid.[10]

While today taken for granted, the electric network is probably the greatest innovation catalyst of our age. The radio, the air conditioner, the computer and other giant innovations have all depended on a predictable and reliable supply of electric current. This multipurpose network is like the railways of the 19th century or the first roads of ages past: among the foundations of the national economy.

Openists point to the electrical grid and say it is successful precisely because we don't care about electricity as a product, but care instead about what the electric grid makes possible. It provides a standardized platform for the development of appliances that serve human needs, such as the hair dryer. Sony and IBM do business safe in the assumption that American electricity will be predictable, standardized and provided without preference for certain brands or products. There is no built-in favoritism for the VCR over the DVD player. You do not ask the electric companies permission before plugging in a new cordless phone. This makes the electric grid, openists say, one of the greatest models of network neutrality the world has ever known.

The electric grid model returns us to the Vonage story that opened the section. The long-term vision is a future where still other services long centralized will finally be decentralized. Freestanding IP-televisions, IP-stereos, and many other services should be available based on plug-in devices, developed by independent, competing companies. This is a vision that can be reached, but is not inevitable, for it requires defense of the network against any force that might seek to close the network to market entrants.

THE DEREGULATIONISTS

The contrasting vision of the communications future begins with the decades-old idea of *media convergence*. Convergence means a natural technological progression toward a single network for communications services. Voice, data, and video, historically carried over different networks will, in the future, be carried over a single "pipe." There was a time, namely the 1990s, when twin visions of "convergence" and "commons" could maintain a peaceful coexistence. But today the visions are rivals, for the underlying principles are in conflict.

The convergence vision focuses on the *owners* of the networks and the services they will offer on the converged network "telecosm."[9] As Peter Huber puts it:

> Convergence among technologies is doing more than networking the networks. It is transforming the services; the vast capacities of broadband networks make nonsense of the traditional regulation distinction between "carriers" and "broadcasters"....Broadcasters, in short, are mastering the art of keeping the "broad" while switching the "cast." Telephone companies are keeping their switched, addressable capabilities while widening their bandwidth and their reach. Nobody casts drift nets anymore. They are all fly fishermen now.[10]

The deregulationist position can also be reduced to several principles. First, is the *Propertization* principle: any given resource will generally reach its best use when mapped out as property, and assigned to owners. When deregulationists think "commons," the word "tragedy" is never far from mind. Property owners can be expected to maintain and steward only what they have the right to exclude others from.[11] Additionally, the creation of transferable property rights will facilitate private, welfare-enhancing transactions. As Frank Easterbook put it in *Law of the Horse*: "we need to bring the internet into the world of property law ... without which welfare-increasing bargains cannot occur."[12]

The second principle is the *Incentive* principle, which is just a simple reminder that communications networks are expensive investments and that companies will only build when given the prospect of a reasonable return on investment.[13]   To speak, as openists do, of a pure public infrastructure may have made some sense when the Government was funding and building the network, but now is seriously out-of-date. Some deregulationists will accept that aspects of the internet have the character of a public good or natural monopoly and therefore might be best provided by an entity outside of the market (internet addresses might be an example). But in general, and for most of the network and its applications, the private sector responding to appropriate incentives will drive and fund the future.

The final principle is *Deregulation* itself. The deregulationist is naturally suspicious of government regulation outside of the assignment of property rights. This can be understood as a different interpretation of the internet revolution: the greatest factor in the success of the internet, deregulationists argue, was the fact that the Federal Communications Commission largely stayed out of the way. The idea of technological destinies, discussed above, is important to this position. Deregulationists are generally technological realists, believing that power more than ideas determine the course of history. Government may slow but it cannot stop the inevitable. So while openists may try to slow or stop it, in the long term the power of private network owners will drive the next-generation internet.

Much of this is as abstract as the idea of an internet commons. When asked for a more concrete vision of what deregulationist policies may lead to, deregulationists have turned to the vision of the "smart pipe." The smart pipe (also known as the "Quality of Service (QoS) internet" or the "value-added service connection") is the central dogma of innumerable industry white papers. The basic idea is this: broadband operators will increase revenue and profit by selling applications bundled with a basic connection. Stated in industry jargon, broadband operators using "next-generation" technologies can offer their customers a host of "value-added" services, such as telephony, video-on-demand, and so on.[14] The incentive, at least on the authority of projection: profits that far exceed what can be earned from selling "commodity bandwidth."

Equipment vendors have pushed this vision aggressively for the last decade. As a current Cisco White Paper instructs cable operators:

> Tomorrow's cable business growth, however, will come from offering value-added services to consumers such as video on demand (VOD), interactive TV, and cable telephony. .... Every competitive MSO [cable operator] has been challenged to plan and build an IP infrastructure that can deliver a full range of differentiated network services and provide absolute network control.[15]

In short, deregulationists predict that the next great wave of innovation will occur at the center of the network, not the ends.[16] That directly contradicts the end-to-end principle, but that's fine: most deregulationists believe blind adherence to the end-to-end principle is what is in fact slowing technological progress today. Economists Bruce Owen and Gregory Rosston, for example, argue that "openness inevitably has a price," and that certain innovations "have been slowed or even blocked because of the [e2e's] requirement that the network not have embedded intelligence."[17]

Finally, while openists favor the story of internet founders, deregulationists invoke a different prescriptive saga: the birth of cable television. As Peter Huber puts it "Cable was the prototype of the broadband future."[18] The development of the cable networks was a story of private ingenuity's victory over governmental perfidy and, in the mind of many deregulationists, a story with clear lessons for 2000 broadband.

The Commission in the 1960s was anxious to preserve certain ideal visions of television. The two most important were that it be free and that it be local. Whatever the theoretical merits of those views, deregulationists point out that the practical effect was to slow the spread of cable television for a full decade and to stop it from penetrating urban markets.[19] It was only by the 1970s that the Commission finally relaxed its grip and let competitive forces run their course. (Today cable companies are the TV's dominant players, so much so that cable operators rather casually bid to acquire broadcasters, their one-time overlords.[20])

This, the deregulationists would suggest, is what is happening in broadband policy, though our proximity makes us incapable of realizing it. There are certain parallels that anchor the obstructionist story. First, physical broadband networks, whether cable, twisted pair, or wireless spectrum, are indeed the subject of intensely complex federal and state regulation, rather like those to which the cable industry was subjected in the late 1960s and early 1970s. (One writer described the cable regulations of 1972 as the "most complicated scheme ever devised by the mind of man."[21]) The ongoing regulatory asymmetry of DSL, cable, and wireless services is perhaps the most obvious example of a governmentally introduced distortion.

Second, the Commission in this view is still attached to some inappropriately utopian visions, which do not correspond with technological destiny. Today, the deregulationist would contend, replacing "localism" and "free television" are similarly impractical ideals like the "end-to-end principle," "open access" and, of course "network neutrality."

A related similarity is what deregulationists decry as an effort to prop up doomed businesses in the name of lofty ideals. In the 1960s, the Commission placed much hope for the future of television in a new generation of UHF broadcast stations.[22] UHF stations did have many appealing qualities: they were locally owned, free over the air for recipients and available in greater quantity than VHF stations. But UHF was hopeless as a technological competitor to cable. Today, they contend, we see the scenario is repeating itself. Independent Internet Service Providers ("ISPs") are kept alive in the vain hope that they may somehow make the broadband world a better place.

So what is the deregulationist's vision of the future? Some argue that the FCC and internet old-timers are holding back, not promoting the natural progress of broadband networks. Innovation, they contend, can happen anywhere, not just at the "ends." Dreams of a neutral network may be holding back the next communications revolution, one that will arise from the center of the network. That vision will necessarily be driven by private network owners and will bring consumers both what they want and are willing to pay for and what the old internet could never have provided.

It is between substantive visions of the future where the openist – deregulationist divide is most stark. That is perhaps because the contrasting utopias depend mainly on intuition and aesthetics, and degrees of trust in the private and public sectors, respectively. Yet nonetheless the sides are not precise opponents. Openists are primarily focused on the "ends"—the innovation commons. Deregulations care most about the means, most of all wanting to prevent disastrous and long-lasting governmental intervention.

SHARED ECONOMIC FAITHS

SCHUMPETER

It is worth reemphasizing that the greatest unifying belief as between openists and deregulationists is a common idolization of innovation. When all is said and done, both sides worship at the shrine of economist Joseph Schumpeter and his concept of innovation as "creative destruction."[23]

The core of what is agreed upon can be stated simply. Both sides take innovation, not price competition, as the principle driver of economic growth. Proximity to the industries of high technology leads naturally to favoring or at least acknowledging dynamic economic models. The market equilibrium central to neo-classical economics is not a state of affairs recognizable to those who today work in the fast-changing world of telecommunications. These beliefs, for both sides, put innovation policy at the center of national economic policy.

How, then, does innovation happen? The two sides, in their nature, subscribe to Schumpeter's "capitalist" or "competitive" theory of innovation centered on "creative destruction." Both sides can agree that capitalism's leading feature is its "process of industrial mutation ... that incessantly revolutionizes the economic structure from within, incessantly destroying the old one, incessantly creating a new one. This process of Creative Destruction is the essential fact about capitalism."[24]

Both sides also agree with Schumpeter that the greatest barrier to innovation is "ordinary routine." As he put it "knowledge and habit once acquired becomes as firmly rooted in ourselves as a railway embankment in the earth."[25] As a result, even "in the breast of one who wishes to do something new, the forces of habit raise up and bear witness against the embryonic project." The greatest threat is social resistance, particularly from "the groups threatened by the innovation."[26]

With all this agreement, where do the differences arise? The difference between openists and deregulationists in Schumpeterian terms is over who the active agents of creative destruction are. It boils down to something quite simple: different attitudes toward size. Many deregulationists, like the later Schumpeter, see large and powerful companies as the central agents of creative destruction. Big firms are the winners, the success stories, the smartest and strongest. Openists see things quite differently. For the Openist, size is not necessarily a sign of continuing success but instead suggestive of complacency and some knack for blocking market entry. The openists like the early Schumpeter with his focus on the entrepreneur as the seed of creative destruction. The difference in opinion over size can be as intractable as how one sees Sport Utility Vehicles or modern skyscrapers. Some see a mighty work of man, others see a wasteful monster. Yet Schumpeter himself managed to reconcile the role of large and small in his work, so it ought be possible for his latter-day followers.

The deregulationist view that large, private and unregulated companies will always be the most significant champions of progress and innovation finds support in the later works of Schumpeter: "What we have got to accept" he said in 1943, is that the "large-scale establishment" is "the most powerful engine of [economic] progress and in particular of the long-run expansion of total output."[27]   Putting faith in "perfect competition" among numerous competitors was, in his view, folly, for "the firm of the type that is compatible with perfect competition is in many cases inferior in internal, especially technological, efficiency."[28]

The reasons for this belief can be specified more carefully. First, in a dynamic market, when a firm successfully establishes a new market through product innovation, the result is inevitably at least a short-term market advantage, even a monopoly. Yet that market power is no cause for concern, as it will erode quickly under the pressure of capitalistic competition. Indeed, short-term monopoly profits are a not social ill but rather social boon. For it is the very existence of potential monopoly profit that fires the pistons of creative destruction. It is only the possibility of a giant and seemingly unfair payoff that motivates risky and otherwise irrational innovative behavior. Under Capitalism, Schumpeter said, "spectacular prizes much greater than would have been necessary to call forth the particular effort are thrown to a small minority of winners, thus propelling much more efficiously than a more equal and more 'just' distribution would."[29]

Second, large, powerful firms have advantages that in this view make them the only entities truly capable of producing meaningful progress. One idea, not strictly Schumpeterian, is that the large firm with a secure market may carry out product innovation in a planned and careful way, and decrease the waste from competing innovative processes.[30] Another idea from Schumpeter is that large firms are simply smarter, stronger, and better. Schumpeter argued that "there are superior methods available to the monopolist," and that "monopolization may increase the sphere of influence of the better, and decrease the sphere of influence of inferior brains."[31]

In the broadband context, this vision sees the great firms—mainly, the greatest of cable operators and powerful Bell Operating Companies—as the agents of perpetual revolution. Their battle for the giant profits that await the champion, the single broadband monopolist, are the driving force behind broadband innovation and the future of the internet.

But this faith in great firms should be tempered, both by the work of Schumpeter himself, and the work of later evolutionary economists. The first starting point is also Schumpeter, but the early, German-language Shumpeter who spent his time on individual entrepreneurs, and the challenges they face.[32]

Schumpeter may be misunderstood in believing that the large firm had an inherent advantage over the small firm. As economist Jan Farberberg argues, "In fact, Schumpeter seemed to be much more concerned with the difference between new and old firms than between small and large firms."[33] And Schumpeter's theory of entrepreneurs is distinct and compelling. They are to him unusual characters, risk-seeking individuals with a "special quality," who are spread through the population like undercover superheroes. What distinguished this class of individuals, said Schumpeter (foreshadowing the "open source" movement), was that profit would be but one motive and not the most important one. Instead, the entrepreneur was generally driven by "the dream or will to found a private kingdom;" "the will to conquer: the impulse to fight, to prove oneself superior to others" and finally the "joy of creating."[34]

The work of recent evolutionary economists like Richard Nelson and Sidney Winter should also be paid close attention to by those of the Schumpeterian faith. An essential element of such neo-Schumpeterian work is the emphasis on the uncertainty and contingency of technological outcomes. It predicts multiple possible equilibria, rather than a single, predictable outcome. One reason is that this branch of economic thinking takes a much more sophisticated view of how firms decide what to do, rejecting the premise that firms will generally arrive at "maximizing" decisions.[35] Firms instead generally depend on a set of routines that survive unless the firm dies or manages to mutate its way of doing business. This latter capacity is limited by the limits of humans' ability to predict or foresee the future. There is, for writers such as Nelson, simply too much information to process: firms will usually lack the capacity to understand it all and understand what routines it needs to change to arrive at the best of all possible worlds. The odds, then, of any single actor treading the optimal path of technological development are exceedingly low.

When cognitive limitations combine with the phenomenon, in at least some markets, of path dependence (that is, technological "lock-in," or "network externalities"),[36] then reaching suboptimal technological outcomes is not only possible but likely. Evolutionists, pace Dilbert, consider firms to be unimaginative creatures whose ideas of the future tends to be closely tied to the present, like a 19th century farmer who asks for a better ox instead of a tractor. The "network" benefits of doing business in accord with the way everyone else does it adds to the problem. The result can quite easily become technological complacency, which to Schumpeterians means an economic swamp.

Here lies the link between neo-Schumpeterian economics and the end-to-end principle described above. The end-to-end principle can be understood as the implementation of an evolutionary innovation policy. E2e mandates that innovation is the job of the many (the ends), not the few (the center). By prescribing non-discrimination, it also sets conditions necessary for a fair fight, so that what survives is the truly the fittest and not merely the favored. E2e can help erase through competition the invariable mistakes that a centralized network planner will make.

This hostility toward centralized, planned innovation should, for openists in particular, spill over to an attitude toward government. Government, no more than any human entity, is likely to have a good idea of what the future should be; so centralized technological planning is no better option. But the developments in evolutionary economics and post-Schumpeterian thought should direct rethinking for the deregulationist. It cannot be denied that the unregulated companies favored by the deregulation can become among the forces that resist the new. The new work suggests that this is not only possible, but likely.

Several policy prescription come from the consensus neo-Schumpeterian analysis here. The insight that all should agree on is that maintaining lowest-cost market entry as possible is the foundation of the innovation theories that all subscribe to. That means preventing any single actor, governmental or otherwise, from becoming lord of the technological future. A multiplicity of innovating actors, even if suffering from the same inability to accurately predict the future, may nonetheless stumble upon the optimal path. But all should understand that the process will be an ugly, Darwinian affair, an interminable exercise in trial and error, and not the well-calculated elegance of monopolistic prophecy.

Vertical Integration & New Institutional Economics

While the study of vertical integration may seem a technical topic, it has become central to understanding the division between openists and deregulationists and what the possibilities for reconciliation are.[37] For the work in this area proposes that the ends favored by openists – namely, the innovations commons -- may be reached by deregulationist means. The analysis of vertical integration has highlighted weaknesses in the openist position, or at least means of regulation that its adherents have advanced. Strong opposition to all vertical integration, expressed in the "open access" laws, has failed to answer to the challenge implicit in examples of "good" vertical coordination.

Why any attention to vertical integration at all? The specific reason is the "open access" debate. Some openists, early on, have suggested that the best means of preventing an erosion of the neutrality of the network

Figure:
Vertical Division

Content
Application
Transport

would be laws limiting vertical integration of broadband carriers with internet service providers.   Keeping these two economic units separate, suggested Lawrence Lessig and Mark Lemley in early work, is likely to prevent content discrimination on the internet.[38] The counter-argument is by now familiar for those who follow the debate. First, as Phil Weiser and Joseph Farell remind us in their paper, vertical integration often leads to important efficiencies.[39]   Second, as Jim Speta and others have pointed out, broadband operators, even if vertically integrated, want to make their product as valuable as possible and can therefore be expected to provide their customers with wide access to content and services.[40]   Weiser and Farell express this as the "ICE presumption," a presumption that a platform monopolist will "internalize complementary externalities."[41]

The literature has focused on a narrow but crucial question: how likely are private firms to arrive at the innovation commons approach themselves? The way to ask the question begins by recognizing that the value of a broadband operator's (or any platform owner's) service ultimately depends on what applications and content are available for use on it. The value of the X-Box game console to a consumer is chiefly a function of the games you can play on it (imagine a game console that offered only "Pong"). We ought therefore to expect the broadband operator to do everything possible to maximize the platform's value to its customers, including the adoption of whatever strategies will lead to the best application development. For example, a service that only allowed Comcast customers to email Comcast customers would be less valuable, so Comcast is not likely to impose such a limitation. Similarly, if an "open" application development model yields the best applications, then the platform owner will provide an open model.

On the other hand, there may be services where vertically coordinated, "hand-in-glove" cooperation results in more value for the customer. A car that arrived with no speedometer or tachometer would be less desirable despite the fact that the automobile and gauge market are arguably separate. In the broadband context, Comcast might, for example, want to offer its customers an integrated and quality-guaranteed Voice-over-cable product. Doing so might be better with vertical coordination between itself and a telephony carrier. In short, some applications are better provided in a closed fashion, and some open. What is better open and better closed is ultimately an empirical question,[42] and one that the platform owner is best situated to answer.

But what if the platform owner is a monopolist: won't it try to "leverage" its platform monopoly into a second monopoly? For example, might a monopolist broadband operator begin to try and give itself a monopoly over all Voice-over-IP revenue? Here, for a deregulationist, the relevance of the "single-monopoly profit" principles emerges. To a platform monopolist, the applications are its inputs, and the monopolist has the same interest as any other party in minimizing its input costs.[43] Hence, if allowing open application development saves the monopolist money, then it will do so. An example comes from Microsoft, monopoly owner of the Windows platform. Microsoft does not categorically bar any foreign applications, but instead integrates some functions into the operating system platform (such as, say, disk defragmentation utilities), and leaves others open to some degree of competition (such as word processors). While the merits of Microsoft as a model are debatable, the point is that a platform owner is making a choice between what is vertically integrated and what is left to competing application developers.

This analysis leads to a presumption that, in the telecommunications market, vertically integrated companies, even with monopoly power, should generally be left unregulated, absent special conditions, or exceptions. Weiser and Farell provide a useful summary of the exceptions that have emerged from the economic literature. Some of the most relevant to the broadband context include interests in price discrimination or disadvantaging potential platform rivals.[44]

But from both Weiser and Farell's work, and from the neo-Schumpeterian work discussed above, there is a central reason to suspect even competing firms may not implement optimal innovation policies themselves. Weiser and Farell call it the problem of "incompetent incumbents."[45] In the terminology of Nelson and Winter, it is the observatio that firms operate on the basis of routines that do not allow for suitable decisional flexibility. Perhaps most simply: the clearest problem is that no company will plan its own death, even if its death is in the social interest.

How can we know, if the platform owner chooses a closed system is it actually trying to internalize complementary externalities or, in Schumpeter's phraseology, "resisting to new ways" in an effort to prevent its own inevitable demise?[46] As Schumpeter put the matter, in an ideal state of capitalism a platform owner faces "competition which commands a decisive cost or quality advantage and which strikes not at the margins of the profits and the outputs of the existing firms but at their foundations and their very lives."[47]   If innovation presents a firm with a threat to its very existence, then its interest in a closed system may have much less to do with "internalization of complementary externalities" than it does with basic survival.

There is a moderate, reconciliatory position among these attitudes toward vertical integration. It is reasonable to agree that certain applications may be more efficiently provided open and others closed, and still see industry education as the primary challenge. The moderate view disagrees with the premise that internal processes of firm-decision will even be likely to lead to good decisions. The primary reason is that the information and signals that broadband operators are exposed to can be biased. Equipment vendors have, as described earlier, spent years convincing broadband operators that great profits lie in capturing the applications market for themselves. In my experience, Wall Street analysts tend to reward broadband operators in the short term for announcing plans to move into the applications market without serious analysis of the second-monopoly profit problem. Neither group has much to lose from sending such messages, but both operators and consumers do. A vivid example came in 2000, when broadband operator Enron announced bold moves into the Video-on-Demand market and was cheered by financial and industry analysts (though obviously punished later).[48] In that case the problem wasn't quite that the operator didn't understand the one monopoly profit rule; it seemed to be that analysts didn't seem to care.

This view sees industry education as paramount. One important tool in this respect is the regulatory threat, which can be important as a kind of signaling tool.[49] It can counteract information broadband operators get from other sources. It is worth noting that FCC Chairman Michael Powell has taken steps toward an educational policy. Powell has encouraged broadband owners to guarantee the neutrality of the network for their own sake as well as for that of consumers. His approach challenges operators to respect "four freedoms" of the internet consumer to guarantee a better network for all.[50] This message, if it reaches operators, may balance the urgings of others, such as equipment vendors and sometimes Wall Street, to seek a second (unachievable) monopoly profit.

RECONCILIATION

In what is perhaps an excess of optimism I consider reconciliation to be plausible. As the discussion above suggests, the insights of the openists and deregulationists are not necessarily in tension. Consider that both sides are basically interested in innovation and promoting market entry. The openists are principally concerned with ends (an open network), and the deregulationists, means (non-governmental methods). That suggests room for agreement.

NETWORK NEUTRALITY

Based on the positions developed here, I believe neither deregulationists nor openists should oppose user-centered network neutrality rules. Such network neutrality rules are most closely akin to the deregulation of equipment attachment rules begun in *Hush-A-Phone*, and therefore should be an easy case for both sides. Stated otherwise, neither side should have much reason to oppose a rule that creates a right of users to use whatever legal and non-harmful application "attachments" they want. Network Neutrality rules also do much to advance the Schumpeterian interest in as wide-open market entry as possible.

Network Neutrality (NN) rules are distinguished by creating rights in *users*. Rights, that is, to attach equipment or access any application or content one wants, so long as not harmful or illegal.

(b) *General Right of Unrestricted Network Usage.* Broadband Users have the right to use their internet connection in ways which are not unlawful or harmful to the network. Accordingly neither Broadband Operators nor the Federal Communications Commission shall impose restrictions on the use of an internet connection except as necessary to: [prevent uses illegal under statute or uses harmful to the network].[51]

This distinguishes NN rules from competitor-centered rules like the various state-law "open access" regimes, or the approach of §251 of the 1996 Telecommunications Act. For example, the Portland merger condition at issue in the original AT&T open access case creates rights in Internet Service Providers, not users.[52]

The attraction to openists of an NN rule is perhaps more intuitive. What is the attraction to the deregulationist? The key point is that creating rights in users can and will serve deregulatory purposes. American law is full of such deregulatory rights, economic and otherwise: the rights created by the dormant commerce clause to be free from discriminatory state regulation are a good example.[53] Hence, a user-centered NN rule is as deregulatory in spirit as *Hush-A-Phone* and *Carter-Phone*[54] were. It prevents government from acting as in the *Hush-A-Phone* case and agreeing to regulations that block application or network attachment. While less likely in recent years than in the 1950s and 1960s, the possibility of such action should not be discounted, for the reasons for doing so in the future cannot be predicted today. NN rules are, in short, like other rights-regimes, a pre-commitment rule for both government and industry. They prevent now what may be temptations tomorrow.

In addition, the broadband industry and some deregulationists may be overlooking the extent to which NN rules prevent government from blocking *operator* entry into the application market. If the user has the right to access lawful applications and content that includes those provided by the operator itself, NN rules thereby prevent quarantine — precluding state actions that prevent operators from offering competitive, vertically integrated applications themselves. NN rules have a value to the operator industry that should not be minimized.

Finally, NN rules are at bottom rules designed to free market entry, and should therefore be supported by those with Schumpeterian leanings, which means nearly everyone in communications policy. The NN rules create a structural bias that favors entry of any player, operator or application, or equipment-developer into the market for consumer usage of the internet. They are designed to make the Vonage story repeat itself, and even if Vonage dies, the Schumpeterian will admit it will have succeeded in bringing the network forward. The NN rules also do not do anything in particular to prevent "facilities-based" entry. If anyone thinks they have a better idea than the TCP/IP protocol, they are free to build that network and see how it goes.

One deregulationist who has not overlooked these arguments and the desirability of NN principles is Commission Chairman Michael Powell. Powell has spoken powerfully on the normative desirability of "network freedom," his phrase for network neutrality. "Network freedom," he says, means "ensuring that consumers can obtain and use the content, applications and devices they want."[55] Doing so, he says, is "critical to unlocking the vast potential of the broadband internet," and (in Schumpeterian language), "essential to nurturing competitive innovation."

Powell's discussion of "network freedom" focuses also on user rights: notably, the four "freedoms:"

> **Freedom to Access Content.** First, consumers should have access to their choice of legal content.

> **Freedom to Use Applications.** Second, consumers should be able to run applications of their choice.

> **Freedom to Attach Personal Devices.** Third, consumers should be permitted to attach any devices they choose to the connection in their homes.

> **Freedom to Obtain Service Plan Information.** Fourth, consumers should receive meaningful information regarding their service plans.[56]

These principles advocated by Powell, while done as part of an educational campaign, underline why openists and deregulationists should find common ground in advocacy of user-centered network neutrality rules. A shared faith in consumer choice and open market entry augurs such a result.

CRITICISM OF NETWORK NEUTRALITY

While some deregulationists, like Chairman Powell, have endorsed principles of network neutrality, many industry players and some deregulationists have mounted challenges to network neutrality proposals. I suggest that these challenges are generally lacking in merit, for reasons that follow.

The industry's most common challenge is this: while neutrality might be an attractive goal, any neutrality regulation is a solution looking for a problem. Such regulation or even a threat thereof, violates the principle of *Primum Non Nocere* (first, do no harm).[57] At its worst, network neutrality regulation might become a tool in the hands of application developers used to block competition from broadband operators. Imagine, for example, a rule that required FCC permission before a broadband operator could offer any service beyond a basic connection.

There are several problems with the *Primum Non Nocere* objection. First, it simply raises a question of dueling baselines. The existing design of the internet is neutral. So why should it not be private entities who follow the principle of "do no harm" before monkeying with the proven strengths of the existing design? In this sense the slogan does nothing but restate the underlying difference in visions.

Second, the objection relies on an anti-regulatory straw man. Because it is possible to imagine a *bad* network neutrality law, *any* network neutrality regulation is suspect. Yet it is unclear how Chairman Powell's or other suggestions create the means for preventing competition among applications. The cable industry, which is the leading exponent of the do-no-harm view, has very meager support for its claim that a NN rule would block operator entry into the applications market. Its sole support is a proposal from Amazon that would bar cable operators from adding pop-up ads to web content.[58] That's far from a rule that prevents operators from entering the applications market. And as discussed above, a NN-rule that creates user's rights will give operators as much as anyone else a right to enter the applications or equipment markets.

A more powerful challenge to network neutrality rules runs as follows. It may be true that the basic, neutral internet creates positive externalities, like the electrical grid or other neutral networks. But the metaphor is inapt for the following reason: one thing the electric grid model fails to take into account is the possible need to improve the grid or infrastructure itself, and the creation of proper incentives to do so. As Howard Shelanski puts the point, using roads as a metaphor: "at some point the road needs to be improved and that work can be disruptive. So the question is not one of never disrupting the flow of traffic, but of knowing when to let cars run freely on the road and when to tear up the road to make it work better."[59]

This returns us to the "smart-pipe" discussion and the argument that much innovative potential is trapped in the core of the network, a point Christopher Yoo makes.[60] Yoo argues that it is critical, in a market with many vertical layers, that competition be encouraged at the layer that is least competitive. As he states, "Modern economic theory suggests that consumers will not realize all of the available benefits unless competition at each stage of the chain of production is sufficiently vigorous."[61] Looking at broadband, he thinks that in the application and content market, competition is robust and needs no favors. Yet he sees competition at the physical layer (between cable and DSL) as least vigorous and therefore the most in need of freedom from government restraints. Network neutrality regulation, in Yoo's view, would mandate dumbness and therefore slow deployment of proprietary "smart" networks.[62]

According to Yoo, the answer is to allow or even encourage the deployment of divergent proprietary, as opposed to standardized, broadband networks. He sketches the possibility of consumers being served by three entirely different and non-standardized broadband infrastructures: "The first network could be optimized for conventional internet applications, such as e-mail and website access. The second network could incorporate security features designed to appeal to users focusing on e-commerce. The third network could prioritize packet routing in the manner needed to facilitate time-sensitive applications such as VoIP."

Yoo's conclusions are overstated and demand several responses. First, it is unclear why Yoo believes that the existence of a neutral internet would be a barrier to "facilities-based competition," that is, the market entry of entire new network facilities.[63] If an operator wanted to build an entirely new network designed, as Yoo suggests, focusing on voice services, it is free to do so—the fact that the internet is kept neutral or not seems irrelevant. Indeed Yoo seems to have it backward: if the neutral network is no good for certain applications, that would drive facilities-based competition, not inhibit it. A neutral network should be expected to drive an efficient mix of shared and facilities-based competition: those applications that can be run over the open network will be, and for those that require entirely new facilities, new facilities will be built.

And in fact such facilities-based competition is our present reality. The existing telephone network is Yoo's "prioritized" network that facilitates a time-sensitive application, telephony, as are the mobile-phone networks. Meanwhile, the cable television network is a network specialized for "one-to-many" video. Perhaps Yoo's point is that these various specialized networks are likely to remain in our lives, but that doesn't say much about how the internet should be regulated.

Second, Yoo's premise that vigorous competition at every layer is always better for the consumer is overstated. He downplays, to the point of elimination, the basic economic benefits of standardization. And when it comes to technology platforms or other areas of economic development it is easy to envision scenarios where standardization means less competition but is nonetheless socially beneficial, which impeaches Yoo's premise.

Here is an intuitive demonstration of the point. Most people in the United States speak a standard language, English. This undoubtedly leads to some sacrifice. We lose, for example, the elegance and righteousness of French; we lack the Chinese vocabulary for food; and we lose the precision of German. But few would argue that vigorous and ongoing competition for a standard American language would clearly serve consumer welfare. It would be, instead, the Tower of Babel.

The same observation holds for standardized technology platforms such as the Windows operating system or the TCP/IP protocol, which bring a variety of benefits for application-developers and end users. Application writers need only write for a single platform, for example, and can expect to reach a much larger addressable market, thereby justifying greater investments. End-users, given a single standard, share information with ease. All of these advantages usually go under the rough heading of network externalities, or the economic benefits of standardization. Yoo is, in essence, failing to take seriously the benefits of platform standardization in his product differentiation model. To be sure, as with language, there are costs from uncompetitive platform markets. The result will in all likelihood be an inferior platform (for want of competition), and the possibility of anti-competitive conduct. But the fact that we face a balance of costs and benefits shrinks Yoo's point. We are left instead with the empirical question: how valuable are neutral standards and networks, and when are they worth a loss in competition in the network?

Yoo and others who favor the encouragement of market entry should in fact favor basic network neutrality rules. True enough, such rules may slow some competition for the standards for the internet's basic protocols. But if that's truly the case, nothing in NN rules prevent full facilities-based competition. And, meanwhile, NN rules facilitate market entry on the standardized and highly successful network we do have. These and other reasons should prompt those deregulationists opposed to network neutrality principles to ask whether they are on the wrong side of the argument.

CONCLUSION

I have suggested here that reconciliation of the broadband debate is plausible, but unfortunately that doesn't make it inevitable. A serious contribution to this problem has come from the winner-take-all approach of some of the groups on each side. The Internet Service Providers have seemed committed to achieving full open access rules through litigation, perhaps demonstrating that companies are not comfortable recommending their own demise. And the cable industry, while it has laudably adhered to neutral practices during the last period of intense scrutiny, still seems unwilling to agree with a simple neutrality rule that would codify its existing practices and do much to remove regulatory scrutiny. It should be recognized that the age of regulatory uncertainty surrounding broadband will soon reach its first decade. That fact alone should prompt all interested parties to seek reconciliation sooner rather than later.

EX PARTE SUBMISSION IN CS DOCKET NO. 02-52

In a series of comments and ex parte letters submitted over the last year, various interested parties have addressed the desirability of a "network neutrality" regime for cable broadband.   On November 18, 2002, the Coalition of Broadband Users and Innovators submitted a short letter arguing that "[g]overnment must ensure that transmission network operators do not encumber relationships between their customers and destinations on the network." The National Cable & Telecommunications Association ("NCTA"), meanwhile, has submitted two letters dated December 10, 2002, and February 21, arguing that regulation is unnecessary and questioning the Commission's authority.   Other submissions on this matter include comments from the High Tech Broadband Coalition, ex parte letters from Amazon.com, Comcast Inc., Cox Cable Inc., and others, along with numerous oral ex parte presentations.

Larry Lessig and I write to the Commission, not as stakeholders, but to address deeper questions of communications policy implicated by the Commission's consideration of a neutrality regime. In short, we believe that the Commission has done much to successfully encourage investment and inter-platform competition in the market for broadband infrastructure. It has yet, however, to pay the same kind of attention to broadband applications. The arguments that support regulatory parity and a fair fight between cable, DSL, and other broadband platforms also favor promoting fair competition among applications on a neutral network. But so far, the Commission has devoted little attention to ensuring either the security of investments in broadband applications, or fair conditions of competition. We believe that a neutrality regime is a first and salutary step in that direction.

This proposal addresses three matters. First, it explains how a neutrality regime might relate to more general goals of the Commission's broadband policy. Second, it addresses two arguments made by the cable industry. It explains why a regulatory solution is preferable to self-regulation in this instance, and refutes the occasional arguments that the First Amendment would prohibit neutrality regulations. Finally, it introduces a sample neutrality regime designed to be simple while promoting the security of investments in broadband applications and fair competition in the market.

WHY A NEUTRAL NETWORK?

The debate so far reflects paired accusations. Application developers accuse the cable industry of "discrimination" and "blocking content," and say it must be stopped.[64] The cable industry accuses developers of manipulating governmental regulation to gain a competitive advantage.[65] Less attention has been devoted to why the Commission might consider network neutrality an independently valuable objective, or to explain how a neutrality regime might reflect broader goals of the Commission's broadband policy.

Fundamentally, should the Commission care if the Internet remains a "neutral" network—more precisely, one that does not favor one application (e.g., the World Wide Web), over others (e.g., mass online gaming)? Is it of any concern to the public if the Internet is biased to favor some things over others?[66]

The answer is yes. There are two reasons the Commission should care about maintaining a neutral network, both reflecting the Commission's interest in "stimulat[ing] investment and innovation in broadband technology and services."[67] First, guaranteeing a neutral network eliminates the risk of future discrimination, providing greater incentives to invest in broadband application development today. Second, a neutral network facilitates fair competition among applications, ensuring the survival of the fittest, rather than that favored by network bias. These arguments will be explained in the sections that follow.

Securing Investments in Innovation

A network that is as neutral as possible is predictable: all applications are treated alike. Since the Commission wants to maximize the incentives to invest in broadband applications, it should act now to eliminate the unpredictability created by potential future restrictions on network usage.

The value of network neutrality can be seen clearly in another context: the nation's electric system. Because it remains neutral, the electricity network has served as an important platform for innovation. The electronics industry designs new and better electronics, safe in the assumption that American electricity will be provided without preference for certain brands or products. When consumers buy a new toaster made by General Electric they need not worry that it won't work because the utility company makes a competing product.

At the heart of this success story lies the predictability of the network and a certain security of investment. The uniformity of the electric grid is a safeguard against the risk of restrictions and uneven standards. It provides designers and consumers alike with a baseline on which they can rely.

Unfortunately the nature of today's broadband networks makes investment in mass broadband applications a far riskier proposition. The nation's broadband network is in its infancy, just now reaching tens of millions of users, like the narrowband Internet in the mid-1990s.[68] At this critical juncture, the broadband networks, particularly those operated by cable operators, have imposed a confusing patchwork of contractual and technical restrictions, enforced in an unpredictable manner. The reasons for these bans and restrictions are a mix: they range from legitimate security concerns all the way to interests in promoting competing products. Since every provider acts independently, neither developers nor consumers can predict whether a new, innovative application will be banned in certain parts of the country. It as if a new toaster were to work well in Connecticut and California, but not in Wisconsin or Wyoming.

The recent story of Virtual Private Networks (VPNs) illustrates the problem. VPNs, which allow employees to work more efficiently from home, are a good example of the kind of productivity-enhancing application that broadband makes possible. However, when cable operators became aware of the usage of VPNs, the results were messy.[69] Some cable operators decided to ban their usage outright, or demand additional fees. Others banned them without any enforcement. Still others allowed VPNs without comment. The unpredictability and variance in these restrictions has been expensive. It has imposed unnecessary costs on the developers of VPN technology, the companies who might benefit from VPN technology, and, of course, on workers themselves.

Over the last year, many of the VPN bans have been relaxed, mainly as a result of the publicity stemming from the instant inquiry.[70] But the VPN episode is generally indicative of a problematic tendency: the restriction of new and innovative applications that broadband operators see as either unimportant, a competitive threat, or a chance to make money. The result is that the effects of usage restrictions fall hardest on small and startup developers—the kind without the resources to file comments before the Commission. By definition, startup application developers push the envelope of what is possible using the Internet's architecture.[71] Their funding depends on the existence of a stable, addressable market for their products. Such developers would benefit the most from knowing that they can rely on a broadband network that is consistent throughout the homes and businesses of America.

A long-standing goal of the Commission in broadband is to "stimulate investment and innovation in broadband technology and services."[72] The Commission has done much, successfully, to encourage the build-out of a broadband infrastructure. It should now provide the necessary security for investments in new services and new applications, by making the environment for investment in broadband applications similarly consistent and secure. By instituting a well-reasoned neutrality regime, it may do just that.

ENCOURAGING COMPETITION AMONG APPLICATIONS

In addition to increasing the predictability of investments in broadband, a neutrality regime also promotes policies of innovation through competition that the Commission has repeatedly endorsed. Most recently, in its broadband infrastructure inquiries, the Commission has favored "multiple platform competition," promoting a fair fight between DSL, cable, and other broadband access infrastructures.[73] The same underlying principles, namely, an evolutionary model of technological innovation, favor the promotion of a neutral network today.

In the academic literature, the Commission has endorsed the evolutionary, or competitive model of innovation.[74] It holds that the process of technological innovation proceeds most rapidly through a survival-of-the-fittest competition between new technologies, and it encourages policies to ensure a fair fight among competing innovations.

If this "Darwinian evolution" is the best path of innovation, it follows that the most promising path of development will be difficult to predict in advance. Hence despite the "waste" generated by a competitive process, the results will be superior to planned innovation directed by a single prospect holder, however well-intentioned.[75] That entity will suffer from cognitive biases (such as a predisposition to continue with current ways of doing business) that make it unlikely to come to the right decisions, even if it means well.[76]

There is a direct link between these evolutionary theories of innovation and the market for broadband Internet applications. The Internet has long functioned as a figurative "platform" for a fierce and highly innovative competition between applications. Popular applications like email, the World Wide Web, and chat programs are the survivors of an ongoing battle for the attention and interest of users. Over the last two decades, applications like "gopher" and "archie" have been largely surpassed by newer and better applications. Every year, new and unforeseen uses of the Internet arise, like the mass network gaming applications that have recently taken the Internet by storm.[77]

This evolutionary process was directly facilitated by the early Internet's design. As articulated in 1981 by Professors Jerome H. Saltzer, David P. Reed, and David D. Clark,[78] the Internet's "end-to-end" design assured innovators that the network itself would not interfere with new applications. Instead, by vesting intelligence at the edge, or "end" of the network, the Internet shifted the capacity to discriminate from the network to the user.[79] The architecture thus removed the possibility that network owners, for competitive or strategic reasons, would interfere with new applications.

Today, the Commission is faced with the challenge of promoting broadband, and it has largely adopted an approach that favors fair competition among competing technologies. In the race for the "last-mile," the Commission could have simply chosen to overtly favor the success of DSL, cable, or wireless broadband, based on its best guess. But instead, it has promoted "the development and deployment of *multiple* platforms," and said that the Commission "should avoid policies that have the unintended consequence of embracing too quickly any one technology or service."[80] It embraces intermodal parity, seeking to develop a regulatory framework that is "consistent across multiple platforms."[81]

These policies are nothing but a restatement of the central principles of evolutionary innovation. Through its commitment to intermodal parity, the Commission has endorsed a policy of leveling the playing field to let the best technology win. But the job is incomplete. The same promotion of competition among last-mile infrastructures is now needed for the broadband application market. Restrictions on usage, however well- or ill-intended, tend to favor certain applications over others. They are the functional equivalent of the Commission choosing a winner in broadband. They threaten to replace survival-of-the-fittest with survival-of-the-favored.

By requiring operators to justify deviations from neutrality, a neutrality regime would prevent both unthinking and ill-intentioned distortion of the market for new applications. Again, the Commission has a powerful example before it in what it has done to ensure intermodal competition among broadband infrastructures. It would be advised to take the same pro-competitive course for the application market.

IS SELF-REGULATION SUFFICIENT?

In its filings with the Commission and other materials, the cable industry has suggested that it agrees with the basic premises of a neutral network. It says that "consumers should have access to all lawful Internet content unless they choose otherwise." It wants to be trusted to maintain the network, asserting that it has no particular plans to block access to one or another application. In speeches, cable executives have described neutrality rules as "a solution looking for a problem."[82]

There are no reasons to doubt the good intentions of the cable industry or other broadband providers. A healthy broadband Internet is as good for the cable industry as everyone else, as they rightly point out. And while cable today delivers the fastest and therefore most attractive broadband connections, truly egregious restrictions on Internet usage would indeed eventually lead consumers to switch to cable's technologically inferior competitors, like DSL, or even prompt a retreat to narrowband access methods. So the industry is correct to note that there is *some* outer limit on what it might do to its users without losing business.

But the record over the last several years confirms that the alignment of the public and cable industry's interests is inexact. Contrary to the assertions of the NCTA,[83] individual providers have a recent and continuing history of placing unacceptable contractual and technical limits on the use of their networks, sometimes for short-sighted reasons.

Consider, for example, the case of home networking (networks that interconnect several home computers to a single broadband connection, often using WiFi technology). Today, the restrictions on home networking are a patchwork. At one extreme, some DSL providers explicitly allow home networking.[84] Many operators express no clear opinion. But others have banned home networking, and at least one major cable provider has threatened home networkers with criminal punishment. It defined the use of a home-network as "Theft of Service," and tells its users that sharing the connection within the home "is a violation of federal law" that "can result in both civil and criminal penalties."[85]

Bans like these sacrifice the potential of home-networking in the hope of drumming up marginal extra business. Ultimately such behavior is not a surprise, for basic economic logic suggests that restrictions on usage can be both good for the provider and bad for the country at the same time. Requiring that home networking equipment (like home WiFi) be purchased and installed by the cable operator generates additional revenue. This revenue may be greater than the revenue lost to users who do not subscribe to cable because of the restrictions, hence making it rational for the provider to enforce the ban. However, the policy exacts a range of costs that the provider does not absorb — what economists call an "externalized cost."[86] It hurts the manufacturers of home networking equipment who face a smaller market for their products. It hurts developers of applications that assume the existence of a home network, because of the unpredictability of local restrictions. And it hurts consumers who decide to forgo home networking because of the restriction and the higher prices charged by the operator. These deadweight losses form the core of the economic case against self-regulation in this instance.

Cable providers have also argued that the problem is, in effect, not yet ripe. Despite the troubling and well-documented examples of discrimination against VPNs, home-networks, and online gaming, the cable industry has argued that the amount of discrimination in broadband Internet services is not significant. It suggests that "in the absence of market failure, there is no reason to [act.]"[87] The Commission, it its view, should wait to see if discrimination becomes a more serious problem.

But this argument misses an obvious point. The potential for discrimination has an obvious effect upon innovation today, whether or not there is any actual discrimination now. The question an innovator, or venture capitalist, asks when deciding whether to develop some new Internet application is not just whether discrimination is occurring today, but whether restrictions might be imposed when the innovation is deployed. If the innovation is likely to excite an incentive to discrimination, and such discrimination could occur, then the mere potential imposes a burden on innovation today whether or not there is discrimination now. The possibility of discrimination in the future dampens the incentives to invest today.

WOULD A NEUTRALITY REGIME PRESENT A FIRST AMENDMENT PROBLEM?

Some have suggested that however desirable a neutral network might be, the Commission's power to regulate broadband operators to prevent discrimination among applications is precluded by the First Amendment. This argument relies on an interpretation of the First Amendment unsupported by Supreme Court precedent.

As the Commission is well aware, there has long been a distinction between the First Amendment's treatment of publication or broadcasting on the one hand, and mere carriage on the other.[88] The distinction reflects the expressive qualities of the former as opposed to the latter, and contains a certain practical wisdom. If carrying data were expressive conduct, the traffic laws that affect postal trucks might suddenly be subject to first amendment scrutiny, as would the entire scheme of telephony regulation.

The Supreme Court has never endorsed the position that every aspect of operating a communications network is protected speech, and the consequences of such a view would be untenable. Instead it has been careful to distinguish what, if any, the expressive aspect of operating a network might be. For example, in the television context, the Supreme Court has suggested that the First Amendment protection of cable operators comes from their exercise of editorial discretion in the selection of channels and content. As the Court explained in City of Los Angeles v. Preferred Communications, Inc., beyond original programming, an operator's expression consists of "exercising editorial discretion over which stations or programs to include in its repertoire."[89]

When applied to the broadband network, it is difficult to find a similar exercise of editorial discretion in the transmission of content. Primarily, it is the ends—the user of the Internet or a remote speaker—who decide on the content of transmission, not the broadband operator. The only influence the operator has over the content of what it carries is through the act of restricting usage or blocking content. Hence it is the act of banning virtual private networking, or the attachment of home networking equipment that the broadband operator would need to rely upon to claim First Amendment protection.

As such it is quite unclear whether imposing network restrictions would qualify as protected "speech." As an exercise of "editorial discretion," it lacks what cable operators had in cases like Preferred Communications: a decided judgment to create a particular package of content or programming for known customers. It is true that the act of banning certain types of usage might instead be cast as some form of expressive conduct. Unfortunately, the conduct that the Court has recognized as expressive, like the burning of draft cards in United States v. O'Brien,[90] is that which clearly communicates a message (like opposition to the draft). In contrast, when a cable operator bans VPNs or stops people from hooking up home networks, it is unclear what message, if any, this is meant to communicate. Finally, it is also true that exclusion or bans sometimes relate to an interest in "expressive association," like that claimed in Boy Scouts of America v. Dale,[91] where the Boy Scouts fired a gay scoutmaster. Yet it remains similarly unclear what the cable operator's associational message might be. Cable operators, unlike the Boy Scouts, cannot plausibly claim that they need to exclude certain uses of the network to preserve some deeper aspect of a cable operators' associational identity. The general point is that in the absence of any identifiable message or editorial policy informed by usage restrictions, it is hard to see how imposing network restrictions would be seen as protected speech under the First Amendment.

Whether restricting use of the network amounts to speech doesn't ultimately matter, for the Commission's authority is secure in either case. The bans on discrimination that are at the center of any neutrality regime are a textbook case of a content-neutral regulation of conduct, supported by substantial government interests. Under the familiar authority of cases like O'Brien, and Ward v. Rock Against Racism,[92] neutrality regulation is not a hard case.

Stated otherwise, the Commission's authority follows a fortiori from the Turner litigation.[93] A general ban against discriminating among network uses is content-neutral; if anything, more so than the "must-carry" rule in Turner that required carrying specific television channels.[94] And the interests recognized by the Supreme Court in Turner as substantial government interests are the same: "promoting the widespread dissemination of information from a multiplicity of sources, and ... promoting fair competition in the market for television programming."[95]

The obvious result of forbidding bans on usage or content is to promote "widespread dissemination of information" from the widest number of sources possible. But it is perhaps easier to see a neutrality regime in First Amendment terms as simply a form of competition regulation, the second interest identified above. As the Supreme Court has stated, "Government's interest in eliminating restraints on fair competition is always substantial, even when the individuals or entities subject to particular regulations are engaged in expressive activity protected by the First Amendment."[96]

It is also clear that a neutrality regime would leave open ample "alternative channels" of communication, as the Ward standard requires.[97] A cable operator who banned VPNs to express its belief that people ought not work at home is perfectly free to express such sentiments in other forums. Indeed, the operator could use the Internet itself to promulgate its views, to a broad and likely receptive audience.

We add it is of course possible to imagine a "bad faith" neutrality regime that would in fact run afoul of the First Amendment. For example, a regime that prohibited cable operators from making their own content available on their networks might create serious First Amendment problems. But the regime we propose here does not contain any such restriction.[98] A content-neutral ban on discrimination in the carriage of content, like that proposed in this letter, is extremely unlikely to run afoul of the First Amendment.

In short, some of the First Amendment arguments advanced in the network neutrality debate have relied more on the charisma of the claim than any analysis of Supreme Court precedent. Under mainstream First Amendment analysis as enumerated by the Court, there is little basis for doubting the Commission's authority.

A PROPOSAL FOR NETWORK NEUTRALITY

Today's problem of Broadband usage restrictions is mirrored by the problem the Commission and courts faced in the telephony context in the 1950s. The question then was for what reasons AT&T might restrict "foreign attachments" to its network. In the well-known Hush-A-Phone decision, AT&T sought to ban the use of a simple plastic cup used to facilitate the privacy of telephone conversations as an "unauthorized foreign attachment." The deeper question was the same as that presented today: when do a carrier's restrictions on network usage create public injury?

The D.C. Circuit's solution was a "harm" requirement. It interpreted the 1934 Communications Act to find that the subscriber has a "right reasonably to use his telephone in ways which are privately beneficial without being publicly detrimental."[99] The Commission, in turn ordered the Bells to allow telephone customers to attach devices that "do not injure

... the public in its use of [Bell's] services, or impair the operation of the telephone system."[100]

The same basic requirement remains with us today. The Hush-a-Phone decision led to the Commission's broader Carterfone decision,[101] and finally Part 68. Part 68 is still focused on balancing the user's freedom to use his telephone as he likes against the need to prevent harm to the network itself.[102] The proposal that follows adapts these principles to the particular context of Broadband communications.

Recognizing that discrimination in broadband service is a potential problem is one thing; constructing an approach to dealing with it, is another. The open-access proposal, as we saw earlier, advocated structural separation between Internet service providers and broadband operators. This approach has the advantage of simplicity, but it has the disadvantage of retarding potential efficiencies of integration. This approach also may fail to deter other forms of discrimination.

What follows is a proposed antidiscrimination principle (a rule, only if necessary). The effort is to strike a balance: to forbid broadband operators, absent a showing of harm, from restricting what users do with their Internet connection, while giving the operator general freedom to manage bandwidth consumption and other matters of local concern. The principle achieves this by adopting the basic principle that broadband operators should have full freedom to "police what they own" (the local network) while restrictions based on inter-network indicia should be viewed with suspicion.

This non-discrimination principle works by recognizing a distinction between *local network* restrictions, which are generally allowable, and *inter-network* restrictions, which should be viewed as suspect. The principle represents ultimately an effort to develop *forbidden* and *permissible* grounds for discrimination in broadband usage restrictions.

LET OPERATORS POLICE WHAT THEY OWN

Broadband carriers are members of two networks. They are each members of a local network, which they own and manage individually. They are also members of the inter-network, which they collectively manage with other service providers.

Once we recognize that carriers are engaged in a collective management scheme, the origin of the externalized cost problem described above becomes clear. The effects of local network restrictions will, usually, affect only the network run by a single service provider. Such restrictions moreover, are necessary for good network management. In contrast, by definition, restrictions at the inter-network layer or above will always affect the entire network, and can create externality problems.

THE NEUTRALITY PRINCIPLE

What follows is an example of a network neutrality law:

§1.   *General Right to Unrestricted Network Usage.*   Broadband Users have the right reasonably to use their Internet connection in ways which are not illegal or harmful to the network. Accordingly neither Broadband Operators nor the Federal Communications Commission shall impose restrictions on the use of an Internet connection except as necessary to:

(1) Comply with any legal duty created by federal, state or local statute, or as necessary to comply with any executive order, warrant, legal injunction, subpoena, or other duly authorized governmental directive;

(2) Prevent physical harm to the local Broadband Network caused by any network attachment or network usage;

(3) Prevent Broadband users from interfering with other Broadband or Internet Users' use of their Internet connections, including but not limited to neutral limits on bandwidth usage, limits on mass transmission of unsolicited email, and limits on the distribution of computer viruses, worms, and limits on denial-of-service or other attacks on others;

(4) Prevent violations of the security of the Broadband network, including all efforts to gain unauthorized access to computers on the Broadband network or Internet;

(5) Serve any other purpose specifically authorized by the Federal Communications Commission, based on a weighing of the specific costs and benefitS of the restriction.

§2. As used in this section,

(1) "Broadband Operators" means a service provider that provides high-speed connections to the Internet using whatever technology, including but not limited to cable networks, telephone networks, fiber optic connections, and wireless transmission;

(2) "Broadband Users" means residential and business customers of a Broadband Operator;

(3) "Broadband Network" means the physical network owned and operated by the Broadband Operator;

(4) "Restrictions on the Use of an Internet Connection" means any contractual, technical, or other limits placed with or without notice on the Broadband user's Internet Connection.

This law expresses the inter-network neutrality principle, operationally, as a non-discrimination rule. As the analysis above recognized, the concept of a total ban on network discrimination is counterproductive. Rather, we need to distinguish between forbidden grounds of discrimination, those that distort secondary markets, and permissible grounds, those necessary to network administration and to prevent harm to the network.

Reflecting the dual-network membership just described, it will be inter-network criteria of discrimination that cause concern. In technical terms, this means discrimination based on IP addresses, domain name, cookie information, TCP port, and others as we will describe in greater detail below. Hence, the general principle can be stated as follows: absent evidence of harm to the local network or the interests of other users, broadband carriers should not discriminate in how they treat traffic on their broadband network on the basis of inter-network criteria.

The negative inference (expressed most clearly in exceptions (a)(3) and (4)) is that operators generally may discriminate in their treatment of traffic on the basis of local network criteria. In technical terms, this means imposing restrictions on the basis of what network engineers call "link" or "layer 2" information, like bandwidth, jitter, or other local Quality of Service indicia.

In Practice: Online Gaming

Popular online gaming applications[103] like Everquest, Asheron's Call, or Online Quake tend to be bandwidth intensive, particularly compared with episodic applications like email. As seen above, concerned broadband carriers have therefore been inclined to restrict the usage of such applications. However, with the neutrality principle in mind, we can distinguish between a "better" and a "worse" way for this to happen.

First, in today's environment, a broadband carrier could block traffic from gaming sites. It could do it either by enforcing a contractual provision in a usage agreement, or in the future, using its control of the local network to block traffic from gaming sites based on either application information, or the IP address of the application provider.[104] Some carriers might elect, for a given supplemental fee, to remove the filter for specified users.

Under the neutrality principle here proposed, this approach would be frowned upon. Instead, a carrier concerned about bandwidth consumption would need to invest in policing bandwidth usage, not blocking individual applications. Users interested in a better gaming experience would then need to buy more bandwidth—not permission to use a given application.

The neutrality of such control would prevent the distortion in the market for Internet applications. If carriers choose to block online games in particular, this gives a market advantage to competing applications that have not been blocked. But if broadband carriers only police bandwidth, the result is an even-playing field. It may be that the expense of more bandwidth leads people to choose different ways to spend their money. But if so, that represents a market choice, not a choice dictated by the filtering policy of the broadband carrier.

Borrowing from Well-Established Categories

One advantage of the proposal is that it relies on well-established legal and technological criteria to achieve its consumer-welfare goals. Respectively, it borrows from principles of harm requirements and non-discrimination familiar to lawyers, along with a local/inter-network distinction that is fundamental to Datacom networks.

The Harm Requirement

In the telephony context, the "foreign attachment" problem discussed above was addressed by a "harm" rule; that is, a rule barring the Bells from preventing attachment of equipment unless harm to the network could be shown. Its origins are found in the Hush-a-Phone case, where the FCC ordered Bell to allow telephone customers to attach devices that "[do] not injure . . . the public in its use of [Bell's] services, or impair the operation of the telephone system."[105]

In the broadband context, it is discrimination against certain content and applications that is the major problem. But the practice of requiring public harm to justify restrictions can be usefully employed.

Local/Inter-Networking

Finally, on the technological side, the distinction between inter-networking and local networking is very well established in the Datacom industry. While the distinction is best reflected, and usually discussed, in the context of the OSI network reference model (as the difference between layer 2 and layer 3 networks),[106] it is in fact independent of OSI. As a practical matter, different physical equipment and different protocols run the different networks. In a given network, "switches" run local networks, while "routers" collectively manage the layer 3 network. Services can be offered at both levels—for example, VPNs and telephony can be offered either as a layer 2 service or as a layer 3 service.

In addition, other schema used to describe network layers embody the same, fundamental, local / inter-network distinction. For example, the TCP/IP network model maintains a distinction between the "link" layer and the "network" layer. This is exactly the same distinction as the layer 2/layer 3 distinction in the OSI model, and the local/inter-network distinction more generally. Again, this is no surprise, because virtual description simply reflects the physical network design. The existence and pervasiveness of the local / inter-network distinction makes it a natural dividing line for reasonable restrictions on use.

Objections to the Proposed Network Neutrality Regime

Before concluding, it is useful to consider some objections and challenges to the proposed network neutrality regime. We consider (1) whether it overly interferes with broadband carriers' ability to earn a return on their infrastructure investment, (2) whether local restrictions can be used to achieve the same problems as inter-network control, and (3) whether the principle interferes with administration of Internet addressing.

Return on Investment

First, does the neutrality principle restriction overly impinge on the ability of broadband carriers to earn a return from their infrastructure investments? While a full analysis of broadband economics is beyond the scope of this proposal, we can nonetheless suggest that the neutrality principle is unlikely to interfere with the special advantages that a carrier gains from building its own infrastructure.

The simple answer is that investing in a local network infrastructure creates its own rewards, as it creates particular advantages in the offering of network services. We can see this clearly by considering the particular example of Virtual Private Networks under the neutrality principle. A broadband operator who owns the local infrastructure has a natural advantage in offering local VPN services. The advantage comes from the fact that they can offer service level guarantees that cannot be provided on a shared network. Nothing in the neutrality principle would prevent a broadband operator from being in the unique position to sell such services.

But the principle would prevent operators from blocking use of Internet VPNs – that is, VPNs that used the Internet to reaches sites that no single local network can encompass. For example, a home user on the East Coast will almost certainly need to use an Internet VPN to connect to his business on the West Coast. In offering this service, a broadband operator is in the exact position as any other Internet VPN provider. Restricting use of Internet VPNs should therefore not be allowed, to preserve undistorted competition for this application.

Can Local Control Disrupt Application Markets?

Some might observe that the local and inter-network are interdependent in certain ways. Won't broadband operators simply use their control over the local network to achieve the same distortion of application markets?

No rule can perfectly stamp out all undesirable behavior. The point of the network neutrality principle is to make interference with the application markets much harder. Without the ability to discriminate on the basis of the origin of a packet or the application being used, the broadband carrier is left with the far blunter tools of local restrictions.

It might be argued that the address resolution protocol (ARP)[107] could be used to achieve the same goals as IP-address filtering, since the job of ARP on a typical network is to convert IP addresses into Ethernet MAC addresses. But, in fact, a broadband carrier manipulating ARP could only succeed in making his own users unreachable. The ARP-cache only holds the information to match up local physical addresses with local IP addresses. ARP has no idea how to stop a user from reaching a specific IP address, other than making that user unreachable. The example shows, in fact, the power of limiting a broadband carrier to local control.

The Need to Administer IP

Finally, some might point out that broadband carriers need some control over the Internet Protocol side of their network. They must, for example, be able to allocate static and dynamic IP addresses, maintain routing tables, and so on. Does the network neutrality principle interfere with this?

The point of the neutrality principle is not to interfere with the administration of the Internet Protocol side of a broadband carrier's network. It is, rather, to prevent discrimination in that administration. Since it is phrased as a non-discrimination principle, a negative inference is that most aspects of IP administration can be conducted without concern. For example, the allocation and administration of IP addressing should not pose any discrimination problems, so long as the administration of such addresses is in an even-handed manner.[108]

CONCLUSION

The goal of this paper was to make an initial case for a broadband discrimination regime as an alternative to the structural remedy of open access to achieve the goal of network neutrality. At this point, the newness of the concept means much unavoidable vagueness as to its operation. It is easier to point out examples of application discrimination that seem unjustified than to elucidate a standard that neatly separates the legitimate from the suspect. For example, there remains much work to better define what the concepts of network neutrality and discrimination would fully entail as a regulatory matter, or even as a regulatory threat. Should neutrality be defined by IETF standards? The intuitions of network theorists? Government definition? Any workable regime designed to achieve network neutrality will need a more precise conception of this and other matters. Nonetheless, the hope is that the general framework described here might serve to begin the effort to discourage the most blatant or thoughtless disfavoring of certain application types through network design.

Structurally, this network neutrality regime creates a non-discrimination rule with several exceptions. The exceptions are important and reflect the need to allow certain grounds of discrimination: those necessary to network administration and to prevent harm to the network or other users. .

The structure of the exceptions reflects the fact that Broadband Carriers are members of two logically distinct networks. Each Broadband Carrier owns a local network, which it manages individually. But each is also a member of the Internet, which all service providers manage collectively.

It is hardly news to recognize that the Commission's "horizontal" model of telecommunications regulation is an uneven match with the "vertical" structure of today's communications networks.[109] But the Commission is fully aware of this fact, and is in the midst of a salutary and important transition between the horizontal and vertical models. Its ongoing effort to achieve regulatory parity in broadband is an important step toward a vertical orientation.

Yet the job remains incomplete. It is now focused exclusively on infrastructure. Neutrality is also the baseline for promoting fair competition in the application market. It is the starting point for the Commission to begin creating a clear environment that facilitates both investment in broadband applications and competition among them. The full realization of the Commission's broadband policy objectives demands no less.

ENDNOTES

[1] Forthcoming as *Broadband Policy A User's Guide* in J. TELECOM. & HIGH TECH. My thanks to participants at the 2004 Silicon Flatirons conference, and the March 26, 2004 Policy Forum "The Future Of The Internet In The Broadband Age" organized by the Consumer Federation of America and the Stanford Center for Internet and Society, specifically for comments from Phil Weiser and Mark Cooper, discussions with Jim Septa, Christopher Yoo and Mark Lemley, and to Lee Kovarksy for research assistance.

[2] See Tim Wu, *Network Neutrality, Broadband Discrimination,* 2 J. TELECOM. & HIGH TECH 141 (2003) (expanding on this point).

[3] *See* Hush-A-Phone Corp. v. United States, 238 F.2d 266, 269 (D.C. Cir. 1956) (Holding that the FCC cannot block the attachment of reasonable network attachments, namely the "Hush-A-Phone" device that attached to a handset and insulated telephone conversations against background noise.)

[4] See Stephen Wildstrom, *At Last, You Can Ditch The Phone Company VOIP Lets You Make Clear, Fast Calls Over The Net, Using A Plain Phone*, BUSINESS WEEK, May 17, 2004.

[5] See, e.g., Lawrence Lessig, *The Internet under Siege*, FINANCIAL POST, November 1, 2001.

[6] Mark Cooper, Remarks at Silicon Flatirons, Feb 8, 2004.

[7] See Remarks of Michael J. Copps, "The Beginning Of The End Of The Internet? Discrimination, Closed Networks, And The Future of Cyberspace" New America Foundation, Washington, DC, October 9, 2003

[8] In the telecommunications industry, the term "end-to-end" is used for a variety of purposes, many of which are quite meaningless, or roughly synonymous with "good." See, e.g., Motorola, End-to-End, http://broadband.motorola.com/nlc/solutions/endtoend.asp. Christopher Yoo, meanwhile, writes in this volume that the end-to-end principle as originally described by the network engineering literature has been misunderstood by openists. See Yoo at 16 to 21.

[9] The idea of a "telecosm" was described most vividly in George Gilder, TELECOSM (2000).

[10] Peter Huber et al., FEDERAL BROADBAND LAW §1.2.4 (1995).

[11] Cf. Garrett Hardin, *The Tragedy of the Commons*, 162 SCIENCE 1243 (1968).

[12] Frank Easterbrook, *The Law of the Horse*, 1996 U. CHI. LEGAL F. 207, 212-213 (1996).

[13] *See, e.g.,* Adam D. Thierer, *Net Neutrality" Digital Discrimination or Regulatory Gamesmanship in Cyberspace?* CATO POLICY ANALYSIS Jan. 12, 2004.

[14] See, e.g., Ira Brodsky, *Telecom Carriers Need to Smarter Up their Pipes*, NETWORK WORLD, Jan. 15, 2001.

[15] Cisco, WHITEPAPER, CISCO CONTENT DELIVERY NETWORK SOLUTION FOR THE ENTERPRISE, (Apr. 2002), available at http://www.cisco.com/warp/public/cc/so/neso/ienesv/cxne/cdnen_wp.htm.

[16] See, e.g., Bruce Owen and Gregory Rosston, *Local Broadband Access: Primum Non Nocere or Primum Processi? A Property Rights Approach*, STANFORD LAW AND

ECONOMICS OLIN WORKING PAPER No. 263, 21-23 (2003). Available at http://ssrn.com/abstract=431620.

[17] Id. at 21.

[18] Peter Huber, LAW AND DISORDER IN CYBERSPACE 62 (1997).

[19] See Leonard Chazen & Leonard Ross, Federal Regulation of Cable Television, the Visible Hand, 83 HARV. L. REV. 1820, 1820 (1970); Stanley M. Besen & Robert W. Crandall, *The Deregulation of Cable Television*, 4 LAW & CONTEMP. PROBS. 77, 81-91 (1981) ("Cable entered the 1970s as a small business relegated primarily to rural areas and small communities and held hostage by television broadcasters to the Commission's hope for the development of UHF.")

[20] See New York Times, Comcast Disney ABC Story (discussing how Comcast consider acquiring ABC as part of its bid to purchase Disney).

[21] Besen and Crandall, *The Deregulation, supra* note 19 (documenting FCC activity constraining the growth of cable).

[22] This was one of the arguments of the 1958 Cox Report. See Kenneth Cox, The Problem of Television Service for Smaller Communities. Staff Report to the Senate Committee on Interstate and Foreign Commerce, 26 December 1958.

[23] Primarily for his account of the capitalism as a system of growth through innovation as opposed to price competition, see CAPITALISM, SOCIALISM, AND DEMOCRACY (1957) Ch. VII, and not for Schumpeter's more controversial prediction of the inevitable collapse of the capitalist system. See id. at 61 ("Can capitalism survive? No. I do not think it can.").

[24] Schumpeter, Capitalism Socialism and Democracy, *supra* note 25, at 83.

[25] Joseph Schumpeter, A THEORY OF ECONOMIC DEVELOPMENT (1912) [hereinafter "Economic Development"], at 84.

[26] *Id.*

[27] Schumpeter, Capitalism, Socialism & Democracy, *supra* note 25, at 106.

[28] *Id.*

[29] *Id.*

[30] Cf. Edmund W. Kitch, The Nature and Function of the Patent System, 20 J.L. & ECON. 265 (1977).

[31] Schumpeter, Capitalism, Socialism & Democracy, *supra* note 25, at 101.

[32] Schumpeter, Economic Development, *supra* note 27.

[33] Jan Fagerberg, A LAYMAN'S GUIDE TO EVOLUTIONARY ECONOMICS 15 (2002).

[34] Economic Development at 93.

[35] See, e.g., Richard Nelson & Sidney Winter, AN EVOLUTIONARY THEORY OF ECONOMIC CHANGE 14 (1982) ("we reject the notion of maximizing behavior as an explanation of why decision rules are what they are.").

[36] See generally, W. Brian Arthur, INCREASING RETURNS AND PATH DEPENDENCY IN THE ECONOMY (1994).

[37] A far better overview of this aspect of the debate is provided by Joseph Farrell & Phillip Weiser, *Modularity, Vertical Integration, and Open Access Policies: Towards a Convergence of Antitrust and Regulation in the Internet Age*, 17 HARVARD J. OF L & TECH. 85 (2003).

[38] See Mark A. Lemley & Lawrence Lessig, *The End of End-to-End: Preserving the Architecture of the Internet in the Broadband Era*, 48 UCLA L. REV. 925 (2001).

[39] See Farell & Weiser, *supra* note 42, at 100-105.

[40] See James B. Septa, *A Vision of Openness by Government Fiat*, 96 NW. L. REV. 1553, 1565-1566 (2001); James B. Septa, *Handicapping the Race for the Last Mile? A Critique of Open Access Rules for Broadband Platforms,* 17 YALE J. ON REG. 39 (2000).

[41] See Farell & Weiser, *supra* note 42, at 101.

[42] Cf. Douglas Lichtman, *Property Rights in Emerging Platform Technologies*, 29 JOURNAL OF LEGAL STUDIES 615 (2000) (describing certain situations in which a platform owner might choose an open platform).

[43] See Richard A. Posner, ANTITRUST LAW 177–78 (2d ed. 2001).

[44] Weiser & Farell, *supra,* n. 42, at 105-119.

[45] *Id.* at 114-117.

[46] Schumpeter, Economic Development, *supra* note 27, at 86.

[47] Schumpeter Capitalism, Socialism, and Democracy, *supra* note 25, at 84.

[48] See Cecily Barnes, BLOCKBUSTER TESTS VIDEO STREAMING, CNET NEWS, http://news.com.com/2100-1023-250126.html

[49] Wu, Network Neutrality, *supra* note 2, (suggesting regulatory threat may force operators to consider the value of openness).

[50] See remarks of Chairman Powell, Silicon Flatirons.

[51] See below.. This is the most recent version of regulations first proposed in Tim Wu & Larry Lessig, Ex Parte Letter CS 52-02 (filed Aug 22, 2003) available at http://faculty.virginia.edu/timwu/wu_lessig_fcc.pdf.

[52] *AT&T Corporation V. City Of Portland*, 216 F.3d 871, 874 (9th Cir. 2000).

[53] See, e.g., *Kassel v. Consolidated Freightways Corporation,* 450 U.S. 662 (1981) (discussing the rights created by the dormant commerce clause).

[54] *See Use of the Carterfone Device in Message Toll Tel. Serv.*, 13 F.C.C.2d 420 (1968) (Decision).

[55] "Preserving Internet Freedom: Guiding Principles For The Industry" Remarks of Michael K. Powell, at the Silicon Flatirons Symposium, February 8, 2004.

[56] *Id.*

[57] See Owen & Rosston, *supra* note 18.

[58] See National Cable and Telecommunications Association, *Ex Parte Letter to FCC*, February 21, 2003.

[59] Howard Schelanski, Remarks at Silicon Flatirons, Feb 8 2004.

[60] Christoper Yoo, *Would Broadband Network Neutrality Help or Hurt Competition?: Understanding the Complex Economics of End-to-End,* SILICON FLATIRONS CONFERENCE, 2004, forthcoming in J. TELECOM. & HIGH TECH.

[61] *Id.* at 28.

[62] Adam Thierer makes the same point. See ARE 'DUMB PIPE' MANDATES SMART PUBLIC POLICY? VERTICAL INTEGRATION, 'NET NEUTRALITY,' AND THE NETWORK LAYERS MODEL (draft on file with author).

[63] Cf. Randal Picker, ENTRY, ACCESS AND FACILITIES-BASED COMPETITION (working paper 2004).

[64] *See, e.g.*, High Tech Broadband Coalition Ex Parte Letter, June 17, 2002; Coalition of Broadband Users and Innovators Ex Parte Letter, Nov. 18, 2002.

[65] *See, e.g.*, National Cable & Telecommunications Association Ex Parte Letter, Feb. 21, 2003.

[66] Of course, it is inevitable that by its design the internet or any communications network will invariably create some favoritism for certain uses. Pure neutrality is more of an aspiration than a fully achievable design principle. The point of the argument is the minimization of bias, not the total elimination of all conceivable forms. Cf. Lamb's Chapel v. Center Moriches Union Free Sch. Dist., 113 S. Ct. 2141, 2149-50 (1993) (Scalia, J., concurring) (on the meaning of neutrality in the context of church and state).

[67] FCC Statement of Broadband Policy, available at http://www.fcc.gov/broadband/

[68] *See* Tam Harbert, *Broadband Penetration in U.S. Continues*, ELECTRONIC BUSINESS, July 1, 2003, at 26 (citing American Electronics Association study placing number of broadband Internet users in U.S at 16.2 million as of June 2002).

[69] *See* Tim Wu, *Network Neutrality, Broadband Discrimination*, 2 COLO. J. TELECOMM. & HIGH TECH. L. 11—12, 20—21 (forthcoming 2003).

[70] *See, e.g.*, Cox Communications Ex Parte Letter, April 7, 2003; Comcast Corporation Ex Parte Notice, May 15, 2003.

[71] *See generally*, Clay Christiansen, The Innovators Dilemma (1997) (suggesting that large firms, focused on consumers' present needs, will be unlikely to develop the products of the future).

[72] FCC Statement of Broadband Policy, available at http://www.fcc.gov/broadband/

[73] *Appropriate Framework for Broadband Access to the Internet over Wireline Facilities, Universal Service Obligations of Broadband Providers*, CC Docket No. 02-33, Notice of Proposed Rulemaking (*"Wireline Broadband NPRM"*) ¶ 4 (rel. Feb. 15, 2002).

[74] *See, e.g.*, John Ziman, *Evolutionary Models for Technological Change*, in TECHNOLOGICAL INNOVATION AS AN EVOLUTIONARY PROCESS 3 (John Ziman ed., 2000); Richard Nelson, UNDERSTANDING TECHNICAL CHANGE AS AN EVOLUTIONARY PROCESS (1987).

[75] These ideas are also discussed in the legal literature. *See, e.g.,* Richard Posner, THE ECONOMIC STRUCTURE OF INTELLECTUAL PROPERTY LAW 364 (forthcoming, on file with author). *See also* Edmund W. Kitch, *The Nature and Function of the Patent System*, 20 J.L. & ECON. 265 (1977).

[76] *See* Clay Christiansen, The Innovators Dilemma (1997) (explaining that firms that pay too much attention to current customer needs often fail to reach the highest levels of innovation).

[77] *See, e.g., Console Wars: Video Games Grow Up*, The Economist, June 22, 2002.

[78] *See* Jerome H. Saltzer et al., *End to End Arguments in System Design*, in INNOVATIONS IN INTERNETWORKING 195 (Craig Partridge ed., 1988) (available at http://web.mit.edu/saltzer/www/publications/endtoend/endtoend.pdf).

[79] These arguments are described in greater depth in Written Ex Parte of Professor Mark A. Lemley and Professor Lawrence Lessig, In re Application for Consent to the Transfer of Control of Licenses MediaOne Group, Inc. to AT&T Corp. (FCC Dec. 15, 1999) (No. 99-251).

[80] *Wireline Broadband NPRM, supra* note 9, ¶ 4.

[81] *Inquiry Concerning High-Speed Access to the Internet over Cable and Other Facilities, Internet Over Cable Declaratory Ruling, Appropriate Regulatory Treatment for Broadband Access to the Internet over Cable Facilities*, CS Docket No. 02-52, Declaratory Notice and Notice of Proposed Rulemaking, ¶ 6 (rel. Mar. 15, 2002).

[82] Robert Sachs, Remarks to NARUC/NECA Summit on Broadband Deployment II (Apr. 28, 2003) (available at http://www.ncta.com/pdf_files/RJS_NARUC_04-28-03.pdf).

[83] *See, e.g.*, National Cable & Telecommunications Association Ex Parte Letter, Dec. 10, 2002. One particular oddity in this respect is the NCTA's claim that the development of the Data Over Cable Service Interface Specifications (DOCSIS) standard in some way demonstrates that the cable networks are "open." While it is true that DOCSIS is itself a neutral standard, the existence of DOCSIS itself does nothing to prevent cable operators from placing other forms of technical limitations on cable service, or enforcing contractual restrictions on usage of the network.

[84] *See* Verizon Service Agreement ¶ 3.6(B), http://www.verizon.net/policies/internetaa.asp.

[85] This language was in the December, 2002, AT&T Broadband Acceptable Internet Use Agreement, then available at

http://help.broadband.att.com/faq.jsp?content_id=1107&category_id=34. It has since been replaced by the present Comcast Acceptable Use policy and subscriber agreements, available at http://www.comcast.net/terms. As for home networking, the current subscriber agreement policy says that users may not use their cable service as "as an end-point on a non-Comcast local area network." See http://www.comcast.net/terms/subscriber.jsp. Whether this is meant to allow home networking or not is unclear.

[86] *See* 2 THE NEW PALGRAVE: A DICTIONARY OF ECONOMICS 263, 263-65 (John Eatwell et al. eds., 1987).

[87] *See, e.g.*, National Cable & Telecommunications Association Ex Parte Letter, Dec. 10, 2003.

[88] *See, e.g.*, Angela J. Campbell, *Publish or Carriage: Approaches to Analyzing the First Amendment Rights of Telephone Companies*, 70 N.C. L. REV. 1071, 1097 (1992); Geoffrey Stone et al., CONSTITUTIONAL LAW 1004 (2001).

[89] 476 U.S. 488, 494 (1986). *See also FCC v. Midwest Video Corp.*, 440 U.S. 689, 707 (1979).

[90] 391 U.S. 367 (1968).

[91] 530 U.S. 640 (2000)

[92] 491 U.S. 781 (1989); *see also* United States Civil Serv. Comm'n v. National Ass'n of Letter Carriers, 413 U.S. 548 (1973) (upholding content neutral restrictions on the speech of federal employees).

[93] *See Turner Broadcasting System, Inc. v. FCC (Turner I)*, 512 U.S. 622 (1994); *Turner Broadcasting System, Inc. v. F.C.C. (Turner II)*, 520 U.S. 180 (1997).

[94] "[L]aws that confer benefits or impose burdens on speech without reference to the ideas or views expressed are in most instances content neutral." *Turner I*, 512 U.S. at 643.

[95] *Turner I*, 512 U.S. at 662; see also *Associated Press v. United States*, 326 U.S. 1, 20 (1945) (First Amendment "rests on the assumption that the widest possible dissemination

of information from diverse and antagonistic sources is essential to the welfare of the public, that a free press is a condition of a free society.").

[96] *Id.* at 664. This philosophy did not originate with the *Turner* litigation – its origins are much deeper. As Justice Black stated in *Associated Press v. United States*, 326 U.S. 1, 20 (1945):

> It would be strange indeed however if the grave concern for freedom of the press which prompted adoption of the First Amendment should be read as a command that the government was without power to protect that freedom. The First Amendment...provides powerful reasons to the contrary. That Amendment rests on the assumption that the widest possible dissemination of information from diverse and antagonistic sources is essential to the welfare of the public, that a free press is a condition of a free society. Surely a command that the government itself shall not impede the free flow of ideas does not afford non-governmental combinations a refuge if they impose restraints upon that constitutionally guaranteed freedom.

[97] 491 U.S. at 791 (content neutral restrictions must "leave open ample alternative channels for communication of the information.").

[98] *See, e.g.*, Amazon.com Ex Parte Letter, Appendix B, Dec. 10, 2002.

[99] Hush-A-Phone v. United States, 238 F.2d 266, 268 (D.C. Cir. 1956).

[100] Hush-A-Phone Corp. v. AT&T, 22 FCC 112, 114 (1957).

[101] 13 F.C.C.2d 420 (1968)

[102] See 47 CFR §68 *et seq.*

[103] Also commonly referred to as "Massively Multiple Online Games," or MMOGs.

[104] For an explanation of how a broadband carrier would do so, *see, e.g., The Cisco Content Delivery Network Solution for the Enterprise*, Cisco White Paper (Apr. 2002), *available at* http://www.cisco.com/warp/public/cc/so/neso/ienesv/cxne/cdnen_wp.htm; *See also* Cosine Communications., *Digital Subscriber Lines and Managed Network-based Services: A Perfect—and Profitable—Marriage*, White Paper, *available at* http://cnscenter.future.co.kr/ resource/rsc-center/vendor-wp/cosine/dslwp.pdf.

[105] Hush-A-Phone Corp. v. AT&T, 22 FCC 112, 114 (1957). This led in turn to the broader *Carterfone* decision, 13 F.C.C.2d 420 (1968), and finally Part 68, which adopted a protective circuitry approach to protecting the telephone network, *see* 47 CFR §68 *et seq.*

[106] *Cf.* Andrew Tanenbaum, Computer Networks 10-18 (4th ed. 2002).

[107] Described in IETF RFC 826, *available at* http://www.ietf.org/rfc/rfc1027.txt.

[108] In today's environment, the scarcity of IPv4 addresses does appear to justify a form of discrimination: charging more for static addresses, than dynamic addresses. This forms a good example of "permissible" discrimination.

[109] *See, e.g.*, Kevin Werbach, *A Layered Model for Telecommunications Policy*, 1 Colo. J. Telecomm. & High Tech. L. ___ (2002); Lawrence Solum & Minn Chung, *The Layers Principle: Internet Architecture and the Law*, Loyola-LA Public Law Research Paper No. 15 (2003) (available at http://ssrn.com/abstract=416263).

VIII. ACCESS DENIED

THE FCC'S FAILURE TO IMPLEMENT OPEN ACCESS TO CABLE AS REQUIRED BY THE COMMUNICATIONS ACT

INTRODUCTION

As demand for high-speed, or broadband, internet connections grows at an ever-increasing rate, so too has competition grown between cable companies and traditional telephone companies for the opportunity to serve that demand. With cable companies seeking to strengthen their present position as the leading providers of residential high-speed internet access, [1] the issue of which rules govern the marketplace behavior of those cable companies becomes increasingly important. [2] The answer to the question of what rules apply to the provision of internet access and other information services over cable facilities has tremendous implications not only for information service providers ("ISPs"), cable companies and telephone companies, but also for consumers of all communications services.

The issue has been prominently debated under the label of "open access" [3] to cable facilities that are used for internet access. The open access debate has had its most recent practical applications in the merger of AT&T and TCI, the pending merger of AT&T and MediaOne and the just announced merger of AOL and Time Warner. [4] These merger proceedings before the Federal Communications Commission (the Commission), and those before local cable franchise boards around the country, will continue to focus well-deserved attention on the question of whether cable companies that provide internet access using their cable facilities must make the underlying transmission capacity available on a nondiscriminatory basis to ISPs that are not affiliated with the cable company. Under the governing federal law, there are two related issues: the first is whether the Communications Act of 1934 [5] ("the Communications Act" or "the Act") defines the transmission of internet access and other information services to the public over cable facilities as a common carrier service that is regulated under Title II of the Act; the second is whether those services can be transmitted to consumers as a cable service protected from common carrier regulation under Title VI of the Act.

Although the issue appears on its face to be (and is in fact) one of straight statutory construction, the debate over open access has led the industry and the Commission away from the statute and into a policy squabble that bears no relation to the decisions made by Congress when it amended the Communications Act in 1996.[6]

This article attempts to return the focus to the words of the statute, as amended, which is the sole authority for the regulatory actions of the Commission and the ultimate arbiter of what cable companies can and cannot do in the internet access marketplace. Because this issue, like other major issues arising out of the 1996 amendments, will most likely be heard by a panel of federal judges whose first concern will be the actual language of the statute, the authors suggest that interested observers and participants would be well served now to return their focus to the Communications Act. A review of the statute as amended indicates that the Commission is on the wrong course, and that it must return to a path within the authority of the Communications Act before its present "parallel universe" policy[7] becomes so embedded in the internet access marketplace that it causes irreparable harm to competition, consumers, thousands of independent ISPs and the structure of the global internet itself.

That the Commission's approach will harm consumers stems from the fact that the underlying premise of cable regulation is that the facility owner in general may control the content and who may offer services that are transmitted over its cable facilities.[8] Such control is the antithesis of the present day internet.[9] In contrast, the underlying premise of common carrier regulation is that the facility owner must make those facilities available to all who wish to use them, and in general may not control the content or services offered by others over those facilities.[10] What the authors advocate is that the Communications Act as amended by Congress in 1996 requires the Commission to apply to cable facilities used to transmit internet access and other information services to the public the same open access rules that require all telecommunications facility owners to share the underlying transmission "conduit" with unaffiliated ISPs and others who wish to offer their content and services to consumers over those facilities.

Application of existing rules requiring open access to the conduit to cable facility "conduit" used to transmit internet services is not new "regulation" of the internet. Rather, it is simply a continuation of the successful government policy that resulted in the competitive market for internet services that exists today.[11]

THE COMMISSION BELIEVES IT CAN TAKE A DISCRETIONARY APPROACH

The current debate over "open access" to cable facilities used for the provision of internet access and other information services flows largely from a failure by the Commission to carry out its statutory duty under the 1996 Act.[12] A fundamental assumption of the current Commission appears to be that persons engaged in the transport of information services to the public at large are only common carriers if, and when, the Commission affirmatively determines their status.[13] Thus, for example, the Commission appears to believe that it can simply refuse to determine the regulatory status of internet access and other information services provided over cable facilities, thereby protecting cable operators from basic open access requirements that would otherwise apply to the transport of information services.[14] Under this discretionary approach, the Commission believes that it can promote its policy goal of rapid broadband access by not regulating the underlying transmission service used to provide information services over cable facilities until there is a "market failure" that requires some affirmative action.[15]

THE COURTS AND CONGRESS HAVE BOTH DETERMINED THAT ACTIONS, NOT A COMMISSION DETERMINATION, DECIDE WHO IS REGULATED

The Commission's discretionary approach is contrary to the plain language of the Communications Act. As the D.C. Circuit Court of Appeals noted in *National Association of Regulatory Utility Commissioners v. FCC*, "we reject an unfettered discretion in the Commission to confer or not confer common carrier status on a given entity, depending upon the regulatory goals it seeks to achieve."[16] Further, the court stated that a "particular system is a common carrier by virtue of its functions, rather than because it is declared to be so."[17]

None of the amendments made by Congress in the more than 20 years since the *NARUC* court made its ruling has changed or undermined the validity of that ruling. In fact, since 1993, Congress has twice considered and rejected the discretionary approach that the Commission has adopted in its quest to be viewed as a non-regulatory body whose primary task is to promote broadband deployment. In both cases Congress opted instead to follow the *NARUC* I approach, classifying an entity for purposes of the Communications Act based on the services it provides, rather than the affirmative judgments of the Commission.

In the 1993 amendments to the Communications Act that added section 332(c) regarding "commercial mobile services," Congress required that all commercial mobile service providers including those formerly determined by the Commission and the courts to be non-common carriers, "shall" be treated as common carriers to the extent of such service.[18] Further, Congress gave the Commission explicit authority to deal with market power issues, by providing statutory authority to forbear from applying to wireless common carriers many otherwise applicable provisions of Title II of the Communications Act.[19]

Congress repeated and expanded upon its 1993 approach in the 1996 Act amendments. A "telecommunications carrier *shall* be treated as a common carrier under this Act only to the extent that it is engaged in providing telecommunications services."[20] So discretion is left to the Commission to determine whether or not telecommunications carriers are or are not common carriers. It is the act of offering a service to the public for a fee, in this case offering "telecommunication"[21] that determines a provider's regulatory status under the statutory definition of "telecommunications service."[22] The statute does not delegate to the Commission the authority to determine whether the common carrier requirements of the Act apply based on a determination of market power, market failure, or any other criteria, the Commission may decide.[23] Instead, Congress once again chose to provide discretion to the Commission to forbear from applying requirements of the Act otherwise applicable to persons who by their actions are telecommunications carriers under the criteria set forth in the statute.[24] In the absence of the Commission exercising that forbearance authority in accordance with the Act (and it has not), a provider that meets the statutory definition of a telecommunications carrier is subject to common carrier regulation under Title II.[25]

THE 1996 ACT WAS INTENDED TO CREATE A LEVEL PLAYING FIELD, WHERE THE SAME RULES APPLY TO THE SAME SERVICES, REGARDLESS OF THE FACILITIES USED

Unfortunately for consumers and competitors, the Commission's current approach undermines the very regulatory parity and technological neutrality that Congress sought to adopt in the 1996 Act."[26] Worse, it will likely result in a decrease in the number of competitive choices for consumers instead of the increase Congress intended. The 1996 Act eliminated state and local barriers to entry in the business of providing telecommunications service.[27] It also lifted the ban on the provision of cable service by companies that also provide local telecommunications service in the same geographic area.[28] By removing these barriers to competition, Congress intended for the two types of providers to enter each other's lines of business and compete directly.[29] As a result numerous changes had to be made to "level the playing field"[30] between the disparate regulatory regimes applicable to the different industry segments.

At issue in the present "open access" debate is whether Congress intended to apply different rules to the cable and telecommunications facilities that were now expected to compete directly with each other to transmit information services to consumers. The Commission itself recently stated that "there are two types of communications service networks, . . . broadcast, and . . .switched . . . The first type of network best describes cable service; the second type most accurately depicts telecommunications and information services."[31] Given Congressional intent that the two main wires into the home compete on a "level playing field" with each other, and the Commission's apparent understanding that information services are provided over telecommunications networks, it seems incongruous that the Commission refuses to apply the same open access requirements that apply to all other telecommunications facilities to cable facilities when those cable facilities are used to transport internet access and other information services to the public.[32]

The Commission and some FCC staff have suggested that perhaps the Commission could develop a new regulatory regime for internet access provided over cable facilities as an "advanced telecommunications capability" under the aegis of section 706 of the 1996 Act.[33] Section 706 defines "advanced telecommunications capability" as a "high-speed, switched, broadband telecommunications capability that enables users to originate and receive high-quality voice, data, graphics, and video telecommunications using any technology."[34]

This definition would certainly appear to include internet access and other information services delivered over a cable facility. However, this proposed solution once again ignores the statutory reality of what Congress did in the 1996 Act. As the Commission properly observed in the Advanced Services Order, section 706 does not confer any independent regulatory authority on the Commission. Instead, "the better interpretation of section 706 is that it directs [the Commission] to use, among other authority, our forbearance authority under section 10(a) [of the Communications Act] to encourage the deployment of advanced services."[35] Section 10 of the Act permits the Commission to forbear from applying any provision of the Communications Act to a telecommunications carrier or telecommunications service (but not a cable service), if application of such provision is not necessary to protect consumers, ensure rates are just and reasonable, or protect the public interest."[36] Further, Congress provided in section 3(b) of the 1996 Act that the terms used in 1996 Act have the same meaning as those terms have in section 3 of the Communications Act (as amended by the 1996 Act), so there is no question that the term "telecommunications" has the same meaning in both section 706 and the Communications Act.[37] Thus it is clear that Congress believed that "advanced" services would be offered to the consumer over telecommunications facilities, which in general are subject to the open access obligations of Title II.

INSTEAD OF PROMOTING COMPETITION, THE COMMISSION'S PRESENT POLICY MAY ALLOW AN OLIGOPOLY TO USE CONTROL OF LAST MILE FACILITIES TO DOMINATE THE INTERNET

Carried to its logical conclusion, the Commission's present policies may result in the establishment of a communications oligarchy dominated by a few national integrated service providers. Each of these providers will seek to use its control of local exchange facilities-either the existing local exchange networks or cable facilities-to offer consumers an exclusive package of internet access, other information services, wireless services, video services and voice services.[38] In each case, the local connection will be used to control the customer's choice of providers for other services.[39] Internal cross-subsidization from a bundled package of services will make it difficult for small or single service providers to compete.[40] As a result, competition will be diminished, and, in a bizarre reversal of fortunes, residential subscribers will be used by the few large, integrated service providers to subsidize competition among themselves for business customers. A review of the arguments demonstrates that the law clearly compels that a cable facility used to provide internet access to the public for a fee is subject to the same requirements that apply to every other competitive telecommunications carrier.[41] Given that these same rules do not seem to be hampering the ability of other competitive local exchange carriers ("CLECs"), which are common carriers, it appears that the Commission's fears of over-regulation and a delay or stifling of cable broadband investment are both unfounded and dangerously misplaced.

CONGRESS ADOPTED THE COMPUTER II MODEL IN WHICH UNREGULATED INFORMATION SERVICES "CONTENT" MUST BE CARRIED TO THE PUBLIC ON A REGULATED TELECOMMUNICATIONS "CONDUIT"

THE STATUTORY DEFINITIONS SHOW THAT CONGRESS INTENDED THAT ALL INFORMATION SERVICES WOULD BE PROVIDED USING TELECOMMUNICATIONS FACILITIES

The 1996 Act added numerous new provisions, including the definitions of "information service" and "telecommunications." An "information service" is defined as "the offering of a capability for generating, acquiring, storing, transforming, processing, retrieving, utilizing, or making available information *via telecommunications . . .* "[42] "Telecommunications" is defined as "the transmission, between or among points specified by the user, of information or the user's choosing without change in the form or content of the information as sent and received.[43] Incorporating the defined term "telecommunications" in the definition or information service clearly indicates, as the Commission itself recently noted in its *amicus brief* in the *Portland* case, that "information service is distinct from, but uses, telecommunications."[44] The plain meaning of the definition of "telecommunications" provided by Congress is that the transmission is at the direction of the user, and the information concerned is under the control of the user.[45] As a result, the definition leaves little room for doubt that, for purposes of the Communications Act, a service is only an "information service" if it provides the listed capabilities for use with information chosen or supplied, and transmitted to or from any point on the network, as directed by the user.

THE COMMISSION HAS REPORTED TO CONGRESS THAT INTERNET ACCESS IS AN INFORMATION SERVICE THAT USES TELECOMMUNICATIONS

In April 1998, the Commission sent a report to Congress on the key definitions adopted in the 1996 Act.[46] The report, conducted pursuant to a Congressional mandate, reviewed all of the Commission's rulemakings up to April 1998 with respect to internet access[47] and information services.[48] In the *Report to Congress,* the Commission reaffirmed several notions including: (1) its understanding that Congress adopted the Computer II[49] framework in the 1996 Act; (2) Computer II continued to apply with respect to information services and internet access, and (3) all "enhanced services"[50] are "information services" under the 1996 Act.[51] In addition, the Commission determined that internet access is a type of information service[52] and said that when a provider offers an information service it "uses telecommunications to do so."[53] Finally, the *Report to Congress* stated emphatically that sections 25 I and 254 of the Communications Act should "apply regardless of the underlying technology those service providers employ, and regardless of the applications that ride on top of their services.[54] Further, the Commission has said that, to promote equity and efficiency, it "should avoid creating regulatory distinctions based purely on technology"[55] and that "this functional approach is consistent with Congress' direction that the classification of a provider should not depend on the type of facilities used. A telecommunications service is a telecommunications service regardless of whether it is provided using wireline, wireless, cable, satellite, or some other infrastructure.[56]

The issue of open access and control of facilities was at the heart of the debate in the Computer II decision 16 years prior to the enactment of the 1996 Act. In 1980, the Commission stated that the "essential thrust" of the Computer II proceeding was to "provide a mechanism whereby non-discriminatory access can be had to basic transmission services by all enhanced service providers. Because enhanced services are dependent upon the common carrier offering of basic services, a basic service is the building block upon which enhanced services are offered."[57] In reaching its decision, the Commission also found that the "[i]mportance of control of local facilities, as well as their location and number, cannot be overstate[d]. As we evolve into more of an information society, the access/bottleneck nature of the telephone local loop will take on greater significance.[58] That access to local facilities is as critical today as it was then-as is evidenced by the expensive steps some companies have taken to obtain local access, for example, AT&T's purchase of TCI and now Media One, and the AOL merger with Time Warner.[59] Yet it appears that the present Commission has decided to choose the opposite solution from the open access approach that it picked in 1980.

With respect to internet access providers, the Commission in the *Report to Congress* seemingly took no notice of the fact that, with the passage of the 1996 Act amendments to promote local competition for both telecommunications and cable service, the rules had changed. The Commission stated, "Internet access providers typically own no transmission facilities . . . they lease lines and otherwise acquire telecommunications from telecommunications providers-interexchange carriers, incumbent local exchange carriers, competitive local exchange carriers, and others."[60] The Commission's statement reflects the world as it was until recently, when local exchange service – the "last mile" access to the consumer – as generally provided through a single company that was the de facto monopoly provider of the transmission service.[61] However, these companies were required to share the underlying transmission service with all internet access and other information service providers.[62] The 1996 Act broke open that de facto monopoly,[63] making it possible for internet access providers, for example AT&T' through its affiliated entity @Home, to own both the ISP and the last mile facility needed to offer internet access and other information services directly to consumers. Even after the acquisition of TCI by AT&T, and the further proposed acquisition of Media One and the AOL-Time Warner merger, the Commission has yet to indicate that it understands that its core assumption – that ISPs generally do not own facilities – is no longer valid with respect to some national players.[64]

The Commission did indicate in the *Report to Congress* that there may be some information service providers that own the facilities that they use to provide transmission services to themselves.[65] While declining to consider those information service providers as common carriers for purposes of universal service contributions, the Commission noted that "[i]t is the facilities owners that, in a real sense, provide the crucial telecommunications inputs underlying internet service[.]"[66]

It is the Commission's refusal to recognize that the world has changed that is creating the central problem discussed in this article. In light of these statements regarding technological neutrality and the detailed analysis of the definitions provided to Congress, it is difficult to understand how the Commission can be so confused by the statute that it is uncertain whether Congress intended that the same regulatory regime should apply — "regardless of the facilities used"[67]— to all transmission facilities used to provide internet access to the consumer.[68] We turn now to a detailed examination of the statutory language.

GIVEN THE STATUTORY REQUIREMENT THAT INFORMATION SERVICES ARE PROVIDED "VIA TELECOMMUNICATIONS," CABLE FACILITIES USED TO PROVIDE INTERNET ACCESS MUST BE TELECOMMUNICATIONS FACILITIES

THE CABLE INDUSTRY CLAIMS THAT INTERNET ACCESS IS A "CABLE SERVICE"

The cable industry currently refuses to provide unaffiliated ISPs with common carrier access to the underlying transmission capability that the cable operators and their affiliates use to transmit internet access and other information services to consumers who are cable accessible. Cable facility owners like AT&T base their refusal on the grounds that internet access and other information services, when provided by a cable operator, are "cable services."[69] As a result, AT&T claims

> that it merely uses broadband cable facilities to provide information services or other cable services to cable subscribers. Accordingly, none of the common carrier obligations of Title II can he applied to any [AT&T owned] TCI cable system either today or during the period after the [AT&T and TCI] merger when these systems continue providing cable service.[70]

The advantage of AT&T's approach to the cable operator is obvious. Section 621 (c) of the Communications Act specifically states that a cable operator may not be subjected to the common carrier requirements of Title

11 of the Act "by reason of providing a cable service."[71] As a result, under the AT&T approach, a cable operator can use its cable facilities to provide internet access and other information services in direct competition with the telephone companies, but without having to provide open access to the underlying transmission facility as its competitors are required to do.

INTERNET ACCESS IS NOT A "CABLE SERVICE" AS DEFINED BY THE COMMUNICATIONS ACT

AT&T and the cable industry are incorrect as a matter of law that internet access and other information services meet the definition of "cable service" as set forth in section 602(6) of the Communications Act.[72] The statutory definition of "cable service" in the Communications Act has remained substantially unchanged since Congress first adopted it in 1984.[73] In particular, subparagraph (A) of the definition, which contains the two mandatory criteria for determining when a service qualifies as a cable service, has never been amended. Congress did make a minor change in 1996 to subparagraph (B) of the definition, but the statutory construction of the definition makes it clear that the additional criteria in subparagraph (B) are discretionary. They become relevant to the definition only if a service first meets the two required criteria in subparagraph (A). If the service does not meet both of those criteria, then nothing in the language of subparagraph (B), even as amended, can make an otherwise ineligible service qualify as a cable service.

As amended, Section 602(6) of the Communications Act defines "cable service" as "(A) the one-way transmission to subscribers of (i) video programming, or (ii) other programming service, and (B) subscriber interaction, if any, which is required for the selection or use of such video programming or other programming service."[74] This definition tracks the fundamental distinction relied on by the courts and the Commission prior to 1984 to treat cable television systems as non-common carrier facilities, namely that they were being used to retransmit television programming normally regulated under Title III.[75] From the plain language of the definition, it is clear that the two conditions set forth in subparagraph (A) must always be met for a service to be classified as a "cable service." First, the service must provide "a one-way transmission to the subscriber." Second, that transmission must consist of either "video programming" or an "other programming service."

Therefore, for internet access or any other information service to be provided as a "cable service," the information at issue would have to be provided via a "one-way transmission to the subscriber," and the information the service provided would have to meet the definition of either "video programming" or an "other programming service."[76] Under the specific criteria set forth by Congress to define an "information service" it is apparent that neither of these two required conditions in the definition of "cable service" can be met.

The definitions of "video programming" and "other programming service" have also remained unchanged since Congress first included them in the Communications Act in 1984. Section 602 (3) defines "video programming" as "programming provided by, or generally considered comparable to programming provided by, a television broadcast station."[77] Section 602 (14) defines "other *programming* service" as "information that a cable operator makes available to all subscribers generally."[78]

It is fairly plain that "video programming," which is programming provided by, or comparable to, that provided by a television station (i.e., a station licensed for one-way, over-the-air broadcasting of signals to any subscriber equipped with a television set to receive those signals) does not qualify under the statutory definition of "information services." Under no circumstance can a television station, much less programming provided by a television station, be said to be engaged in the "offering of a capability for generating, acquiring, storing, transforming, processing, retrieving, utilizing, or making available information via telecommunications,"[79] a transmission of information that is chosen by and transmitted under the direction of a user.[80] With "video programming" eliminated as a possible option, internet access and apparently any other information service accessible through a cable facility must be an "other programming service" if it is to be considered a "cable service" subject to exclusion from common carrier obligations under section 621 (c)1 of the Communications Act. [81]

In 1984, the similarity between the editorial control over content exerted by a broadcaster, and that asserted by a cable operator, was the nexus Congress chose for determining which services would be exempt from the common carrier requirements of the Communications Act. As a result, Congress maintained the linkage to broadcasting services in the other statutory component of the definition of "cable service." An "other programming service" is defined as "information that a cable operator makes available to all subscribers generally."[82] Further, Congress explained in the legislative history that the definition was intended to include services that are ancillary to broadcasting.[83]

AT&T claims that because it makes internet access "available" to all subscribers, its service meets the definition of an "other programming service."[84] For AT&T's argument to be even facially plausible, one would have to believe that the term "information" has the same meaning as the term "information service" for purposes of the Communications Act. Clearly it does not.[85]

Both the statutory language used by Congress and the explicit legislative history demonstrates that "information services" are not included in the definition of "other programming service."[86] Looking at the plain meaning of the words used, an "information service" is "the offering of a capability for generating, acquiring, storing, transforming, processing, retrieving, utilizing, or making available information via telecommunications."[87] A cable operator that makes available to all subscribers information selected by the cable operator cannot be said to be offering each subscriber the "capability for" individually manipulating that information."[88] The statutory criteria describe two completely different services. They are not interchangeable.

Information selected by the cable operator is provided to all users under the statutory definition of "other programming service."[89] The subscriber or user is a passive participant, in much the same manner that a television broadcast viewer is. In contrast, the subscriber or user of an "information service" is clearly an active participant under the terms of the statutory definition."[90] Information selected, created, or changed by a user, or which the user is "making available" to others, cannot be said to be "information that a cable operator makes available" and therefore cannot be an "other programming service" as defined by the Communications Act.[91]

Even if the plain language of the statute leaves any room for doubt, the legislative history of the Cable Act does not.[92] In the 1984 Cable Act Congress adopted the House definition of "other programming service,"[93] and the *House Cable Act Re*port states that the "definition of other programming services requires that the information provided in a cable service must be made available to all subscribers generally and may not include information that is subscriber-specific . . . services providing subscribers with the capacity to engage in transactions or to store, transform, forward, manipulate, or otherwise process information or data would not be cable services."[94]

It was no accident that the *House Cable Act Report* tracks so closely the terms the Commission and the courts defined as "enhanced" or "information" services. The Commission adopted its Computer II "basic/ enhanced" dichotomy in 1980, just four years before the enactment of the Cable Act. Two years before the Cable Act, the Modification of Final Judgment in the antitrust case against AT&T defined "information services" as "the offering of a capability for . . . storing, transforming, processing, retrieving, utilizing . . . information by means of telecommunications."[95]

Thus, the very activities that are at the heart of information services and internet access were clearly intended by Congress in 1984 to be excluded from the definition of "cable service." In fact, the *House Cable Act Report* could not make the point more clearly when it states "[s]ome examples of non-cable services would be: shop-at-home and bank-at-home services, electronic mail, one-way and two-way transmission of non-video data and information not offered to all subscribers, data processing, video-conferencing, and all voice communications."[96]

Even though the world wide web was still nearly 10 years in the future, Congress in fairly unambiguous terms included what are now internet services in the list of services *excluded* from the definition of "cable service" that was enacted in the Cable Act.[97] However, the cable industry claims that in 1996 Congress completely reversed itself, adopting through a two word change a sweeping evisceration of the limitations it so clearly and deliberately adopted in 1984.[98] It is on this slender thread that the cable industry hangs its entire legal argument.

THE 1996 AMENDMENT TO THE DEFINITION OF CABLE SERVICE DID NOT EXPAND THE DEFINITION OF "CABLE SERVICE" TO INCLUDE "INFORMATION SERVICES"

In the 1996 Act, Congress amended the definition of "cable service" to include the phrase "or use" in subparagraph (B).[99] As amended, "cable service" is now defined to mean "(A) the one-way transmission to subscribers of (i) video programming, or (ii) other programming service, and (B) subscriber interaction, if any, which is required for the selection or use of such video programming or other programming service.[100]

Other than the addition of "or use," the definition has not changed. The basic mandatory criteria remain: Cable service is limited to "the one-way transmission to subscribers of (i) video programming or (ii) other programming service."[101] Nevertheless, the cable industry argues that the addition of "or use" was intended by Congress to overturn the explicit statutory limitations adopted by Congress in 1984.[102] In support of its position the cable industry and others rely on a single sentence in the 1996 *Act Conference Report,* as well as a floor statement made by a single member of the House of Representatives.[103] Unfortunately for the cable industry, the statutory construction of subparagraph (B) makes that subparagraph an optional add-on to, and not a part of, the subparagraph (A) definition. Thus, subscriber interaction, "if any," may be provided as part of the "cable service," but only if it is "required for the selection or use of such video programming or other programming service."[104] It is only after a service has met both statutory criteria in subparagraph (A) that the "or use" amendment applies, and only to the extent that the cable operator choses to permit such selection or use.

The *House Cable Act Report* stated that "a cable service may not provide subscribers with the capacity to communicate instructions or commands to software packages such as computer or video games."[105] Arguably, the addition of "or use" could imply limited two-way interaction by the subscriber, for example to send commands to a video game stored and operated at the computer headend. This would expand the 1984 Act definition slightly to allow interactive gaming among multiple cable subscribers without the exception swallowing the rule, as the cable industry would have the Commission believe.[106] Whatever intentions AT&T and the cable industry might suggest, the statutory construction of the definition as amended makes the amendment insignificant to the determination of whether or not an "information service" can also be a "cable service." Notwithstanding the confusing reference to "information services made available to subscribers by a cable operator" in the *1996 Act Conference Report,*[107] an apparent congressional intent as revealed in a conference report does not trump a pellucid statutory directive."[108]

DESPITE THE COMMISSION'S CONFUSION, THE CONGRESS DID NOT LEAVE THE REGULATORY CLASSIFICATION OF 1NFORMATION SERVICES PROVIDED OVER CABLE FACILITIES UNRESOLVED

CONGRESS INTENDED THE DEFINITION OF CABLE SERVICE TO CLEARLY MARK THE BOUNDARY BETWEEN SERVICES

The legislative history of the Cable Act also demonstrates that Congress carefully limited the definition of "cable service" in order to "mark the boundary between those services provided over a cable system which would be exempted from common carrier regulation under section 62 1 (c) and all other communications services that could be provided over a cable system."[109]

Congress recognized that "non-cable communications services [provided over cable systems] are subject to regulatory authority"[110] and that "state and Federal authority over non-cable communications services [offered over cable systems] under the status quo shall be unaffected by the provisions of Title VI."[111] The *House Cable Act Report* also states that "nothing in Title VI shall be construed to affect authority to regulate any cable operator to the extent that such operator provides *any communications service other than cable service,* whether offered on a common carrier or private contract basis."[112]

Finally, the report goes on to state, for example, that "[m]aking available a cable system for voice communication between subscribers would not be a cable service . . . Similarly, offering cable system capacity for the transmission of private data . . . would not be a cable service ."[113]

Given these very specific examples, it is apparent that in 1984 Congress did not intend to permit cable facilities to be used to provide telecommunications services under a different regu1atory regime than the one that applied to common carriers.[114] The "level playing" field concept of the 1996 Act continued this longstanding intent.

CABLE FACILITY- OPERATORS PROVIDING INFORMATION SERVICE TO
SUBSCRIBERS ACT AS COMPETITIVE LOCAL EXCHANGE CARRIERS TO THE
EXTENT THEY PROVIDE NON-CABLE SERVICES

If internet access and information services are not "cable services,"
then AT&T and other cable facility operators act as competitive local
exchange carriers when they provide broadband internet access and other
information services to the public over cable facilities. When discussing
internet access provided by incumbent local exchange carriers, the
Commission stated recently that an end-user may utilize a
telecommunications service together with an information service, as in the
case of internet access. In such a case, however, the two services are treated
separately. The first service is a telecommunications service (e.g., the xDSL-
enabled transmission path), and the second service is an information service-
in this case internet access.[115] The internet access provided by a cable
operator through @Home is no different from the internet access provided
by any other local exchange carrier (incumbent or competitive) through its
own affiliated ISP. The Commission itself describes cable modem service
and in particular the service provided to AT&T's customers through
@Home-in terms of separate services that are bundled together when offered
to the consumer.[116] One of the services is "the underlying transport service"
or "use of the cable network for data deliver services," while the others are
described as "internet access" and "content."[117] Further, AT&T itself has
already admitted that it would be a competitive local exchange carrier when
it provides "telecommunications service" over its cable facilities, albeit
with the caveat that it is not yet one because it may provide internet access
and other information services its cable system as a "cable service," rather
than "via telecommunications" as all other local exchange carriers do.[118]
Unfortunately for AT&T's position, it is the statute and not the carrier that
determines who is a local exchange carrier.

Since 1983 Congress has made it clear that a cable operator can be
regulated as a telephone company when it provides non-cable services.
The new definitions Congress added in the 1996 Act make it even clearer.[119]
One of the goals of the 1996 Act was to provide competitively neutral
requirements for the provision of similar services.[120] Thus Congress made
it clear that a cable facility operator can also be a telephone company or
more precisely a "local exchange carrier[121] under the statutory definitions
in the Act. As part of the proceedings to implement both section 251 of the

Act and section 706 of the 1996 Act, the Commission found that advanced services like packet-switching and xDSL service are "telecommunications" and that when advanced services are provided by an incumbent local exchange carrier they are either "telephone exchange service" or "exchange access."[122] Any person - incumbent or not – who provides "telephone exchange service"[123] or "exchange access"[124] is a "local exchange carrier" for purposes of the Communications Act.[125] Further, the Commission noted, "[n]othing in the statutory language or legislative history limits [the terms "telephone exchange service" and "exchange access"] to the provision of voice, or conventional circuit switched service . . . The plain language of the statute thus refutes any attempt to tie these statutory definitions to a particular technology."[126]

Other than the nature of the facilities used, there is no significant difference between broadband internet access offered over cable facilities and that offered by local exchange carriers using DSL transmission. As a matter of law there is no support in the Communications Act for different regulatory treatment of these identical services based solely on the type of facilities used,[127] nor does the Communications Act draw any distinction between types of local exchange carriers (i.e., incumbent or competitive) or the facilities used to provide a transmission service for purposes of deciding who is a "local exchange carrier[128] or a telecommunications carrier.[129]

THE CHANGES MADE TO TITLE VI BY THE 1996 ACT DEMONSTRATE THAT CONGRESS INTENDED TO PRESERVE THE DISTINCTION BETWEEN CABLE SERVICES AND TELECOMMUNICATIONS SERVICES

If one broadens their review of the changes made in the 1996 Act beyond the addition of "or use" that is so often cited by the cable industry, a clearer pattern emerges. Congress made extensive changes to Title VI with respect to the heart of the issue raised in this debate, namely the relationship between cable services, information services and telecommunications services.

In particular, Congress took considerable pains to add several new sections to Title VI. Paragraph V of Title VI, titled "Video Programming Services Provided By Telephone Companies," seems to have escaped the Commission's notice entirely when it comes to examining the relationship between information services provided over cable facilities and those same services provided over more traditional facilities.[130] In addition, Congress added explicit provisions to existing sections of Title VI to prohibit local franchising authorities from requiring a cable operator to provide a telecommunications service as part of its franchise obligations.[131]

Section 651 (a) of the Act[132] establishes a common regulatory treatment of video programming provided by a common carrier for each different type of transmission media regulated by the Act. Common carriers and any other person using radio communications to provide video programming are all to be regulated under Title III.[133] Common carriers only transmitting video programming are to be regulated only under Title II. Any other use of common carrier facilities to provide video programming to subscribers must be done either through a cable system subject to parts I through IV of Title VI[134] or through an open video system subject to section 653 of the Act.[135] In either case the facilities are subject to regulation under Title II for all non-cable services and to the appropriate sections or section of Title VI for cable services.

Section 651 (b) of the Act most clearly illustrates that Congress had a specific demarcation point between services in mind. That section states that "[a] local exchange carrier that provides cable service through an open video system or a cable system shall not he required, pursuant to Title II of this Act, to make capacity available on a nondiscriminatory basis to any other person for the provision of cable service directly to subscribers."[136]

This section demonstrates that Congress was concerned that, absent this explicit limitation reinforcing the exemption from common carrier requirements for "cable service" in section 621 (c), common carrier requirements might be applied to permit competing cable service providers to use the local exchange facilities of a "telephone company" that also used those common carrier facilities provide its own cable service. This would undo the "level playing field" Congress sought to create because cable operators do not have to share their facilities with competing cable service providers. As. a result, as the legislative history of section 631 (b) indicates, Congress intended that a common facility could be used for both cable services and telecommunications services, and specific language was included so that the common facilities could be regulated appropriately under Title II for telecommunications services and under Title VI for cable services.[137]

That a cable facility could be used for more than one type of regulated service was not a new or novel idea on the part of Congress in 1996. In the *NARUC v. FCC* case the court stated that "it is at least logical to conclude that one can be a common carrier for some activities but not others."[138] During consideration of the 1984 Cable Act the House Commerce Committee expressed a similar view, stating " [W]hile cable operators are permitted under the provisions of Title VI to provide any mixture of cable and non-cable services they choose, the manner in which a cable service is marketed would not alter its status as a cable service . . . the combined offering of a non-cable shop-at-home service with service that by itself met all the conditions for being a cable service would not transform the shop-at-home service into a cable service, or transform the cable service into a non-cable communications service."[139] Twelve years later the view of Congress had not changed. Services that are not cable services remain subject to regulation under other titles of the Act. The cable industry, and perhaps the Commission, appears to believe that part V of Title VI only applies to companies that started life as a telephone company.[140] However, there is nothing in the Act or the legislative history of the 1996 Act that supports such a limited view.[141] If internet access and other information services are included under the definition of cable service, as the cable industry advocates, then any local exchange carrier, including an incumbent local exchange carrier such as Bell Atlantic, could escape any obligation to provide open access to ISPs or unbundled network elements and interconnection to competitive local exchange carriers who wish to provide internet access services.[142] This would be the case because section 651 (b) of the Act states a local exchange carrier is under no Title II obligation to make capacity available for the provision of cable service.[143] The explicit limitations Congress so carefully imposed in the definition of "cable service" would be made meaningless, and facilities-based ISPs, including incumbent local exchange carriers like Bell Atlantic and SBC, would be free to determine their own regulatory regime.[144] It is clear that Congress did not intend for this to be possible under the plain language of the Communications Act.

CONCLUSION

The Commission's choice so far to ignore the explicit requirements of the Communications Act as they apply to cable facilities used to provide internet access cannot ultimately be upheld by the courts. By allowing cable companies to create oligopolies in the high speed internet access marketplace, the Commission dooms to extinction any number, perhaps even thousands, of smaller ISPs whose presence is the driving force behind internet access competition and technological innovation. Ironically, it is the competitive internet marketplace that the Commission insists it is seeking to promote when it willfully abdicates its statutory responsibilities and allows increasingly concentrated and powerful cable facility operators to avoid their obligation to make their underlying telecommunications transmission facilities available on a common carrier basis.

Destruction of a vital and competitive internet services market would in itself be disastrous, and it would represent a perverse outcome for a policy largely justified by the disingenuous cry of "don't regulate the internet." If the Commission allows the cable industry to "interpret" the language of the Communications Act out of existence in order to avoid its common carrier responsibilities, how can the Commission continue to require that an incumbent or competitive telephone company providing the same service make its facilities available to all ISPs on a non-discriminatory basis? The answer, of course, is that it cannot, with the result that the entire regime designed by the Commission and Congress to foster meaningful competition and consumer choice is gutted, to be repaired, if at all, at the cost of years of unnecessary litigation. Both industry and the consuming public would be far better served if the Commission were to re-examine its policies-this time in the full light of the statute-and correct its course before it is too late.

BRIEF OF PETITIONER EARTHLINK, INC. , BRAND X INTERNET SERVICES, ET AL., V. FEDERAL COMMUNICATIONS COMMISSION

This appeal is from the Declaratory Ruling released by the Federal Communications Commission ("FCC" or "Commission").[145] The central issue decided by the Commission and now before this Court is whether the transmission component of an Internet access service offered to the public for a fee by cable companies using their own facilities is a "telecommunications service" within the meaning of section 3(46) of the Act.[146]

The Commission decided that such transmission does not constitute a telecommunications service. If, contrary to the Commission's decision, the transmission component of cable-based Internet access service is a "telecommunications service," then that transmission is by definition a "common carrier" service.[147] Common carriers are required under sections 201 and 202 of the Act[148] to sell their telecommunications services on nondiscriminatory terms and conditions to any legitimate purchaser that requests them unless the Commission relieves the common carrier of that obligation by exercising its forbearance authority under section 10 of the Act.[149] Therefore, if the transmission services here at issue are common carrier telecommunications services, then cable companies that provide those services must sell them on nondiscriminatory terms to unaffiliated ISPs, something that cable companies have refused to do.

The statutory classification issue has been popularly referred to over the past several years as the "cable open access" debate. At stake is whether ISPs that are not affiliated with cable companies have a statutory right to demand and receive transmission service at reasonable rates and on nondiscriminatory terms from cable companies that use their own transmission facilities to provide Internet access service to the public. The simple question of whether the transmission component of an Internet access service offered to the public by a cable company is a common carrier telecommunications service has been presented to the Commission at least six times over the past four years.[150] The Declaratory Order is the first and only time that the Commission has chosen to address the question.

This case turns on the relationships among three defined terms in the Act: "information service," "telecommunications," and "telecommunications service."

The challenged Declaratory Ruling issued by the Commission held that an Internet access service offered to the public for a fee by a cable company is an "information service" that is offered "via telecommunications," but that the telecommunications involved is not a "telecommunications service."[151] The Commission's stated reason for this last finding is that the telecommunications over which the information service of Internet access is delivered is not offered to the consumer "separately" or on a "stand-alone" basis" from the information service.[152]

Cable-based transmission is the most widely available mode of delivering high speed or "broadband" access to the Internet, comprising approximately sixty-eight percent of the high speed residential market. Notwithstanding a handful of agency-imposed and voluntary agreements, denial of a statutory right to purchase this transmission service from cable companies effectively prevents EarthLink and other ISPs from providing cable-based Internet access services to customers reached by cable facilities. The Commission's order therefore excludes EarthLink and other ISPs that are not affiliated with a cable company from a substantial portion of the large and growing broadband Internet access market. Viewed from the perspective of the consumer, the Commission's ruling that the cable-based telecommunications underlying Internet access service is not a "telecommunications service" means that the vast majority of consumers today have access to only one cable-based Internet provider – the cable company itself.

In addition to finding generally that the telecommunications underlying Internet access service provided over cable facilities is not a "telecommunications service," the Commission also held specifically that any "stand-alone" transmission service offered to ISPs by AOL Time Warner under order of the Federal Trade Commission would be classified as "private carriage" rather than common carriage. The lawfulness of that decision constitutes the second issue presented.

A third issue presented involves the Commission's "waiver" of the requirements mandated by its 1980 order in the *Computer II* proceeding. The *Computer II* provision waived by the Commission requires that *all* providers of "information services" (such as Internet access service) that use their own transmission networks to deliver those information services to the public must unbundle and sell that underlying transmission capability to competing information service providers on nondiscriminatory terms.[153] The Commission held that the *Computer II* requirement does not apply to cable companies, but nevertheless went on to "waive" that requirement, on its own motion and without notice, to the extent that it might be found applicable to cable companies that also provide local exchange service.

THE COMMISSION WAS WRONG AS A MATTER OF LAW WHEN IT HELD THAT CABLE MODEM SERVICE DOES NOT INCLUDE A TELECOMMUNICATIONS SERVICE.

THIS COURT HAS ALREADY RULED THAT COMPANIES THAT PROVIDE INTERNET ACCESS SERVICE OVER THEIR OWN CABLE FACILITIES ARE PROVIDING TWO SERVICES, ONE OF WHICH IS A "TELECOMMUNICATIONS SERVICE"

The first question presented is a pure exercise in statutory construction: Is the "telecommunications" over which cable companies deliver the "information service" of Internet access a "telecommunications service" under section 3(46) the Act, 47 U.S.C. § 153(46)? The court would ordinarily apply the familiar two-part test announced in *Chevron USA v. N.R.D.C.*, 467 U.S. 837 (1984), to the Commission's interpretation of the statutory term "telecommunications service." Under that framework, the court asks first "whether Congress has directly spoken to the precise question at issue." *Id.* at 842. Only if the court determines that Congress has not directly addressed the question at issue does it then ask "whether the agency's answer is based on a permissible construction of the statute." *Id.* at 843. Congress has directly addressed the precise question at issue and has decided it differently than has the Commission. Thus, the FCC's assertion of statutory ambiguity notwithstanding, no deference is due its interpretation.[154]

This Court's decision in *AT&T Corp. v. City of Portland,* 216 F.3d 871, 878 (9th Cir. 2000), on the precise statutory definition issue here presented also deprives the Commission of entitlement to deference. "Once we have determined a statute's clear meaning," the United States Supreme Court has held, "we adhere to that determination under the doctrine of stare decisis, and we judge an agency's later interpretation of the statute against our prior determination of the statute's meaning."[155]

In *City of Portland*, this Court held that when a cable operator offers an Internet access service over its cable facilities, it is providing two services: an unregulated "information service" and a regulated "telecommunications service:"

> Like other ISPs, @Home consists of two elements: a "pipeline" (cable broadband instead of telephone lines), and the Internet service transmitted through that pipeline. However, unlike other ISPs, @Home controls all of the transmission facilities between its subscribers and the Internet. *To the extent @Home is a conventional ISP, its activities are that of an information service. However, to the extent @Home provides its subscribers Internet transmission over its cable broadband facility, it is providing a telecommunications service as defined in the Communications Act.*[156]

Under this Court's rule that one panel "may not reconsider the correctness of an earlier panel's decisions,"[157] *City of Portland* controls and the Commission's declaration that cable modem service "does not include an offering of telecommunications service to subscribers" must be set aside on that ground alone.

The Commission also suggests – again without quite saying so – that this Court's *City of Portland* holding regarding the telecommunications service component of cable-based Internet service was *obiter dictum*:

> The Ninth Circuit could have resolved the narrow question before it by finding that cable modem service is not a cable service. Nevertheless, in the passage quoted above the court concluded that because there is a "telecommunications" component involved in providing cable modem service, a separate "telecommunications service" is being offered within the meaning of section 3(46) of the Act.[158]

In fact, the Court in *City of Portland* determined that, in order to answer the question before it, "we *must* determine how the Communications Act defines @Home."[159] That the Court itself determined that it was necessary to decide how the Act classified the components of cable-based Internet access service defeats the assertion that its holding was *dictum*.

The Commission's final attempt to cast doubt on *City of Portland* consists of its assertion that "[t]he Ninth Circuit did not have the benefit of briefing by the parties or the Commission on this issue and the developing law in this area."[160] This assertion is misplaced for two reasons.

First, as the court noted, "the FCC has declined, both in its regulatory capacity and as amicus curiae, to address the issue before us. Thus, we are not presented with a case involving potential deference to an administrative agency's statutory construction pursuant to the *Chevron* doctrine."[161] That the Commission had the chance, but chose not to share its thoughts with the court, is no reason for the court now to reconsider – quite the contrary. By the Commission's own admission, "the issue of what, if any, regulatory treatment should be applied to cable modem service dates back to at least 1998. . . ."[162] After *City of Portland* was decided, it took the Commission another year and a half to issue the Declaratory Ruling. Given the Commission's dogged avoidance of the simple statutory question here at issue, it is at best unseemly for the Commission now to suggest that this Court has somehow jumped the gun.

Second, the fact that neither AT&T (because to have done so would have subjected it to common carrier regulation) nor the City of Portland (because to have done so would have placed it within the prohibitions of 47 U.S.C. § 541(b)) chose to brief the "telecommunications service" issue has no bearing on the binding nature of the Court's earlier decision. The parties – and the Commission as amicus curiae – all made the tactical decision that they would try to obtain a favorable ruling without addressing the most obvious issue in their case. For the Commission to suggest that the Court's refusal to sanction the *City of Portland* litigants' failed strategy of avoidance should lead here to a reconsideration of the Court's earlier decision is without legal justification.

For all of the foregoing reasons, *City of Portland* requires that the Commission's holding that cable modem service does not include a telecommunications service must be reversed.

THE PLAIN LANGUAGE OF THE COMMUNICATIONS ACT DEFINES THE TRANSMISSION UNDERLYING INTERNET ACCESS SERVICE OFFERED TO THE PUBLIC FOR A FEE AS A "TELECOMMUNICATIONS SERVICE"

City of Portland controls this case. Even absent that controlling authority, however, the plain language of the Act mandates that the transmission service underlying Internet access service offered to the public for a fee over cable facilities (like the transmission service underlying Internet access service using other transmission facilities) is a "telecommunications service." This case is one in which "Congress has directly spoken to the precise question at issue."

The Commission held that "cable modem service" is an "information service" under the Act:[163]

> E-mail, newsgroups, the ability for the user to create a web page that is accessible by other Internet users, and the DNS are applications that are commonly associated with Internet access service. Each of these applications encompasses the capability for "generating, acquiring, storing, transforming, processing, retrieving, utilizing, or making available information via telecommunications." *Taken together, they constitute an information service, as defined in the Act.* Consistent with the analysis in the Universal Service Report, we conclude that the classification of cable modem service turns on the nature of the functions that the end user is offered. We find that cable modem service is an offering of Internet access service, which combines the transmission of data with computer processing, information provision, and computer interactivity, enabling end users to run a variety of applications. As currently provisioned, cable modem service supports such functions as e-mail, newsgroups, maintenance of the user's World Wide Web presence, and the DNS. *Accordingly, we find that cable modem service, an Internet access service, is an information service.*[164]

EarthLink agrees with the Commission that the "Internet access service" function of cable modem service (i.e., that part of the service that enables users to access interactive services on the Internet)[165] is an "information service" within the meaning of the Act. EarthLink also agrees with the Commission that, "[c]onsistent with the statutory definition of information service, cable modem service provides the capabilities described above 'via telecommunications.'"[166] Where EarthLink and the Commission part ways is at the next stage in the analysis, i.e., whether the "telecommunications" used by cable facility operators (or any other facility operator) to offer "information services" to the public for a fee constitutes a "telecommunications service" under the Act.[167] The Commission concluded that the "telecommunications" here involved is not a "telecommunications service"

> *Cable modem service: is not itself and does not include an offering of telecommunications service to subscribers.* We disagree with commenters that urge us to find a telecommunications service inherent in the provision of cable modem service. Consistent with the statutory definition of information service, cable modem service provides the capabilities described above "via telecommunications." That telecommunications component is not, however, separable from the data-processing capabilities of the service. As provided to the end user the telecommunications is part and parcel of cable modem service and is integral to its other capabilities.
>
> As stated above, the Act distinguishes "telecommunications" from "telecommunications service." The Commission has previously recognized that "[a]ll information services require the use of telecommunications to connect customers to the computers or other processors that are capable of generating, storing, or manipulation information." Although the transmission of information to and from these computers may constitute "telecommunications," that transmission is not necessarily a *separate* "telecommunications service." We are not aware of any cable modem service provider that has made a *stand- alone* offering of transmission for a fee directly to the public, or to such classes of users as to be effectively available directly to the public."[168]

The Commission's analysis is perhaps most remarkable for the fact that it does not even attempt to address the two factors that determine when "telecommunications" is also a "telecommunications service," i.e., whether the telecommunications is offered "*for a fee* directly *to the public.* . . ." *Id.* (emphasis added). Nor does the Commission acknowledge that EarthLink submitted uncontroverted evidence demonstrating that Internet access services are being offered by all major cable companies directly to the public at standard rates. In addition, the Declaratory Ruling ignores the detailed legal argument offered by EarthLink and others applying the definition of "telecommunications service" to cable modem service.[169] Neither the Commission nor any party has questioned that the services at issue are offered "for a fee directly to the public." Nevertheless, the Commission has refused to address the obvious implication of that fact, i.e., that the "telecommunications" component of cable modem service therefore fits perfectly into the definition of "telecommunications service." The Commission's complete failure to apply or even acknowledge the clear two-part statutory definition of "telecommunications service" renders its conclusion legally insupportable.[170]

What the Commission did say is as damaging to its position as what it did not say. Unable to make the Act's definition of "telecommunications service" fit its purpose, the Commission rewrote that definition by adding words of qualification. Specifically, the sole basis offered by the Commission for its holding that the telecommunications here involved is not a telecommunications service is that such telecommunications is not offered "separately" from the information service of Internet access. The Commission succinctly summarized its position in paragraph 40 of the Declaratory Ruling: "Although the transmission of information to and from these computers may constitute 'telecommunications,' that transmission is not necessarily a *separate* 'telecommunications service.' We are not aware of any cable modem service provider that has made a *stand-alone* offering of transmission for a fee directly to the public, or to such classes of users as to be effectively available to the public."[171]

The most fundamental problem with the Commission's analysis is that it relies entirely on words that are not in the statute. Specifically, the Commission reads the definition of "telecommunications service" as requiring the existence of a "separate" or "stand-alone" offering of telecommunications to the public for a fee. These words do not appear in the definition of "telecommunications service," and the Commission has no power to add them.[172] The statutory definition of "telecommunications service" simply does not require that the telecommunications involved (which the Commission admits is present) must be provided on a "stand-alone" or "separate" basis, and the Commission is without authority to add such a requirement. Inasmuch as the Commission's reading of the Act depends entirely on the insertion of those qualifying words, that reading must be rejected.[173]

The Commission's Holding that Cable Modem Service Does Not Include a Telecommunications Service Contradicts Twenty Years of Commission Precedent – Precedent that the Commission Has Held Congress Adopted in the Telecommunications Act of 1996.

The Commission's holding that cable modem service does not include a telecommunications service must be reversed on the grounds that it conflicts with the plain meaning of the statute as derived from both the unambiguous language of the Act and this Court's decision in *City of Portland*. Even if the Act were not clear on its face, however, the Commission has held for over twenty years that facilities-based carriers cannot escape otherwise applicable common carrier regulation of transmission services by bundling those services with unregulated information services. The Commission adopted that bedrock principle in its 1980 *Computer II* decision and had never strayed from it until the Declaratory Order.[174]   Moreover, since the passage of the Telecommunications Act of 1996, the Commission has held on multiple occasions (most recently in the ruling under review) that Congress incorporated the *Computer II* regulatory regime into the Act when it amended the Act in 1996.[175]   Despite this unbroken line of Commission decisions and the adoption by Congress of the *Computer II* framework, the Commission attempts to explain its refusal to apply the *Computer II* rules to cable modem service by stating simply that "[t]he Commission has never before applied *Computer II* to information services offered over cable facilities."[176]

In order to understand how *Computer II* relates to the proper application of the statutory term "telecommunications service" to the transmission component of cable modem service, it is necessary first to examine the precedent that the Commission has here ignored and second to examine how that precedent was incorporated into the Act through the Telecommunications Act of 1996.

Until the Declaratory Ruling, the Commission had consistently held that where facilities-based carriers provide information services to the public over their own networks, the transmission underlying those information services is a common carrier service ("telecommunications service") that the carrier must sell to others on non-discriminatory terms and conditions. That position has its genesis in the *Computer Inquires*, to which the Commission makes reference in the Declaratory Ruling. The Commission makes reference especially to its decisions in the *"Second Computer Inquiry,"* referenced in the Declaratory Ruling and here as *"Computer II."* *Computer II* enunciated a regulatory framework under which computer services that are delivered over telecommunications facilities are divided into two components: "basic services" and "enhanced services."

Computer II made it clear that carriers using their own transmission facilities to provide "enhanced services" (now called "information services") must sell to competing information service providers on nondiscriminatory terms the transmission services ("basic services" in *Computer II* parlance — now "telecommunications services") over which those enhanced services are delivered:

> "[A]n essential thrust of this proceeding has been to provide a mechanism whereby non-discriminatory access can be had to basic transmission services by all enhanced service providers. Because enhanced service providers are dependent on the common carrier offering of basic services, a basic service is the building block upon which enhanced services are offered. Thus those carriers that own common carrier transmission facilities and provide enhanced services, but are not subject to the separate subsidiary requirement, must acquire transmission capacity pursuant to the same prices, terms, and conditions reflected in their tariffs when their own facilities are utilized. Other offerors of enhanced services would likewise be able to use such a carrier's facilities under the same terms and conditions."[177]

> Since its adoption of *Computer II*, the Commission has repeatedly reaffirmed its position that use of a common carrier transmission service to deliver an information service to the public does not change the regulatory classification of the transmission component as a common carrier telecommunications service.[178]

In 1995, on the eve of the passage of the 1996 Act, a bureau of the Commission reaffirmed that the fact that a facilities-based carrier bundles a regulated "basic service" ("telecommunications service") with an "enhanced service" ("information service") does not change the regulated nature of the basic service:

> We also reject AT&T's contention that the contamination theory applies to its frame relay service and renders its entire InterSpan service offering an enhanced service. To date, the Commission has not applied the contamination theory to the services of AT&T or any other facilities-based carrier. Indeed, the Commission rejected that alternative in Computer III and other proceedings.
>
> * * *
>
> Moreover, application of the contamination theory to a facilities-based carrier such as AT&T would allow circumvention of the Computer II and Computer III basic-enhanced framework. *AT&T would be able to avoid Computer II and Computer III unbundling and tariffing requirements for any basic service that it could combine with an enhanced service. This is obviously an undesirable and unintended result.*[179]

The Declaratory Order cites no authority that indicates that the Commission has *ever* read the Act as requiring that a facilities-based carrier using its own transmission facilities to deliver information services to the public must also offer that transmission on a "stand-alone" basis before such transmission will be considered a common carrier telecommunications service, and EarthLink knows of no such authority.

The rules that the Commission adopted in *Computer II* have now been codified as part of the Act. The Commission has held that Congress adopted the basic service/enhanced service concepts when it enacted the Telecommunications Act of 1996:

> The 1996 Act added or modified several of the definitions found in the Communications Act of 1934, including those that apply to "telecommunications," "telecommunications

service," "telecommunications carrier," "information service," "telephone exchange service," and "local exchange carrier." In section 623(b)(1) of the Appropriations Act, Congress directed us to review the Commission's interpretation of these definitions, and to explain how those interpretations are consistent with the plain language of the 1996 Act. Reading the statute closely, with attention to the legislative history, we conclude that Congress intended these new terms to build upon frameworks established prior to the passage of the 1996 Act. *Specifically, we find that Congress intended the categories of "telecommunications service" and "information service" to parallel the definitions of "basic service" and "enhanced service" developed in our Computer II proceeding, and the definitions of "telecommunications" and "telecommunications service" developed in the Modification of Final Judgment breaking up the Bell system.*[180]

In adopting the *Computer II* basic/enhanced framework through the addition of definitions of "telecommunications service" and "information service," Congress did more than merely update the terminology used to describe those services. Reflecting the reality that telecommunications services were being offered and would continue to be offered by cable companies and other businesses that had not historically participated in the market for those services, Congress made it clear that the way carriers were classified (and therefore regulated) did not depend on the nature of the facilities used to provide the service. Congress expressed this functional approach by defining telecommunications service as the "offering of telecommunications for a fee directly to the public, or to such classes of users as to be effectively available directly to the public, *regardless of the facilities used.*" 47 U.S.C. § 153(46) (emphasis added). Accordingly, when Congress codified *Computer II*, it expressly provided that those rules would apply to all facilities used to deliver information services to the public, including cable facilities.

With the following terse statement the Commission dismisses all of its cases that hold that the facilities-based transmission service used to provide information services to the public remains a common carrier telecommunications service despite being combined with an information service:

> These decisions are inapposite. In the cases relied upon by EarthLink and others, the providers of the information services in question were traditional wireline common carriers providing telecommunications services (e.g., telephony) separate from their provision of information services. *Computer II* required those common carriers also to offer on a stand-alone basis the transport underlying that information service. The Commission has never before applied *Computer II* to information services provided over cable facilities. Indeed, for more than twenty years, *Computer II* obligations have been applied exclusively to traditional wireline services and facilities.[181]

"Generally, an agency must follow its own precedent or explain its reasons for refusing to do so in a particular case."[182] Here, the Commission simply states without explanation that it has never before applied the same rules to cable-based information service providers that it has applied to "traditional wireline" information service providers.

The short answer to the Commission's explanation that *Computer II* does not apply here because the transmission at issue is carried over cable lines instead of telephone lines is that such a rationale is categorically foreclosed by the plain language of the Act, which defines "telecommunications service" functionally, "regardless of the facilities used."[183] In other words, if the Commission wishes to treat functionally identical services offered by telephone companies and cable companies differently, it must do so on some basis other than the nature of the facilities employed. Inasmuch as the Commission has offered no such permissible alternative basis for its holding here, however, the Commission's determination that *Computer II* does not compel common carrier treatment of the transmission underlying cable-based Internet access service must be reversed.[184]

The Commission's argument that *Computer II* and its progeny do not apply to cable facilities, but only to "traditional wireline" facilities, is "explained" in footnote 169 of the Declaratory Ruling. There the Commission states that, "[b]y 'wireline,' we refer to services offered over the infrastructure of traditional telephone networks."[185] This is no explanation at all. Nowhere in the Act or in any Commission regulation is there a definition of "traditional wireline common carrier," much less one that defines such entities as "traditional telephone" companies.

Without any hint of irony or self-consciousness, the Commission itself correctly observes in its discussion of the terms "information service," "telecommunications," and "telecommunications service" that "*[n]one of the foregoing statutory definitions rests on the particular types of facilities used*."[186] That statement is clearly consistent with the "regardless of the facilities used" language in the definition of telecommunications service,[187] but it is flatly inconsistent with the Commission's holding that the application of *Computer II* depends upon the nature of the underlying transmission facilities.

Finally, even if the language of the Act did not foreclose the distinction the FCC draws between cable facilities and the "traditional wireline" facilities to which it seeks to limit the holding of *Computer II*, the Commission's position would nonetheless be arbitrary because it constitutes an unexplained and unacknowledged departure from the position that it took earlier in this very proceeding. In the Notice of Inquiry that began this proceeding, the Commission quite clearly proceeded from the assumption that *Computer II* would apply to cable companies that provided information services if those cable companies were found to be common carriers:

> In the event that cable operators are found to be common carriers providing an information service, and therefore subject to the requirements stemming from the Computer Inquiries, should the Commission forebear from enforcing the requirement to unbundle basic services from enhanced?[188]

The Commission's categorical statement in the Declaratory Ruling that *Computer II* and its progeny simply do not apply to information services delivered to the public over cable facilities neither acknowledges nor explains this about-face – a classic example of arbitrary decisionmaking.[189]

For each of the independent reasons given above, the Commission's holding that the transmission component of cable modem service is not a telecommunications service must be reversed.

THE COMMISSION'S HOLDING THAT AOL TIME WARNER OFFERS TRANSMISSION TO ISPS ON A PRIVATE CARRIAGE BASIS IS CONTRARY TO LAW AND UNSUPPORTED BY THE RECORD

The second holding of the Declaratory Ruling that EarthLink challenges is the Commission's finding that, to the extent that AOL Time Warner provides transmission to unaffiliated ISPs, it does so on a private carriage rather than a common carriage basis. The Commission's own statement of its conclusion perhaps best illustrates why that conclusion cannot stand:

> It is possible, however, that when EarthLink or other unaffiliated ISPs offer service to cable modem subscribers, they receive from AOL Time Warner an "input" that is a stand-alone transmission service, making the ISP an end-user of "telecommunications," as that term is defined in the Act. *The record does not contain sufficient facts by which to make that determination.* To the extent that AOL Time Warner is providing a stand-alone telecommunications offering to EarthLink or other ISPs, we conclude that the offering would be a private carrier service and not a common carrier service, because the record indicates that AOL Time Warner determines on an individual basis whether to deal with particular ISPs and on what terms to do so.[190]

In order for its decision to be upheld, the agency "must articulate a rational connection between the facts found and conclusions made."[191] If the Commission does not know whether AOL Time Warner in fact provides telecommunications to unaffiliated ISPs, or on what terms, it has no basis to determine that such transmission is offered on a private carriage basis. Commissioner Copps pointed out this logical flaw in his dissent:

> Next, the Commission addresses the situation in which a cable operator offers its cable modem service as an input provided to an unaffiliated ISP. Although the decision concludes that the record provides insufficient information to determine whether cable operators are offering pure transmission services to ISPs, the majority determines –

with scant analysis – that it expects that any cable operators that offer pure telecommunications in the future would be offering only private carriage. Doesn't insufficient information mean that the Commission should refrain from broad pronouncements until it can acquire the necessary data?[192]

The inquiry into the common carrier status of a service provider is inherently a factual one, and the lack of any relevant facts in the record regarding the service at issue necessarily undermines the Commission's private carriage finding.[193] The Commission itself properly notes that "[t]he Commission and courts have long distinguished between common carriage and private carriage *by examining the particular service at issue.*"[194]

The Commission states that "[t]he record indicates that AOL Time Warner is determining on an individual basis whether to deal with particular ISPs and is in each case deciding the terms on which it will deal with any particular ISP."[195] In footnote 209, which accompanies the immediately preceding quoted passage, the Commission cites to paragraphs 52-54 as support for the assertion that AOL Time Warner "is determining on an individual basis whether to deal with particular ISPs. . . ." As noted above, it is paragraph 54 that contains the Commission's conclusion that "[t]he record does not contain sufficient facts to" determine the nature of the service at issue.[196] Thus, the Commission's circle of citations begins and ends with the same conclusion – that there is no record evidence upon which to base the private carriage finding.

Even if the Commission's private carriage ruling were not facially invalid for lack of a factual basis, it must be set aside because it ignores the fact that cable companies that sell mass market cable-based Internet access services over their own facilities are providing a "telecommunications service," i.e., a common carrier transmission service. That transmission service is the same service whether it is provided by the cable company directly to Internet service subscribers or to ISPs. Thus, even if it were true (which it is not) that AOL Time Warner "is dealing with each ISP on an individualized basis," Excerpt at 0142, that fact would merely prove that AOL Time Warner is impermissibly discriminating among customers with respect to a common carrier service.[197]

It is irrelevant how cable companies might try to structure their future arrangements for selling transmission to ISPs given that those cable companies are already selling the same transmission to millions of consumers on a common carrier basis as the delivery vehicle for the cable companies' own Internet access service:

> [I]t is simply irrelevant to the common carrier analysis that cable companies might seek to negotiate individual terms with ISPs if and when those cable companies decide to offer the transmission used for cable modem service as a stand alone service sold to ISPs. The plain fact is that every major cable company is today holding itself out to millions of individual users to whom it provides its facilities-based Internet access service on standard terms and conditions. As discussed above, that offering includes both the information service of Internet access and the telecommunications service over which that information service rides. Under the standard for common carriage set forth in *National Ass'n of Regulatory Utility Commissioners v. F.C.C.*, 525 F.2d 630 ("*NARUC I*"), holding oneself out indiscriminately to the public to provide a service that permits users to transmit intelligence of their own design and choosing renders one a communications common carrier. . . . Since the cable companies are already actively offering "cable modem service" to millions of people on a common carrier basis, they cannot avoid their common carrier obligations to ISPs simply by refusing to serve them or by negotiating different terms.[198]

The Declaratory Ruling does not even address this argument, an argument that makes the Commission's speculation about the relationships between AOL Time Warner and other ISPs irrelevant. Although it is certainly the case that a single entity may be a common carrier with respect to one service and a private carrier with respect to another,[199] EarthLink is aware of no authority that holds that a single entity may be both a common carrier and a private carrier with respect to the *same* service. Such a result would be counter to the entire concept of common carriage, the fundamental tenet of which is that all subscribers to a particular service may access it on terms that are not unreasonably discriminatory.[200] The Commission would take prohibited discrimination and turn it into "private carriage." This the Commission may not do.

THE COMMISSION'S WAIVER OF THE COMPUTER II UNBUNDLING AND NONDISCRIMINATION REQUIREMENTS FOR CABLE COMPANIES THAT ALSO PROVIDE LOCAL EXCHANGE SERVICE WAS UNLAWFUL

The FCC offers one final way to avoid regulating the transmission component of cable modem service. Just in case the Commission is wrong about whether cable modem service includes a telecommunications service, and just in case it is wrong about whether *Computer II* applies, and if it is wrong about cable-based transmission being private carriage, it simply "waives" the *Computer II* requirements for those cable companies that also offer local exchange service:

> Even if *Computer II* were to apply, however, we waive on our own motion the requirements of *Computer II* in situations where the cable operator additionally offers local exchange service.[201]

This ruling must be set aside for at least four independent reasons.

THE AUTHORITY CITED BY THE COMMISSION IS BY ITS OWN TERMS INADEQUATE TO SUPPORT THE WAIVER

The Commission cites 47 C.F.R. §1.3 as its authority for waiving the *Computer II* requirements. Section 1.3 states in its entirety:

> *The provisions of this chapter* may be suspended, revoked, amended, *or waived* for good cause shown, in whole or in part, at any time by the Commission, subject to the provisions of the Administrative Procedure Act and the provisions of this chapter. Any provision of the rules may be waived by the Commission on its own motion or on petition if good cause therefor is shown.[202]

As discussed above, the Commission has held on several occasions (including in this proceeding) that the *Computer II* rules that are purportedly waived here have been incorporated by Congress into the Act through the adoption in 1996 of the defined terms "telecommunications service" and "information service." As such, *Computer II* is no longer merely a

Commission regulation, and it is therefore no longer a "provision of this chapter" within the meaning of 47 C.F.R. § 1.3. Instead, the *Computer II* distinction between "basic" and "enhanced" service has been codified in the definitions of "telecommunications service" and "information service," with the section 201 and 202 common carrier obligations attaching to the telecommunications service component of Internet access service.[203] It is axiomatic that an agency must follow its own regulations.[204]   By attempting to "waive" a statutory provision as opposed to a provision of the Commission's own regulations, the Commission clearly steps beyond the boundaries that it has itself set for its waiver power.

The Commission Violated the Administrative Procedure Act and Its Own Regulations by Issuing the Waiver Without Notice and Without Providing an Opportunity for Public Comment

Even if the Commission's waiver were not *ultra vires* because of its application to a statute as opposed to a regulation, it is unlawful because it was adopted without any notice to affected parties or any opportunity for comment. The waiver idea appeared for the first time in the Declaratory Ruling.

Commissioner Copps raised the lack of notice in his dissent, but the Commission chose to ignore the issue:

> The Ruling seems uneasy with its own conclusions. Just in case we are wrong, and access requirements were to apply, *they are waived, on the Commission's own motion, with neither notice nor comment.*[205]

The Commission's rule states that waivers are "subject to the provisions of the Administrative Procedure Act."[206] The rule does not specify which Administrative Procedure Act processes must be employed, and it is well settled as a general proposition that an agency has substantial discretion to proceed by either rulemaking or adjudication.[207] For that reason, EarthLink does not take issue as such with the fact that the Commission chose to waive *Computer II* in a Declaratory Ruling, which is at least technically classified as an adjudicatory procedure.[208] Instead, EarthLink objects to the fact that the waiver was issued without any opportunity whatsoever for the affected parties to provide their views to the agency. This is not a case where the court must determine whether a minimal opportunity for public input satisfies the requirements of 5 U.S.C. § 554 and the Due Process clause of the United States Constitution. Because there was absolutely no indication that a waiver was being considered and therefore no opportunity for parties to address that possibility, the waiver fails to meet even the most lenient standard that may be available to the agency by law.

THE WAIVER IMPERMISSIBLY CIRCUMVENTS THE STATUTORY FORBEARANCE PROCEDURES AND STANDARDS IN SECTION 10 OF THE COMMUNICATIONS ACT

Even if the waiver were not defective because it is *ultra vires* and was adopted without notice or opportunity for comment, it violates the substantive and procedural provisions set forth in section 10 the Act, 47 U.S.C. § 160. That section governs the Commission's authority to forbear from applying the Act and the Commission's regulations to telecommunications services and telecommunications carriers. It is firmly established that when Congress has provided a specific procedure for doing something, agencies cannot bypass that procedure.[209]

In 1996, Congress added section 10 to the Act to provide the Commission with substantial authority to forbear from applying "any regulation or any provision...to a *telecommunications carrier* or *telecommunications service.*"[210] As discussed above, the transmission service underlying cable Internet access is a telecommunications service. The waived *Computer II* unbundling requirements by definition deal only with "basic services" — what the Act now calls "telecommunications services."[211] Because the *Computer II* unbundling requirements are grounded in the nondiscrimination provisions of Title II of the Act, which only apply to common carrier telecommunications services, section 10 applies by its clear terms to any Commission action to forbear from enforcing the *Computer II* requirements. Moreover, as discussed in detail above, the Commission itself has held that Congress has codified the *Computer II* regime in the Act. Thus, the Commission is attempting to "waive" provisions of the Act itself, a result that can only be obtained through the section 10 forbearance procedures.

The Commission's invocation of its regulatory waiver authority under 47 C.F.R. § 1.3 is made the more improper by the fact that the

Commission has acknowledged in this very proceeding that section 10 controls the grant of any relief that the Commission may want to provide from the *Computer II* rules. When the Commission began the proceeding that led to the Declaratory Ruling, it clearly indicated that the section 10 forbearance procedure would apply if the Commission wished to release cable companies providing Internet access service from *Computer II* requirements in the event that those cable companies were deemed to be common carriers. In the Notice of Inquiry, the Commission asked:

> In the event that cable operators are found to be common carriers providing an information service, and therefore subject to the requirements stemming from the *Computer Inquiries*, should the Commission forbear from enforcing the requirement to unbundle basic service from enhanced?"[212]

The Commission also recognized the applicability of section 10 when it proposed to use that section to avoid the impact of *City of Portland*.[213] It is unclear whether the Commission merely forgot about the Act's forbearance provisions and related requirements when it attempted to avoid application of *Computer II* by "waiver" in the Declaratory Ruling, or whether the Commission simply determined, for whatever reason, that it preferred to use its own waiver procedure. Whatever the explanation, the substitution of a waiver for the statutorily mandated forbearance procedure is impermissible.

The section 10 requirements clearly state what the Commission must do before it forbears from enforcing a common carrier regulation – namely, it must make three specific determinations. Those determinations are that:

> (1) enforcement of such regulation or provision is not necessary to ensure that the charges, practices, classifications, or regulations by, for, or in connection with that telecommunications carrier or telecommunications service are just and reasonable and are not unjustly or unreasonably discriminatory;

> (2) enforcement of such regulation or provision is not necessary for the protection of consumers; and

(3) forbearance from applying such provision or regulation is consistent with the public interest.[214]

The record is devoid of any indication that the Commission even acknowledged, much less applied, these required criteria. That the Commission did not undertake the required section 10 analysis before issuing the Declaratory Ruling is conclusively demonstrated by the fact that the Commission has requested comment in the contemporaneous NPRM on the appropriateness of section 10 forbearance from common carrier regulation if cable modem service is held to include a telecommunications service.

In sum, the waiver exceeds the authority in the Commission's governing regulation and acts to circumvent entirely the mechanism that Congress prescribed for relieving common carriers of selected obligations under the Act. As such, the waiver is contrary to the Act and must be vacated.

CONCLUSION

After years of avoiding the issue, the Commission in the Declaratory Ruling finally held that there is no telecommunications service included when a cable company offers Internet access service the public for a fee over the cable company's own transmission facilities. In so holding, the Commission ignored the ruling of this court on precisely the same issue, ignored the plain language of the Act, and ignored twenty years of precedent that the Commission itself admits has been codified in the Act by Congress. Not content with those holdings, the Commission hedged its bets by declaring that cable-based transmission services that one cable company might be selling to unaffiliated ISPs constitute private carriage rather than common carriage. The commission made this finding even as it held that it did not have enough information to do so. Finally, the Commission added a piece of twine to its belt and suspenders by "waiving" the requirements of *Computer II* in the event that its other holdings did not obtain the desired result.

For all of the reasons set forth herein, each and every challenged Commission holding is contrary to law and must be reversed. Because the issues presented can be answered conclusively by reference to the plain language of the statute, there is no need or purpose in remanding the matter to the Commission for further proceedings. Instead, EarthLink respectfully requests that the Court find that the offering of Internet access service to the public for a fee using a provider's own transmission facilities includes a telecommunications service, regardless of the facilities used. EarthLink requests further that the Court set aside each of the challenged Commission rulings.

ENDNOTES

[1] *See In re* Annual Assessment of the Status of Competition in the Markets for Delivery of Video Programming, *Sixth Annual Report,* CB Dkt. No.99-230, FCC 99-418, at paras. 58, 62 (released Jan. 14, 2000) (noting that 32 million homes are passed by cable modem access, with 1 million subscribers; there are 159,000 xDSL subscribers) [hereinafter *Sixth Cable Report.* Internet access is not defined under the Communications Act of 1934. In general the term is used to refer to services that permit the user to access information content and other users through transmission services that utilize the Internet protocol. *See infra* note 47.

[2] As the Commission noted in its *Amicus* brief to the court in *AT&T Corp. v. City of Portland,* there is no agreed upon definition of "open access." *See* Amicus Curiae Brief of the Federal Communications Commission at 8 n.2, AT&T Corp. v. City of Portland, No.99-35609 (9th Cir. Aug. 16, 1999), *available at* <WWW.techlawjournal.com/courts/port- land/19990816fcc.htm> [hereinafter *FCC Amicus Brief].* In this article, the term "open access" is used to mean the same "open" access to the underlying transmission conduit that the Commission granted to all enhanced service providers in the *Computer II* proceeding. That proceeding required all common carrier facility operators to permit enhanced service providers, including ISPs, to purchase the underlying conduit or "transmission service" on the same terms and conditions on which the common carrier provides that transmission to itself or its affiliated ISP. *See In re* Amendment of Section 64.702 of the Commission's Rules and Regulations, *Final Decision,* 77 F.C.C.2d 384, 474-73, para. 231 (1980) [hereinafter *Computer II).*

[3] The term "cable facilities" is used in this article to refer to the physical transmission infrastructure of a" cable system " as defined in section 602(7) of the Communications Act of 1934. *See* 47 U.S.C. § 522(7) (1994 & Supp. III 1997). A "cable system" is "a facility, consisting of a set of closed trans- mission paths and associated signal generation, reception, and control equipment that is designed to provide cable service which includes video programming [.]"

[4] *See, e.g., AOL Seen Unlikely to Remain Advocate of Open Access Rules,* COMM. DAILY, Jan. 12, 2001, at 1.

[5] Communications Act of 1934, Title I, ch. 652, 48 Stat. 1064 (codified as amended at 47 U.S.C. §§ 151-221)

[6] Telecommunications Act of 1996, Pub. L. 104-104, 110 Stat. 56 (codified at 47 U.S.C. §§ 151-710.).

[7] *See* Barbara Esbin, *Internet Over Cable: Defining the Future in Terms of the Past,* 7 COMMLAW CONSPECTUS 37, 98 (1998) (noting that "the Commission could reasonably interpret the 1996 Act as permitting the creation of 'parallel universes' for cable and telephony Internet-based services"). As this article demonstrates, such a result would be in conflict with the statutory language. *See also* THE COMMUNICATIONS ACT: A LEGISLATIVE HISTORY OF THE MAJOR AMENDMENTS, 1934-1996, at 374-77 (Max D. Paglin ed., Pike & Fischer 1999) [hereinafter A LEGISLATIVE HISTORY].

[8] *See* 47 U.S.C. § 532(b) (restricting federal, state, and lo- cal authority to require cable channels for use by programmers unaffiliated with the cable operator); 47 U.S.C. § 541 (c) (prohibiting common carrier regulation of cable services).

[9] The "internet" is a term that has many meanings de- pending on who is using it. *See* Harry Newton, NEWTON'S TELECOM DICTIONARY (14th ed. 1998) at 375-76 ("It is very hard to define the Internet in a way that is meaningful or easy to grasp...[the Internet] is basically transparent to what it carries. It doesn't care if it carries electronic mail, research material, shopping requests, video, images, voice phone calls, requests for information, faxes, or anything that can be digitized, placed in a packet of information, and sent."). Part of the confusion in the present debate stems from the fact that the term is used loosely to describe both the underlying transmission facilities (the "conduit"), the TCP /IP protocols used to transmit information over those facilities, and the myriad of computer servers used to store and transform information provided by both service providers and users. For purposes of this article the term "internet" refers to the information content and services provided by and to users over telecommunications facilities, and not to the underlying conduit. The Commission treats all "internet" services as "information services" under the Communications Act.

[10] *See* Newton, *supra* note 8, at 168 (definition of common carrier); *In re* Application for Consent of Transfer of Control of Licenses of MediaOne Group, Inc., to AT&T Corp., *Written Ex Parte of Prof Mark A. Lemley and Prof Lawrence Lessig,* CS Dkt. No.99-251, at para. 20 (noting that "the [common] carrier is not to exercise power to discriminate in the carriage") [hereinafter *Lemley-Lessig Ex Parte*].

[11] *See Lemley-Lessig Ex Parte, supra* note 10, at paras. 30-36.

[12] Section 1 of the Communications Act states that the Commission "shall execute and enforce the requirements of this Act." 47 U.S.C. § 151 (1994).Section I of the Communications Act states that the Commission "shall execute and enforce the requirements of this Act." 47 U.S.C. s 151 (1994).

[13] *See* Federal Communications Commission, Cable Services Bureau, BROADBAND TODAY: INDUSTRY MONITORING SESSIONS 44 (staff report authored by Deborah A. Lathen) (1999) [hereinafter BROADBAND TODAY]; *see also* Federal Communications Commission, Office of Policy Planning, THE FCC AND THE UNREGULATION OF THE INTERNET 25 (authored by Jason Oxman) (1999); Esbin, *supra* note 7, 118 (1998).

[14] *See FCC Amicus Brief, supra* note 2, at 9 ("the Commission saw no reason 'at this time' to require cable operators to open their broadband reason systems to all ISPs").

[15] *See* FCC Chairman William E. Kennard, *How to End the Worldwide Wait,* WALL ST. J., Aug. 24, 1999, at A18; *see also* FCC Chairman William E. Kennard, *Consumer Choice Through Competition,* Remarks to the National Association of Telecommunications Officers and Advisors (Sept. 17, 1999); *FCC Amicus Brief, supra* note 2, at 18.

[16] 525 F.2d 630, 644 (D.C. Cir. 1976) [hereinafter *NARUC* 1].

[17] *Id.*

[18] *See* 47 U.S.C. § 332(c)(I)(A) (1994 & Supp. III 1997). In *NARUC I* the court found that the proposed specialized mobile radio service at issue, which was classified as a private mobile radio service, was not a common carrier service. *See NARUC I,* at 644. In the amendments Congress changed the classification of specialized mobile radio services and several other private mobile radio services to commercial mobile services subject to the common carrier requirement. *See* Omnibus Budget Reconciliation

Act of 1993 § 6002(c)(2)(B) & (d)(3)(B), Pub. L. No.103-66, 107 Stat. 312, 396-97 (1993) (amending the Communications Act of 1934, codified at 47 U.S.C. § 332).

[19] *See* 47 U.S.C. § 332(c) (1) (A) (i)-(iii) (1994 & Supp. III 1997).

[20] 47 U.S.C. § 153(44) (1994 & Supp. III 1997).

[21] 47 U.S.C. § 153(43) (1994 & Supp. III 1997) (defining "telecommunications" as "the transmission, between or among points specified by the user, of information of the user's choosing, without change in the form or content of the information as sent and received").

[22] 47 U.S.C. § 153(46) (1994 & Supp. 1111997) (defining telecommunications service as "the offering of telecommunications for a fee directly to the public, or to such classes of users as to be effectively available to the public, regardless of the facilities used").

[23] In the 1996 Act, Congress elected not to adopt the Senate's "market power" approach, which would have authorized the Commission to determine market power among local exchange carriers and, thus, when the open access provisions of the statute now codified at 47 U.S.C. § 251 would apply. *See.* CONF. REP. No, 104-230, at 117 (1996). Congress instead imposed interconnection requirements on all telecommunications carriers regardless of their market power; imposed certain additional requirements on all local exchange carriers, including new entrants without market power; and compelled additional cost based unbundling and collocation requirements on all incumbent local exchange carriers, again, regardless of their market power. *See id. a* 121-22. Thus, in cornerstone provisions of the 1996 Act Congress has explicitly rejected the "market-based harm" predicate to regulatory action advanced by the FCC staff. *See* BROADBAND TODAY, *supra* note 13,a t 47.

[24] As part of the 1996 Act amendments, Congress added new sections 10 and 11 (47 U.S.C. §§ 160 & 161), regarding regulatory forbearance and regulatory reform, respectively. Section 10 permits the Commission, either by its own initiative or upon request, to waive *any* provisions of the Communications Act that would otherwise apply to a telecommunications carrier if the Commission determines that application of such provisions is neither necessary to protect consumers nor ensure that rates are just, reasonable, and non-discriminatory, and that it is otherwise in the public interest to do so. *See* 47 U.S.C. § 160(a) (1994 & Supp. III 1997). Section 11 directs the Commission to biennially review all of its regulations applicable to providers of telecommunications services, and to repeal or modify any regulations that it finds to no longer be in the public interest. That both of these sections are limited to providers of telecommunications service and make no mention of cable service or cable providers clearly indicates that Congress believed that convergence between the cable and telecommunications sectors would likely lead to most, if not all, facilities based providers being engaged to some degree in telecommunications service. *See* A LEGISLATIVE HISTORY, *supra* note 7, at 55-58 (regarding universal interconnection) and 316-20 (regarding "convergence" between cable and telephony).

[25] *See* 47 U.S.C. § 153(44) (providing that a telecommunications carrier shall be treated as a common carrier to the extent that it provides telecommunications service).

[26] *See In re* Deployment of Wireline Services Offering Advanced Telecommunications Capability, *Memorandum Opinion and Order, and Notice of*

Proposed Rulemaking, 13 FCC Rcd. 24012,24013, para. 11 (Aug. 7, 1998) [hereinafter *Advanced Services Order]* (noting, "Congress made clear that the 1996 Act is technologically neutral and designed to ensure competition in all telecommunications markets").

[27] *See* 47 U.S.C. § 253(a) (1994 & Supp. III 1997).

[28] *See* Telecommunications Act of 1996 § 302(b) (1), Pub. L. No.104-104, 10 Stat. 124 (repealing the cable-telephone cross ownership ban in section 613(b) of the Communications Act); 47 U.S.C. § 533(b).

[29] *See* S. CONF. REP. No.104-230, at 148 (stating that meaningful facilities-based competition to incumbent local exchange carriers is possible given that cable services are available to 95 percent of United States homes). *See also* 47 U.S.C. § 572 (1994 & Supp. III 1997) (providing that cable operators and local exchange carriers are prohibited from buying each other's facilities in areas where their services compete or overlap); 47 U.S.C. § 543(1)(I)(D) (adding provision of video programming by a local exchange carrier as one of the tests for effective competition that will remove rate regulation from a cable company).

[30] *See* 142 CONG. REC. S691-01 (Feb. 1, 1996) (statement of Sen. Stevens) ("...now we have tried to find a way to literally level the playing field and set down the rules for competition."). *See also id.* at S710 (statement of Sen. Kerry) ("these fundamental features...are designed to create a level playing field"); 142 CONG. REC. HI145-06, 1177 (statement of Rep. Casde) ("the legislation has sought to ensure that different industries are competing on a level playing field").

[31] *See FCC Amicus Brief, supra* note 2, at 26..

[32] The structure of the Communications Act fully supports this result. Congress added the definition of "information services" as part of the complete overhaul it made to the Communications Act. *See* 47 U.S.C. § 153(20). *See also* A LEGISLATIVE HISTORY, *supra* note 7, at 31 ("The [1996 Act] brought the most substantial changes in the regulation of telecommunications services since adoption of the Communications Act in 1934."). All of the amendments made by the 1996 Act that include the term "information service" were placed in Title II of the Communications Act. *See, e.g.,* 47 U.S.C. §§ 228,230, 251, 254,256, 257, 259,271,272 & 274. None of the amendments made by Congress to Title VI in the 1996 Act used the term "information service." Instead, the major thrust of the changes Congress made to Title VI of the Communications Act in the 1996 Act were devoted to maintaining the demarcation line between "cable services" and non-cable services *(i.e.,* telecommunications and information services). *See* 47 U.S.C. §§ 571-573 (1994 & Supp. III 1997). Finally, in Title V of the 1996 Act, Congress made numerous changes to the existing law to address concerns about obscenity and violence on the internet and on television. *See* Public Law 104-104, Title V, 110 Stat. 133-43. All of the provisions addressing the internet or computer services were included in Title II of the Communications Act, while no mention of either computers or the internet was included in the provisions dealing with video programming and cable services. *See generally* S. Conf. Rep. No.104-230, at 187-97.

[33] *See FCC Amicus Brief, supra* note 2, at 25; *See also* Esbin, *supra* note 13, at 177.

[34] 47 U.S.C. § 157 (1994 & Supp. 1111997).

[35] *Advanced Services Order,* 13 FCC Rcd. at 24047, para. 77.

[36] *See* 47 U.S.C. § 160 (1994 & Supp. III 1997).

[37] *See* Pub. L. No.104-104, § 3(b) (110 Stat. 61).

[38] *See Sixth Cable Report, supra* note 1, at 34, para. 68. Analysts believe that bundling of multiple services, offered either entirely over an operator's own network. ..reduces churn and increases equity values." *Id.; see also Lemley-Lessig Ex Parte, supra* note 10, at 20-21.

[39] *See Lemley-Lessig Ex Parte, supra* note 10, at 20-21.

[40] *See Cable Operators Finding Success in Local Phone Service,* COMM. DAILY,] June 17, 1999, at 4 (noting that "Cablevision VP Kevin Curran said his company bundles its telephony offering with cable, giving discounts on cable bill in relation to how much consumer spends on telephone. About six percent of customers wind up with free cable as result.").

[41] These include the *Computer II* requirement that a facilities based common carrier that seeks to offer information services must make the underlying transmission conduit available to all other information service providers on the same price, terms and conditions that it makes that transmission available to itself or its affiliates. *See Computer II,* 77 F.C.C.2d at 474, para. 231; *see also* Esbin, *supra* note 7, at 67 ("[T]he [Commission's] order did not distinguish dominant from non-dominant carriers for purposes of the unbundling requirement [for packet-switched frame relay transmission services] ."

[42] 47 U.S.C. § 153(20) (1994 & Supp. III 1997) (emphasis added).

[43] 47 U.S.C. § 153(43) (1994 & Supp. III 1997).

[44] *FCC Amicus Brief, supra* note 2, at 4. The Commission also stated that it has "long distinguished between basic 'telecommunications' or 'transmission' services, on the one hand, and 'enhanced services' or 'information services' ...that are provided by means of telecommunications facilities, on the other hand. Congress in 1996 codified the FCC's long-standing distinction by adding new definitions to the Communications Act." *Id.* at 3.

[45] *See* 47 U.S.C. § 153(43) (the term "telecommunications" means "the transmission, between or among points specified by the use, of information of the user's choosing. ..) (emphasis added).

[46] *See* generally In Re: Federal-State Joint Board on Universal Service, *Report to Congress* 13 FCC 11501 (1988) [hereinafter *Report to Congress*]. None of the Commission's subsequent orders to date have overturned these findings, and in fact the Commission frequently cites the *Report to Congress* in its orders, *See, e.g., Advanced Services Order,* 13 FCC Rcd. 24012; *In re* Deployment of Wireline Services Offering Advanced Telecommunications Capability, *Order on Remand,* FCC 99-413 (Dec. 23, 1999) [hereinafter *Advanced Service Order on Remand*] *Report to Congress,* 13 FCC Rcd. 11501.

[47] Internet access is not defined in the Communications Act. In the *Report to Congress,* the Commission defined Internet access as a combination of "computer processing, information storage, protocol conversion, and routing with transmission to enable users to access Internet content and services." *Report to Congress,* 13

[48] *See generally* 47 U.S.C. § 153(20) (1994 & Supp. III 1997).[4]

[49] *Report to Congress,* 13 FCC Rcd. at 11512, paras. 24-28 (emphasis in original, citations omitted).

> In *Computer II* the Commission classified all services offered over a telecommunications network as either *basic* or *enhanced.* A basic service consisted of the offering, on a common carrier basis, of pure 'transmission capacity for the movement of information.' The Commission noted that it was increasingly inappropriate to speak of carriers offering discrete 'services' such as voice telephone service. Rather, carriers offered communications paths that subscribers could use as they chose.
>
> An enhanced service, by contrast, was defined as 'any offering over a telecommunications network which is more than a basic transmission service.'
>
> The Commission therefore determined that enhanced services, which are offered' *over* common carrier trans- mission facilities,' were themselves not to be regulated under.Title II of the Act no matter how extensive their communications components.

[50] The Commission's regulations define "enhanced service" as "services, offered over common carrier transmission facilities used in interstate communications, which employ computer processing applications[.]" 47 C.F.R. § 64.702(a) (1998). These regulations were not changed by the passage of the 1996 Act.

[51] *See Report to Congress,* 13 FCC Rcd. at 11507, 11516-17, 11524, paras. 13,33, 45.

[52] *See id.* at 11536, para.73.

[53] *Id.* at 11520, para. 39.

[54] *Id.* at 11552, para. 105. Section 251 of the Act requires, among other things, interconnection among all telecommunications carriers. *See* 47 U.S.C. § 251 (a) (1994 & Supp. III 1997). Section 254 requires that all telecommunications carriers contribute to universal service. *See* 47 U.S.C. § 254(d) (1994 & Supp. III 1997).

[55] *Report to Congress,* 13 FCC Rcd. at 11548, para. 98.

[56] *Id.* at 11530, para. 59 (emphasis added).

[57] *Computer II,* 77 F.C.C.2d. at 475, para. 231.

[58] *Id.* at 468, para. 219.

[59] *See In re* Applications for Consent to the Transfer of Control of Licenses and Section 214 Authorizations from TCI to AT&T Corp., *Application, Description of Transaction, Public Interest Showing and Related Demonstrations,* CS Dkt. No. 98-178, at 20 n.36 (Sept. 14, 1998). *See also Cable Carried Incentive for AOL Merger,* WASH. POST, Jan. 18, 2000, at El.

[60] *Report to Congress,* 13 FCC Rcd. at 11540, para. 81.

[61] *See* A LEGISLATLVE HISTORY, *supra* note 7, at 35-37("the Bell System was able to refuse connection to any communications system beyond its effective control"). *See also Lemly-Lessig Ex Parte, supra* note 10, at para. 25..

[62] *See Computer ll,* 77 F.C.C.2d. at 475, para. 231.

[63] *See* 47 U.S.C. § 253 (removing barriers of entry for interstate and intrastate telecommunications service by any provider). *See also* A LEGISLATIVE HISTORY, *supra* note 7, at 54-55.

[64] *See Advanced Services Order on Remand, supra* note 46, at para. 38 (recognizing that their analysis of "exchange access" does not cover traffic where the ISP itself provides the trans- port component of its internet service, but noting that such circumstances are "rare").

[65] *See Report to Congress,* 13 FCC Rcd. at 11528, 11534, paras. 55, 69.

[66] *Id.* at 11535-36, para. 72. The Commission did observe that they "have not yet established the regulatory classification of Internet services provided over cable television facilities." *Id.* at 11535 n.140.

[67] 47 U.S.C. § 153(46) (1994 & Supp. 1I11997).

[68] *See FCC Amicus Brief, supra* note 2, at 19; *see also* Esbin, *supra* note 7, at 98.

[69] *See In re* Petition of Internet Ventures, Inc. and Internet On-Ramp, Inc., *Reply Comments of AT&T Corp.,* Dkt. No. GSR-5407-L, at 6 (Aug. 11, 1999) [hereinafter *AT&T Reply Comments*].

[70] *In re* Joint Application of AT&T Corp. and Telecommunications, Inc., *AT&T's and TCI's Joint Reply to Comments and Joint Opposition to Petitions to Deny or to Impose Conditions,* CS Dkt. No.98-178, at 53 (Nov. 13, 1998) [hereinafter *AT&T/TCI Joint Reply*]. *See also AT&T Reply Comments, supra* note 69, at 6 n.19 (noting, "Federal law prohibits regulating cable systems providing cable services as a common carrier").

[71] 47 U.S.C. § 541(c) (1994 & Supp. III 1997).

[72] 47 U.S.C. § 522(6) (1994 & Supp. III 1997).

[73] *See* Cable Communication Policy Act of 1984, Pub. L. No.98-549, § 2, 98 Stat. 2779, 2781 (1984) (codified at 47 U.S.C. § 522(6» [hereinafter *Cable Act 011984*].

[74] 47 U.S.C. § 522 (6) (8) (1994 & Supp. III 1997).

[75] "The Committee intends to exempt video programming from common carrier regulation in accordance with the traditional conception that the one-way delivery of television programs, movies, sporting events and the like is not a common carrier activity." H.R. REP. No.98-934, at 53 (1984) [hereinafter referred to in text as *House Cable Act Report*]. In fact, the legal underpinning of the exemption of "cable service" from common carrier obligations is the editorial control exercised by the cable operator over the information sent to the subscriber. *See* U.S. v. Southwestern Cable Co., 392 U.S. 157 (1968). If the cable industry is correct, which it is not, then the industry is essentially claiming that the cable facility operator exercises editorial control over all information received by subscribers who obtain Internet access over a cable facility. Given that the very value of the Internet is that it provides nearly unlimited access to content without any editorial control by any single entity, a less plausible contention is difficult to imagine.

[76] The Commission agrees: As it stated to the Court in its *Amicus* brief, "[a] service cannot be a 'cable service' unless it qualifies as 'video programming' or 'other programming ser- vice.' The 1996 Telecommunications Act did not alter the definitions of' video programming' or 'other programming service.' Unless [i]nternet access fits one of these definitions, it cannot qualify as 'cable service.' " *FCC Amicus Brief, supra* note 2, at 23.

[77] 47 U.S.C. § 522(20) (1994 & Supp. III 1997).

[78] 47 U.S.C. § 522(14) (1994 & Supp. III 1997).

[79] 47 U.S.C. § 153(20) (1994 & Supp. III 1997).

[80] AT&T, the National Cable Television Association, and Time Warner Cable all seem to be in complete agreement on this point, arguing in their comments and reply comments in the *IVI Petition* that internet access clearly does not meet the definition of "video programming." *See In re* Petition of Internet Ventures, Inc., Reply Comments of Time Warner, Inc., Dkt. No CSR-5407-L, at 4. (emphasizing that "no serious claim is, or can be, made by IVI or any other ISP that the internet, as a *two-way,* interactive service, is in any fashion comparable, from the consumer's perspective, to the *one-way* video programming generally offered by broadcast stations in 1984"); *see also In re* Petition of Internet Ventures, Inc. and Internet On-Ramp, Inc., *Comments of ATT&TCI,* Dkt. No. CSR-5407-L, at 9 (stating "[t]his is not video programming at all, but rather access to content"); *see also In re* Petition of Internet Ventures, Inc., *Reply Comments of the National Cable Television Association,* Dkt. No. CSR-5407-L, at 6-7 (Aug. 11, 1999) (explaining that "[t]he [i]nternet as a whole is hardly comparable to the programming provided by a television broadcast station"); *see AT&T Reply Comments, supra* note 69, at 5 (stating that "ISPs provide connectivity, not content").

[81] 47 U.S.C. § 541(c) (1994 & Supp. III 1997). Section 621(c) provides that "[a]ny cable system shall not be subject to regulation as a common carrier or utility by reason of pro- viding any cable service." *Id.*

[82] 47 U.S.C. § 602(14) (1994 & Supp. 111 1997).

[83] *See* H.R. REP. No.98-934, at 41 (stating that "[o]ther programming services that make non-video information generally available to all subscribers are included as cable services because they are sufficiently like video programming to warrant a similar regulatory exemption.") This approach makes sense and tracks court decisions regarding the Com- mission's jurisdiction over cable services. *See also Southwestern Cable,* 392 U.S. at 177 (1968) (commenting that the Commission's authority over cable services is restricted to that reasonably ancillary to its effective performance of its responsibilities for regulation of television).

[84] *See AT&T Reply Comments, supra* note 69, at 6.

[85] The term "information" is not defined under the Communications Act. It should be noted that in the 1996 Act Congress chose not to amend the definition of "other programming service" to include the newly defined term "information service," despite adding that definition and making changes to other definitions in Title VI of the Communications Act

[86] *See* 47 U.S.C. § 552 (14) (1994 & Supp. III 1997).

[87] 47 U.S.C. § 153(20) (1994 & Supp. III1997).

[88] *See id.*

[89] 47 U.S.C. § 522(14).

[90] *See* 47 U.S.C. § 153(20).

[91] *See* 47 U.S.C. §§ 153(20) & 522(14).

[92] The Commission quoted extensively from this detailed and clearly stated legislative history in its *amicus* brief in the *Portland* case. *See FCC Amicus Brief, supra* note 2, at 21.

[93] *See* Cable Act of 1984, § 2, 98 Stat. 2779, 2781.

[94] H.R. REP. No.98-934, at 42.

[95] United States v. AT&T, 552 F. Supp. 131 at 179. (D.D.C. 1982), *aff'd sub. nom.* Maryland v. United States, 460 U.S. 1001 (1983). A footnote in the opinion referred to the definition of "information services" in the Modification of Final Judgment (MFJ) as "essentially...equivalent" to the Commission's definition of "enhanced services" in *Computer II. See id.* at 178 n.198. In the 1996 Act, Congress adopted a modified version of the MFJ definition as the statutory definition of "information services" now found in section 3 of the Communications Act. *See* S. CONF. Rep. No.104-230, at 115-16.

[96] H.R. REP. No.98-934, at 44.

[97] *See id.*

[98] *See FCC Amicus Brief, supra* note 2, at 22 (noting that " AT&T and TCI have argued that Congress, by adding the words 'or use,' intended to expend the definition of 'cable service' to include the wide range of interactive services en- compassed by Internet access").

[99] *See* 47 U.S.C. § 522(6) (B) (1994 & Supp. III 1997). 100 *Id.* at § 522(6) (emphasis added).

[100] *See Id.* at § 522(6) (B) (1944 & Supp. III 1997).

[101] *Id.*

[102] *See FCC Amicus Brief, supra* note 2, at 22.

[103] *See* Esbin, *supra* note 7, at 96 (citing S. Rep. No.1 04- 230 at 169 (1996) and 142 CONG. REC. H1156 (daily ed. Feb. 1,1996) (statement by Rep. Dingell).

[104] 47 U.S.C. § 522(6) (A) & (B) (1994 & Supp. III. 1997).

[105] *See* H.R. REP. No.98-934, at 42.

[106] A LEGISLATIVE HISTORY, *supra* note 7, at 374 ("The [amendment] expanded an *exception* to the definition's general requirement that 'cable service' be 'one-way.' Without some limit on the interactivity permitted, the exception would swallow the rule.") (emphasis in original).

[107] *See* S. CONF. REP. No.104-230, at 169.

[108] *See* City of Dallas, Texas v. FCC, 165 F. 3d 341, 349 (5th Cir. 1999). *See also FCC Amicus Brief,* supra note 2, at 24 (observing that "Congress stated that its 1996 amendment of the definition of cable service was not intended to eliminate the longstanding regulatory distinction between telecommunications service and cable service" (citing S. CONF. REP. No. 104-230, at 169».

[109] H.R. REP. No.98-934, at 41.

[110] *Id.* at 60.

[111] *Id.* The Cable Act of 1984 also specifically states, "The provisions in this Act and the amendments made by this Act shall not be construed to affect any jurisdiction the Federal Communications Commission may have under the Communications Act of 1934 with respect to any communication by wire or radio (other than cable service, as defined by section 602(5) of such Act) which is provided through a cable sys- tem, or persons or facilities engaged in such communications." Cable Act of 1984, § 3(b), 98 Stat. 2779,2801 (1984).

[112] H.R. REP. No.98-934, at 63 (emphasis added). Section 621 (d) of the Communications Act allows the Commission or a state to require the filing of

informational tariffs for any intrastate communication service other than a cable service. *See* 47 U.S.C. § 541 (d). The legislative history accompanying this section makes clear that Congress intended the informational tariff requirement to provide the Commission and the states information necessary to determine if a service should be regulated as a common carrier service. *See id.*

[113] *Id.* at 42.

[114] *See generally* Esbin, *supra* note 7, at 66 ("Of particular concern with respect to cable's increasing capacity for two- way transmission services was the effect of telephone subscriber bypass of the regulated local exchange networks in favor of the potentially unregulated provision of voice and data services by the cable companies."). In the 1996 Act, Congress specifically required that all telecommunications carriers must contribute to universal service. *See* 47 U.S.C. § 254(d). This requirement would have little meaning if cable facilities could be used to escape universal service contributions.

[115] *See Advanced Services Order,* 13 FCC Rcd. at 24030, para. 36 (citation omitted).

[116] *See In re* Applications for Consent to the Transfer of Control of Licenses and Section 214 Authorizations from TCI to AT&T, *Memorandum opinion and Order,* 14 FCC Rcd. 3160, 3195, para. 70 (1999) [hereinafter *TCI Order]; see also FCC Amicus Brief, supra* note 2, at 12-13.

[117] *See TCI Order,* 14 FCC Rcd. at 9195, para. 70.

[118] *See Joint Reply of AT&T and TCI, supra* note 51, at 53-54. In fact, the Pennsylvania Public Utilities Commission recently approved AT&T tariffs for local exchange service offered over TCI's cable network in Pittsburgh and its suburbs. *Pa. PUC Approved AT&T Tariffs for Local Exchange Service,* COMM. DAILY, Dec. 17, 1999, at 10.

[119] The authors are aware that some commentators have argued that the new definition of "information service" and the addition of section 230(b) to the Communications Act have removed from the Commission any jurisdiction over Internet access or other information services, even when those services are provided by a local exchange carrier. *See* Leonard Kennedy & Lori Zallaps, *If It Ain't Broke ...The FCC and Internet Regulation,* 7 COMMLAW CONSPECTUS 17, 26 (1999) .The authors disagree with the legal analysis of the article, which relies heavily on a "policy" statement by Congress in section 230 of the Communications Act dealing with indecent con- tent. The article overlooks completely the legislative history of section 230. The section as passed by the House contained an explicit prohibition on FCC regulation of the Internet, but that restriction was deleted in conference. *See* A LEGISLATIVE HISTORY, *supra* note 7, at 379 ("the House bill's Cox-Wyden ...declaration that the FCC was given no new jurisdiction to regulate the Internet was dropped"). In short, there is nothing in section 230-which in any case is concerned solely with Internet content and not transmission- that supports rejection of the fundamental regulatory structure of the Communications Act and the plain meaning of the definitions contained in sections 3 of the Act.

[120] *See* 142 CONG. Rec. S710 (1996) (statement of Sen. Kerry) (commenting that "[t]hese fundamental features of the conference report on S. 652 [the 1996 Act] are designed to create a level playing field where every player will be able to compete on

the basis of price, quality, and service"); 142 CONG. Rec. H1177 (1996) (statement of Rep. Castle) (stating that "the legislation has sought to ensure that different industries will be competing on a level playing field"); 142 CONG. Rec. S691 (1996) (statement of Sen. Stevens) (explaining that "we have tried to find a way to literally level the playing field. ..I do believe we have succeeded").

[121] 47 U.S.C: § 153(26) (1994 & Supp. III 1997).

[122] *See In re* Deployment of Wireline Services Offering Advanced Telecommunications Capability, *Order on Remand,* FCC 99-413, at para. 3 (reI. Dec. 23, 1999) [hereinafter *Order on Remand]* .

[123] "Telephone exchange service" is service "operated to furnish to subscribers intercommunicating service...or comparable service provided through a system of switches, transmission equipment, or other facilities (or combination thereof) by which a subscriber can originate and terminate a telecommunications service." 47 U.S.C. § 153(47) (1994 & Supp. III 1997).

[124] (1998) "[E]xchange access' " means the "offering of access to telephone exchange services or facilities [.] " 47 U. S.C. § 153(16) (1994 & Supp. III 1997).

[125] *See* 47 U.S.C. § 153(26) (1994 & Supp. III 1997).

[126] *Advanced Services Order,* 13 FCC Rcd. at 24011, para.41. *See also Order on Remand, supra* note 122, at para. 21.

[127] As the Commission recently noted to the Court in *Portland,* "it is not readily apparent why the classification of the service should vary with the facilities used to provide the service." *FCC Amicus Brief, supra* note 2, at 25.

[128] The Act merely states, " 'Local exchange carrier' means *any person* that is engaged in the provision of telephone exchange service or exchange access." 47 U.S.C. §153(26) (1994 & Supp. III 1997) (emphasis added). *See also* City of Dallas, Texas v. FCC, 165 F.3d 341, 354 (5th Cir. 1999) (explaining that "Congress also knew how to distinguish among respective groups of LECs ...When Congress wanted to distinguish traditional, incumbent LECs from the new "competitive" LECs (including cable companies) whose entry the Act facilitated, it did so in plain terms.")

[129] A "telecommunications carrier" is any person who offers telecommunications to the public for a fee, regardless of the facilities used. *See* 47 U.S.C. §153(44) & (46) (1994 & Supp. III 1997).

[130] Part V of Title VI is not discussed at all in any of the works cited in footnote 13 in which various FCC staff examined or opined on the issue of internet access and other information services provided over cable facilities.

[131] *See* 47 U.S.C. § 541(b). Section 303 of the 1996 Act, added a new paragraph (3) to section 621 (b) It also amended section 622(b) to limit franchise fees to "cable service" only. *See* 47 U,S.C.§ 542(b); *see also* S. Conf. Rep. No. 104-230, at 180.

[132] 47 U.S.C. § 572 (a) (1994 & Supp. III 1997).

[133] This provision was intended to "create parity among providers of services using radio communications." S. CONF. REP. No.104-230, at 172; *see also* 47 U.S.C. § 336 (Supp. II 1996) (addressing the regulation of the provision of ancillary and supplementary services by broadcast licensees).

[134] 47 U.S.C. §§521 & 561.

[135] 47 U.S.C. §§ 571 & 573 (1994 & Supp. III 1997).

[136] 47 U.S.C. § 571 (b) (1994 & Supp. III 1997).

[137] *See* S. Conf. Rep. No. 104-230, at 172 ("an integrated cable system utilizing its own telephone exchange facilities"); *see also id.* at 178 ("In another effort to ensure parity among video providers, the conferees state that [open video system] fees may only be assessed on revenues derived from comparable cable services"); *id.* at 180 (stating that "the franchise fee provision is not intended to reach revenues that a cable operator derives for providing new telecommunications services over its system").

[138] National Association of Regulated Utilities Commissioners v. FCC, 533 F.2d 601,608 (1976) [hereinafter *NARUC II*].

[139] H.R. Rep. No.98-934, at 44.

[140] As noted earlier, AT&T has in fact been certified as a local exchange carrier in Pennsylvania for the provision of local exchange service using its cable facilities. *See supra* note 112

[141] "[A]s a result of the walls brought down and the forces unleashed by this bill, it is not clear what will constitute a telephone company in the future-perhaps every firm that transmits information by any electronic means." 142 Cong. Rec. 5698 (1996) (statement of Sen. Kerry.)

[142] These requirements are found, among other places in Title II, in new section 251 of the Communications Act, as added by the 1996 Act. As the Commission found in the *Advanced Services Order,* section 251 is one of the "cornerstones of the framework Congress established in the 1996 Act." *Advanced Services Order,* 13 FCC Rcd. at 24011, para. 76. Given the intensity of the debate surrounding the 1996 Act and importance Congress attached to it, it seems unlikely that Congress would overlook, much less permit, such a possibility.

[143] 47 U.S.C. § 571 (b) (stating that "[a] local exchange carrier that provides cable service through an open video system or a cable system shall not be required, pursuant to subchapter II of this chapter, to make capacity available on a nondiscriminatory basis to any other person for the provision *of cable service directly to subscribers")* (emphasis added).

[144] The Commission noted this problem as well in its *Amicus* brief, stating, "Under [the cable industry's] broad statutory interpretation, however, 'other programming service' would arguably include any transmission capability that enables subscribers to select and receive information, including basic telephone service." *FCC Amicus Brief, supra* note 2, at 24. AT&T's interpretation that "cable service" includes internet access and other information services could also permit the Regional Bell companies to escape the in-region interLATA restrictions so carefully imposed by Congress in section 271 of the Act, because the definition of "incidental interLATA services" in section 271(g)(l)(A) of the Act, which are not subject to the ban-includes "video programming" and "other programming service" as defined in section 602 of the Act *See* 47 U.S.C. § 271(g)(l)(A) (1997).

[145] March 15, 2002, in GN Docket No. 00-185, *In Re Inquiry Concerning High-Speed Access to the Internet Over Cable and Other Facilities.* The proceeding was initiated by the Commission's issuance of a Notice of Inquiry, released on September 28, 2000. Excerpt of Record, *Brand X Internet Services et. al v. Federal Communications Commission*, Nos. 02-70518, 02-70684, 02-70685, 02-70686, 02-70879, 02-72251, (9th

Circ. Court of Appeals), at 0113 [hereinafter, Excerpt]. Comments, reply comments, and permitted *ex parte* presentations totaling some 336 separate entries were received in the record. *See* Certified List of Items in the Record, filed by the Commission with the Court on May 29, 2002.

[146] 47 U.S.C. § 153(46).

[147] 47 U.S.C. § 153(44) ("A telecommunications carrier [provider of telecommunications services] shall be treated as a common carrier under this Act only to the extent that it is engaged in providing telecommunications services. . .").

[148] 47 U.S.C. §§ 201 and 202.

[149] *See* 47 U.S.C. § 160. The Commission has not exercised its forbearance authority with respect to these services. The Commission's expressly reserved that issue for further consideration in the NPRM issued along with the Declaratory Order. Excerpt at 0159.

[150] *See National Cable & Telecomm. Ass'n v. Gulf Power Co.*, 534 U.S. 327, 122 S.Ct. 782, 798 (2002) (dissenting opinion).

[151] Excerpt, *supra* note 145, at 0135.

[152] Excerpt, *supra* note 145, at 0135-36.

[153] *Computer II,* 77 F.C.C. 2d at 384, 475. The separation of the underlying transmission from the computer-enhanced portion of the service is commonly referred to as a requirement to "unbundle." "Unbundling" as used in the *Computer II* proceeding is different from the "unbundling" mandated by section 251(c)(3) of the Act, 47 U.S.C. § 251(c)(3). *Computer II* unbundling refers to the requirement that facilities-based carriers that offer information services over their own transmission facilities must separate their transmission services from the computer processing (information service) functions that ride on those transmission services and must sell the transmission component to competing information service providers on non-discriminatory terms. Section 251(c)(3), in contrast, imposes upon incumbent local exchange carriers an obligation to sell separate network elements to competing telecommunications carriers (which may or may not also be information service providers). *Computer II* unbundling requirements apply to all facilities-based carriers that use their own transmission facilities to deliver information services; section 251(c)(3) applies only to incumbent local exchange carriers.

[154] The Commission asserts at paragraph 32 of the Declaratory Ruling that "[t]he Communications Act does not clearly indicate how cable modem service should be classified or regulated; the relevant statutory provisions do not yield easy or obvious answers to the questions at hand. . . ." Excerpt, *supra* note 145, at 0131. The Commission never identifies what it is about the statute that is unclear or ambiguous. To the extent that the Commission "has ignored the plain text and has attempted to manufacture an ambiguity in order to obtain an increased level of judicial deference," that tactic should be rejected. *City of Dallas v. F.C.C.*, 165 F.3d 341, 353 (5th Cir. 1999). To the extent that the Commission's statement that "[t]he Communications Act does not clearly indicate how cable modem service should be classified" constitutes an argument that the statute must specifically refer to "cable modem service" or some equivalent in order to apply to that service, that argument is also without merit. "Merely because a statute's plain language does not specify particular entities that fall under its definition, does not mean that the statute is ambiguous as to all those who do fall under it." *Royal Foods Co. v.*

RJR Holdings Inc., 252 F.3d 1102, 1107 n.6 (9th Cir. 2001), citing *United States v. Monsanto*, 491 U.S. 600 (1989).

[155] *Maislin Indus. v. Primary Steel*, 497 U.S. 116, 131 (1990); *see also Lechmere v. N.L.R.B.*, 502 U.S. 527, 536-37 (1992); *Neal v. U.S.*, 516 U.S. 284, 295 (1996). This Court has adopted the same approach *Ladha v. INS*, 215 F.3d 889, 896 (9th Cir. 2000) (brackets and notations in original).

[156] 216 F.3d. at 878 (emphasis added). That holding is in direct conflict with the Commission's holding that "[c]able modem service is not itself and *does not include an offering of telecommunications service to subscribers.*" Excerpt, *supra* note 145, at 0135 (emphasis added).

[157] *Ladha v. INS*, 215 F.3d at 896,

[158] Excerpt, *supra* note 145, at 0143-44 (footnote omitted).

[159] *AT&T Corp. v. City of Portland*, 216 F.3d 877 (9th Cir. 2000) (emphasis added).

[160] Excerpt, *supra* note 145, at 0144.

[161] *City of Portland*, 216 F.3d at 876.

[162] Excerpt, *supra* note 145, at 0112.

[163] The Commission defines "'cable modem service' to mean the complete retail offering that is provided to subscribers," i.e., the capability to access the functionality of the Internet combined with the transmission over which the customer is connected to that capability. *See* Excerpt, *supra* note 145, at 0131 n.135.

[164] Excerpt, *supra* note 145, at 0134 (emphasis added).

[165] *see City of Portland*, 261 F.3d at 877-878.

[166] Excerpt, *supra* note 145, at 0135.

[167] "Telecommunications" is also defined in section 3 of the Act. *See* 47 U.S.C. § 153(43). The full text of the definition is set forth in the Addendum.

[168] *Id.* (footnotes omitted) (emphasis added).

[169] *See, e.g.,* EarthLink Comments at 24-31, Excerpt, *supra* note 145, at 0026-0033; *see also* EarthLink November 8, 2001, *Ex Parte* Letter at 10.

[170] *See Bell Atlantic Tel. Cos. v. F.C.C.*, 206 F.3d 1, 9 (D.C. Cir. 2000) (failure of FCC to explain application of statutory terms is independent ground for vacating ruling). As is discussed *infra*, the Commission's interpretation also renders meaningless the Congressional command that the definition applies "regardless of the facilities used." 47 U.S.C. 153(46).

[171] *See e.g.,* Excerpt, *supra* note 145, at 0135.

[172] *See Vincent v. Apfel*, 191 F.3d 1143, 1148 (9th Cir. 1999) ("no justification for adding limiting language to a clear and unambiguous statute and regulation"); *see also United States v. Calamaro*, 354 U.S. 351, 359 (1957) (agency cannot add to the statute "something which is not there").

[173] That Congress did not intend "telecommunications service" to include only that telecommunications that is offered to the public for a fee on a "separate" basis is reinforced by the fact that Congress has demonstrated that it knows how to impose such a requirement when it so desires. The definition of "telephone toll service," found at section 3(48) of the Act (47 U.S.C. § 153(48)), states that such service is "telephone service between stations in different exchange areas *for which there is made a separate*

charge not included in contracts with subscribers for exchange service." *Id.* (emphasis added).   Inasmuch as the Commission's Declaratory Ruling hinges on the fact that cable companies bundle transmission and information services in a single-price offering, Congressional designation of such bundling as significant in the definition of one term ("telephone toll service") indicates that bundling is not significant where the definition of a different term ("telecommunications service") makes no mention of a separate charge.

[174] 77 F.C.C. 2d 384.

[175] *See* Excerpt, *supra* note 145, at 0132 n.139.

[176] Excerpt, *supra* note 145, at 0137.

[177] *Computer II*, 77 F.C.C. 2d at 475.

[178] *In Re* Filing and Review of Open Network Architecture Plans, Memorandum and Order, 4 F.C.C.R. 1, 141 (1988) (emphasis added).   In 1988, for example, the Commission had this to say:

> Bell Atlantic seems to reason that because enhanced services are not common carrier services under Title II, the basic services that underlie enhanced services are somehow also not subject to Title II. We do not agree.   Enhanced services by definition are services "offered over common carrier transmission facilities." Since the Computer II regime, we have consistently held that the addition of the specified types of enhancements (as defined in our rules) to a basic service neither changes the nature of the underlying basic service when offered by a common carrier nor alters the carrier's tariffing obligations, whether federal or state, with respect to that service

[179] *In Re* Independent Data Communications Mfrs. Ass'n. Petition for Declaratory Ruling that AT&T's InterSpan Frame Relay Service is a Basic Service; and Am. Tel. and Tel. Co. Petition for Declaratory Ruling That All IXC's Be Subject to the Commission's Decision on the IDCMA Petition, Memorandum Opinion and Order, 10 F.C.C.R. 13717, 13723 (October 18, 1995) (hereinafter "Frame Relay") (emphasis added). The "contamination theory" discussed in the quoted language refers to the rationale under which information service providers that do not own the transmission facilities over which they deliver their information services have been relieved of otherwise applicable common carrier obligations with respect to that underlying transmission. Such non-facilities-based information service providers were known as value-added-network service providers ("VANs"), see Frame Relay at 13718 n.6, in pre-1996 Act language. "Under the contamination theory, VANs that offer enhanced protocol processing services in conjunction with basic transmission services have historically been treated as unregulated enhanced service providers. Under this theory, the enhanced component of their offerings is viewed as 'contaminating' the basic component, and as a result, the entire offering is considered enhanced." Frame Relay at 13720. It is this doctrine, for example, that prevents non-facilities-based Internet service providers such as EarthLink from being treated as common carriers. If the contamination theory were adopted today for the first time, it would have to be done under the Commission's section 10 (47 U.S.C. § 160) forbearance authority. As the language quoted above from Frame Relay demonstrates, the Commission has never applied the

contamination theory to an entity that uses its own transmission facilities to deliver information services to customers.

[180] *In the Matter of Federal-State Joint Board on Universal Service*, Report To Congress, 13 F.C.C.R. 11501, 11511 (1998) (emphasis added); *see also Declaratory Ruling* at ¶ 34 n.139 (basic/enhanced distinction incorporated into 1996 Act).

[181] Excerpt, *supra* note 145, at 0137 (footnotes omitted).

[182] *McClaskey v. United States Dep't of Energy*, 720 F.2d 583 (9th Cir. 1983), citing *Atchison, Topeka & Santa Fe Ry. v. Wichita Bd. of Trade*, 412 U.S. 800, 807-08 (1973).

[183] 47 U.S.C. § 153(46). *See AT&T Corp. v. City of Portland*, at 871, 879, ("Under the Communications Act, this principle of telecommunications common carriage governs cable broadband as it does other means of Internet transmission such as telephone service and DSL, 'regardless of the facilities used.'") (internal citations omitted).

[184] *See Louisiana-Pacific Corp. v. N.L.R.B.*, 52 F.3d 255, 259 (9th Cir. 1995) (agency order must be upheld, if at all, on the same basis articulated by the agency).

[185] Excerpt, *supra* note 145, at 0137.

[186] Excerpt, *supra* note 145, at 0133 (emphasis added).

[187] 47 U.S.C. § 153(46).

[188] Excerpt, *supra* note 145, at 0022 (emphasis added).

[189] *See, e.g., Greater Boston Tel. Corp. v. F.C.C.*, 444 F.2d 841, 852 (D.C. Cir. 1970) ("[a]n agency changing its course must supply a reasoned analysis indicating that prior policies and standards are being deliberately changed, not casually ignored, and if an agency glosses over or swerves from prior precedents without discussion it may cross the line from the tolerable terse to the intolerably mute.").

[190] Excerpt, *supra* note 145, at 0141-0142 (emphasis added).

[191] *Desert Citizens Against Pollution v. Bisson*, 231 F.3d 1172, 1180 (9th Cir. 2000).

[192] Excerpt, *supra* note 145, at 0183.

[193] *See NARUC II,* at 608 ("Nor is it essential that there be a statutory or other legal commandment to serve indiscriminately; *it is the practice of such indifferent service that confers common carrier status.*") (emphasis added).

[194] Excerpt, *supra* note 145, at 0142 (footnotes omitted) (emphasis added). EarthLink notes that the determination of who is and who is not a common carrier is an area in which the courts have afforded little deference to the Commission. The court in a seminal case on communications common carriers put it this way: "The common law definition of common carrier is sufficiently definite as not to admit of agency discretion in the classification of operating communications entities. *A particular system is a common carrier by virtue of its functions*, rather than because it is declared to be so." *National Ass'n of Regulatory Util. Commrs. v. F.C.C.*, 525 F.2d 630, 644 (D.C. Cir. 1976) (emphasis added) ("NARUC I").

[195] *Id.* (footnote omitted).

[196] *Id.* Paragraph 52 of the Declaratory Ruling does include recitations of a number of assertions made by AOL Time Warner regarding the nature of its agreement with EarthLink, an agreement that AOL Time Warner executed under order of the Federal Trade Commission. *See* Excerpt, *supra* note 145, at 0140 n.194 and accompanying

text (referring to the FTC order). Although EarthLink agreed to waive the confidentiality provision included in the AOL Time Warner agreement to allow the Commission to examine the terms of that agreement, to EarthLink's knowledge the Commission never asked AOL Time Warner to do the same, and the Commission never reviewed the agreement. In any event, the agreement is not in the record, and the AOL Time Warner representations regarding the contents of that and other alleged agreements as recited by the Commission in paragraph 52 of the Declaratory Ruling (Excerpt, *supra* note 145, at 0140-0141) have nothing to do with the private carriage/common carriage analysis.

[197] *See, e.g., Southwestern Bell Tel. Co. v. F.C.C.*, 19 F.3d 1475, 1481 (D.C. Cir. 1994) ("carrier cannot vitiate its common carrier status merely by entering into private contractual relationships with its customers").

[198] Excerpt, *supra* note 145, at 0107-0108.

[199] *NARUC II*, 533 F.2d at 608.

[200] *See* 47 U.S.C. § 202.

[201] Excerpt, *supra* note 145, at 0137.

[202] 47 C.F.R. §1.3 (emphasis added).

[203] 47 U.S.C. §§ 153(46), 153(20), 201, 202.

[204] *See, e.g. Memorial, Inc. v. Harris*, 655 F.2d 905, 910-11 n.14 (9th Cir. 1980).

[205] Excerpt, *supra* note 145, at 0183 (emphasis added).

[206] 47 C.F.R. § 1.3

[207] *See, e.g., Chisholm v. F.C.C.*, 538 F.2d 349, 365 (D.C. Cir. 1976). Where the Commission has no discretion, however, is on the issue of whether the Administrative Procedure Act applies at all to substantive determinations like the *Computer II* waiver at issue here. The Commission's waiver of the *Computer II* rules would fundamentally change the effect of those rules by eliminating for all major cable companies the otherwise applicable requirement that they sell transmission to competing ISPs on nondiscriminatory terms. The waiver therefore qualifies as a substantive (rather than interpretative) rule. *See Alcaraz v. Block*, 746 F.2d 593, 613 (9th Cir. 1984) ("Substantive rules are those which effect a change in existing law or policy.") (internal citations omitted); s*ee also Neighborhood TV Co. v. F.C.C.*, 742 F.2d 629, 637 (D.C. Cir. 1984) ("In determining whether a rule is substantive, we must look at its effect on those interests ultimately at stake in the agency proceeding.") Here, the waiver would allow cable companies to refuse to provide their ISP competitors with transmission capability essential to those competitors' ability to offer service. That is a substantive effect by any measure.

[208] *See* 5 U.S.C. §554(e).

[209] *See MCI Telecommunications Corp. v. AT&T*, 512 U.S. 218, 231 n.4 (1994) (agencies "are bound, not only by the ultimate purposes Congress has selected, but by the means it has deemed appropriate, and prescribed, for the pursuit of those purposes.*")*; *Amalgamated Transit Union v. Skinner*, 894 F.2d 1362, 1364 (D.C. Cir. 1990) ("Where Congress prescribes the form in which an agency may exercise its authority . . . we cannot elevate the goals of an agency's actions, however reasonable, over that prescribed form."); *Beverly Enters., Inc. v. Herman*, 119 F. Supp.2d 1, 11 (D.D.C. 2000) ("[i]t is not the province of this Court to authorize substitution of a potentially more effective method where Congress has provided for one in the statute."); *see also In Re Sealed*

Case, 237 F.3d 657 (D.C. Cir. 2001); *PDK Labs v. Reno*, 134 F. Supp.2d 24, 35 (D.D.C. 2001).

[210] 47 U.S.C. §160(a) (emphasis added).

[211] *See Computer II*, 77 F.C.C. 2d at 429; *see also Universal Service* Report To Congress, 13 F.C.C.R. 11501, 11511.

[212] Notice of Inquiry at ¶ 54, Excerpt, *supra* note 145, at 0022.

[213] Declaratory Ruling at n. 219, Excerpt, *supra* note 145, at 0144.

[214] 47 U.S.C. §160(a)(1)-(3).

IX. A HORIZONTAL LEAP FORWARD

LETTER TO EVANS AND POWELL

May 20, 2002

The Honorable Donald Evans
Secretary
United States Department of Commerce
1401 Constitution Avenue, N.W.
Washington, D.C. 20230

The Honorable Michael Powell
Chairman
Federal Communications Commission
445 12th Street, S.W.
Washington, D.C. 20554

Dear Secretary Evans and Chairman Powell:

I am writing you both today out of a desire to assist in your deliberations regarding proposed changes in this nation's public policies governing the deployment and use of so-called "broadband" telecommunications technologies. As the Department of Commerce considers adopting a national broadband policy, the Federal Communications Commission has embarked on a number of rulemaking proceedings pertaining to broadband deployment. From my perspective, the Commission appears poised to take certain steps which could undo much of the pro-competitive promise of the Telecommunications Act of 1996, and consign American consumers to a broadband future controlled by the dominant telephone and cable bottlenecks. As I explain below, I believe strongly that U.S. policymakers should heed important historical lessons about the rise and success of the Internet, and ensure that competitors and consumers alike have access to the still-developing broadband world through open, nondiscriminatory telecommunications platforms.

Over the course of twenty-five years of working with the Department of Commerce and the FCC, my experience has proven that regardless of the issue, both agencies have stood steadfastly for a vision of public policy that fosters robust competition and innovation in all Internet and telecommunications-related markets. Over the past few months I have engaged in especially helpful meetings on a number of issues with Assistant Secretary Nancy Victory. I was particularly honored to be included as a participant in her broadband "roundtable" last October, which served as a precursor to the broadband deployment proceeding initiated by NTIA in November. I also was honored to address the Commission this past February as part of the Chairman's "Distinguished Lecture" series, and to have the opportunity to meet and talk with Chairman Powell.

Today, I want to offer you my view of key elements of broadband policy, and convey my concerned observations about several broadband-related regulatory proceedings now underway at the FCC. In my view, the policy direction suggested by these proceedings could have a profoundly negative impact on the Internet, and the availability of the high-capacity telecommunications connections so necessary to its current and future openness and competitive nature. I believe the FCC direction is paradoxically self-inconsistent and at odds with the pro-competition philosophy of the Administration in general.

As both of you may know, I have a long history of involvement in the initiation and growth of the "network of networks" we now call the Internet. I derived great satisfaction as an engineer in the mid-1970s from my collaboration with Bob Kahn on the development of a suite of networking protocols, the Transmission Control Protocol and Internet Protocol ("TCP/IP"). The IP protocol in particular proved to be a remarkably potent realization of a multi-network open architecture. By its very design, the protocol was intended to be ubiquitous and open to all types of applications, carrying all kinds of content, over all forms of transmission technology, by all sorts of service providers. Over the intervening years scores of protocols have been layered on top of IP and its adjunct protocol, TCP — from the Domain Name System (DNS) protocols to the World Wide Web protocols (notably HTTP) — but the role of IP as the open standard transcending technologies and modalities remains.

Of course, merely inventing a particular protocol for delivering bits of information from one end of the country to another does not guarantee that one can create applications, services, and content that are able to actually utilize this delivery system. Although the IP protocol has allowed the creation of open, interconnected networks, in reality the networks can only be as open as the various conduits used to reach them. It is here, at the "edge" of these otherwise-open networks, where the dictates of public policy can have such a profound impact. In this regard, the FCC first helped set the stage for small pieces of protocol to leap from blackboards and laboratories into the vibrant marketplace.

The FCC has a long and distinguished legacy of support for non-regulation of information services generally and the Internet in particular. Part of this legacy entails embracing the straightforward concept that all providers of information services, content, and applications have an equal right to use the local telephone network to reach their customers. This policy of nondiscriminatory treatment was established back in the late 1970s in the so-called Computer Inquiry proceedings, and the resulting rules governing how the telephone companies must unbundle and offer their basic transmission services to unregulated enhanced service providers ("ESPs") on the same rates, terms, and conditions that they offer such basic services to themselves. These Computer Inquiry interconnection and unbundling rules have been in place for nearly a quarter century now, and have had a profoundly positive and far-reaching impact on this country's economic and social landscape. In particular, literally thousands of players were free to unleash their creative, innovative, and inspired product and service ideas in the competitive information services marketplace, without artificial barriers erected by the local telephone companies. I am firmly convinced that the Commission's foresight in this area contributed strongly towards the commercial introduction, rise, and incredible success of the Internet.

The 1996 Act built on this regulatory legacy in the information services area (as well as the long distance and equipment markets), by mandating that the local telephone network monopolies be broken open once and for all. Through the establishment of various pro-competitive requirements, such as interconnection, unbundling, collocation, and resale, Congress sought to give would-be competitors the tools they would need to pry open a market that had never seen the light of competition (in that vein, it is especially gratifying that the U.S. Supreme Court last week reaffirmed the FCC's "TELRIC" (Total Element Long Run Incremental Cost) standard as fully consistent with the Telecommunications Act). Indeed, the 1996 Act essentially mirrored the FCC's conclusion in the Computer Inquiry proceedings: access to monopoly-controlled facilities must be provided so that non-monopolies may compete. While we still are a long way from significant competition in the local market, the tools are available - if the regulators are prepared to act on this mandate.

Unfortunately, I am beginning to see troubling signs that the FCC's pro-competitive legacy, and the resulting benefits to American consumers and businesses, may be in serious jeopardy. Over the past few months, the FCC has initiated several interrelated rulemaking proceedings that appear to have at their core the single-minded but mistaken notion that open, nondiscriminatory telecommunications platforms no longer serve the public interest when they are used to provide so-called "broadband" services. In particular, the Commission has suggested an intention to prevent competitive telephone companies ("CLECs") from leasing elements of the incumbent telephone companies' ("ILECs") networks to provide competing services, contrary to the dictates of the Telecommunications Act. Moreover, the Commission has suggested that its longstanding Computer Inquiry rules — which allow Internet service providers ("ISPs") to utilize the underlying telecommunications services necessary to serve consumers — no longer are necessary in a broadband world. In other words, the FCC appears determined to deny CLECs and ISPs the very capabilities they need to survive, let alone flourish, in the market. Together the proposals, if adopted, would effectively wall off the local telephone network from competitive entry and eviscerate any chance of fostering competition and innovation in these interrelated worlds.

As far as I can discern, the Commission appears to premise its suggested approach on a few key mistaken "factual" assumptions: (1) "broadband" is a different sort of animal from "narrowband;" (2) robust "intermodal" competition exists or soon will exist between different facilities-based providers of broadband services; and (3) the incumbent local phone companies in particular require additional incentives to deploy Digital Subscriber Line ("DSL")-based broadband services. From this engineer's perspective, none of these assumptions have any merit.

First, my engineering training and instincts chafe at the notion that something we choose to call "broadband" is something wholly separate and apart from narrowband or, indeed, from the underlying network that supports it. In the context of the local telephone network, DSL technology is merely the latest in a continuing stream of incremental improvements to the use of the existing telephone network. DSL constitutes a group of copper-based technologies that encompasses a family of related protocols, all of which collectively have one job: transmitting information over existing copper local loops. DSL technologies can do this job at higher bit rates than more traditional "dial-up" modems, but there is little else to distinguish them. Moreover, this transmission path should not in any way be confused with one of the more common applications of DSL: Internet access. While DSL essentially is an "edge" technology that can be and is used to reach the Internet, DSL is not in any way equivalent to the Internet. Building an anticompetitive telecommunications policy around the ordinary capabilities of DSL, and one of its many applications, makes no sense to me. Also, the notion that extension of fiber further into the network somehow creates a wholly new network that should be closed off to competitors is equally without merit.

This observation is particularly crucial in the context of new "last mile" access technologies such as Gigabit Ethernet ("GE"). There are two important facts to keep in mind about GE as a means of accessing data networks: (1) it is a thousand times faster than the best cable modem or DSL services, and (2) it is symmetric, meaning it can deliver data at these same speeds in both directions. These are vital differences from currently available high-speed access technologies that tend to be asymmetric, typically supporting higher delivery speeds towards subscribers and slower ones from them. The significant point, of course, is that all of these various "competing" services are delivered on monopoly-controlled channels.

Second, the concept of "intermodal" competition, like many appealing notions, appears profound on the surface, but quickly loses credibility upon closer inspection. Physics gets in the way of the supposed competition. It is true that the phone companies and cable companies compete today in many places to provide high-speed, asymmetric Internet access to residential customers. However, this competition is not ubiquitous. Even with comparatively wider coverage, DSL is still not available to many consumers because of distance from their central offices, while some cable providers may not have invested in the requisite hybrid fiber/coax technology to provide cable modem service.

Moreover, other potential modalities - such as satellite and fixed wireless systems - lack the technical characteristics that would enable them to offer a viable third or fourth alternative to these near-ubiquitous modalities. In particular, satellite-based broadband service (1) is only available by line-of-sight, (2) is vulnerable to precipitation effects and latency problems, (3) utilizes expensive or inefficient technology (including either costly two-way dishes or separate telephone "dial-up" return), and (4) typically yields lower quality and bandwidth. Fixed wireless service (such as MMDS) possesses many of the same technical drawbacks as satellite service, as well as the additional factors of the limited availability of spectrum and shared spectral bands. In short, while these technologies offer the promise of niche services in the broadband market, neither comes close to the widespread reach of the local telephone networks and cable networks.

At best, the residential broadband market is a duopoly-and in the worst case, consumers have only one choice or, in poorly served areas, no choice at all. This circumstance seems hardly likely to result in driving the benefits of lower prices and innovative service offerings that would come from a more thoroughly competitive market. Indeed, the Consumer Federation of America recently released a detailed report exposing the myth of intermodal competition in the residential high-speed Internet market, and demonstrating the negative consequences to consumers of a cable/ telco duopoly. In addition, cable systems generally do not serve businesses, so the vast majority of American businesses continue to rely solely on the incumbent local telephone network. In my view, then, there is no possible justification for effectively closing competitors' access to this network that would result in termination of the robust "intramodal" competition that CLECs seek to bring to the market. Indeed, I am persuaded that open access to all transmission media is the only way to guarantee that every ISP can reach every possible subscriber by every means available. Of course, open access does not mean free access. The suppliers of the alternative transmission media should be fairly compensated for providing such access, as required by the Telecommunications Act. As the Supreme Court held last week, the TELRIC standard provides ample compensation to the ILECs for CLECs' use of their facilities.

Third, I am genuinely puzzled by the notion that the local telephone companies need any additional incentives to deploy broadband services. To begin with, as all competitive enterprises know well, competition is its own incentive. The local telephone companies claim they are battling fiercely with the cable companies, and the few remaining CLECs, to provide broadband services to American consumers. In such an environment, no company can afford to sit on the sidelines and watch its competitors take the market. To the extent the ILECs believe they can choose to do so, of course, it is yet another sign that they have market power in providing broadband services.

In addition, the ILECs' argument that they are not adequately compensated for providing wholesale broadband functionalities, which in turn fails to stimulate facilities-based investment by both ILECs and CLECs, does not bear close scrutiny. No less an authority than the Supreme Court concluded that the ILECs' "lack of incentives" argument "founders on fact." Among other things, the TELRIC standard includes direct and overhead costs, depreciation expense, and risk-adjusted cost of capital. As Justice Souter observed, "TELRIC rates leave plenty of room for differences in the appropriate depreciation rates and risk-adjusted capital costs depending on the nature and technology of the specific element to be priced." The Court ultimately determined that it is reasonable to prefer TELRIC over "alternative fixed-cost schemes that preserve home-field advantages for the incumbents."

More fundamentally, however, there is no lack of broadband deployment. As Assistant Secretary Victory, Under Secretary Bond, and FCC officials uniformly have attested in recent months, broadband deployment in this country is robust. Current figures from numerous studies demonstrate that between 70 to 85 percent of all Americans have ready access to some broadband services. If their claims to shareholders and Wall Street are any indication, the ILECs certainly show no signs of slowing deployment, especially as a result of complying with the Act. Any public policy issue pertaining to broadband should focus on the comparatively low take-rates (somewhere around 10 percent of American consumers). Excessive pricing by the two dominant providers, and a lack of compelling consumer applications, are market realities that cannot be blamed on pro-competitive regulation.

Thus, there appears to be no viable reason for the FCC to step back from the requirements of the Act, its own pro-competitive legacy, and the pro-competitive economic policies of the Bush Administration, to embrace a future where, at best, consumers can only receive what unregulated monopolies and/or duopolies are willing to give them. Certainly such a retrograde step would not be consistent with my own personal vision. I am well aware that some may not share my conviction that consumers are best served by open platforms spread across many competing modalities. Nonetheless, should the United States Government decide that it does not have the will or inclination to require that one of the two dominant modalities — cable — create an open platform, it should not lack the wisdom to ensure that the one remaining platform — telephony — remains open to all. In fact, as I have suggested above, the openly accessible platform of all modalities is the heart and soul of the Internet, and was Congress' intention for the local telecom market when it adopted the Telecommunications Act.

I thank both of you for your attention to this most important public policy matter. I look forward to the opportunity to discuss with you and your staff the constructive ways in which the U.S. Government can help promote and defend competition and innovation within the telecommunications networks residing at the "edge" of the dynamic — and open — Internet.

Sincerely,

Vint Cerf

FORMULATING A NEW PUBLIC POLICY FRAMEWORK BASED ON THE NETWORK LAYERS MODEL

OVERVIEW AND SUMMARY

This white paper proposes that U.S. policymakers develop, apply, and promote a new network engineering-supported public policy framework for all Internet Protocol (IP)-based services, applications, and facilities.[*] The framework would be founded upon the multiple network "layers" or "levels" built into the construct of the TCP/IP protocol stack. If adopted, the tailored principles established by the <u>horizontal layers framework</u> could be used to analyze the viability of specific legislative, regulatory, and administrative proposals. The principles also could provide a compelling new way to frame current policy issues in the larger context of non-arbitrary engineering functionalities.

The proposed horizontal layers framework contained in the MCI Layers Model would help further a number of important objectives in the public policy space, including:

- Create a rational, sustainable legal and regulatory framework for the coming IP-centric world;

- Prevent the unwarranted imposition of legacy telecommunications regulation and new ISP liability obligations on IP-based applications, by the Executive Branch, Congress, the Federal Communications Commission (FCC), the Federal Trade Commission (FTC), and other national regulators;

- Justify preempting intrusive Internet regulation by states and localities;

- Lessen or remove existing legacy retail regulation of competitive telecommunications services (such as traditional voice telephony service); and

- Focus regulatory and antitrust attention and resources on one compelling public policy issue: market power over last-mile physical infrastructure.

In short, the paper proposes nothing less than a comprehensive framework that policymakers should apply to all electronic transmission technologies and services supported by the TCP/IP protocol suite. Moreover, the framework need not be confined to the world of the Internet, as the basic protocol topologies described further below apply equally well to other types of networks, including plain old telephone service networks, as well as frame relay, ATM, MPLS, and Ethernet. At minimum, the network layers principle can have a separate function as a useful tool for analyzing pressing issues in the e-commerce and e-business arena, as well as current telecommunications issues such as local competition, broadband regulation, IP-based voice communications (usually referred to as Voice over IP, or VoIP), intercarrier compensation, and universal service funding. In short, this paper proposes to incorporate the conceptual underpinnings of the layers principle into all facets of current U.S. communications-related public policy debates. Through the judicious use of this principle, public policy choices can be grounded not in vague theoretical abstractions, but in the ways that communications networks actually are designed, constructed, and operated.

Part I of the paper provides the pertinent legal and technical background, and sets the stage for explanation of the "layers principle" in Part II, as described and endorsed by a small but growing number of legal, economic, and technology commentators. Part III applies the layers principle, as formulated most comprehensively by Professor Lawrence Solum, in the context of current e-commerce issues. Because Solum provides a thorough analysis of the layers principle in various e-commerce settings, the bulk of the paper introduces additional corollaries and analyzes regulatory debates in the traditional common carrier context, with a particular focus on broadband, VoIP, and other pressing telecommunications regulatory issues. In this author's judgment, while application of the layers framework does not miraculously provide ready-made answers to every public policy conundrum, at the very least it does allow policymakers to start asking the right kinds of questions.

BACKGROUND

THE WORLD OF LEGACY COMMUNICATIONS REGULATION

In the "old" days before the Internet, the particular communications service offered and the underlying technology utilized essentially were considered as one and the same. For example, the copper telephone line carried voice telephony service, the coaxial cable line carried cable television video service, and radio waves carried broadcast television and radio services. Later, different radio bands were used to provide wireless telephony services and satellite broadcast television service. Communications-related industries, many of them monopolies or oligopolies, developed around the technology platforms and the particular retail services they provided to the public.

As a result of this previously-unquestioned fit of message and medium, U.S. policymakers organized the country's legal and regulatory superstructure around these "vertical" composite systems.[1] Notably, the Communications Act of 1934, and subsequent amendments, bought into this notion of vertically-oriented regulation, and so we have different law provisions – such as Title II (telephony), Title III (television and radio, and wireless communications), and Title VI (cable television) – that apply to different service/technology "silos."[2] Not surprisingly, the FCC adopted the same schema when it formed the Common Carrier (now Wireline Competition) Bureau, the Mass Media Bureau, and later the Wireless Telecommunications Bureau. Figure 1 lays it out schematically.

Beginning in the mid-1960s, the FCC took a first tentative step away from the vertical silos approach in the telephony space by separating out a certain category of new applications and services that happen to utilize basic telephony facilities (see Figure 2). In the initial *Computer Inquiry* decision, the FCC began wrestling with fundamental questions concerning the observed growing convergence between "the modern day electronic computer" and "communication common carrier facilities and services."[3] Even at this early stage, the FCC already had recognized that

Figure 1

The Present "Silo Model" of Regulation

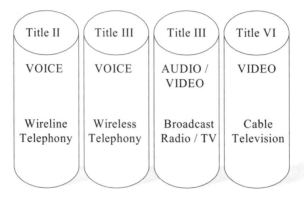

Figure 2

The Birth of the Layered Regulatory Approach

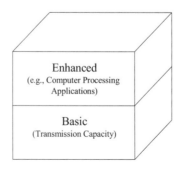

computer-based services are separate from, and increasingly depend upon, communications services, and that a different regulatory regime was necessary to allow the nascent computing industry to compete without undue interference from government regulators or meddling communications carriers.

After several inconclusive starts, in 1980 the FCC issued its seminal *Computer II* order, which distinguished those services which should continue to be regulated as common carriage offerings under Title II of the Communications Act from those services which utilize communications inputs in a highly competitive, and unregulated, "value-added" services marketplace. The Commission classified all services offered over a telecommunications network as either "basic" or "enhanced." Put simply, "basic transmission services are traditional common carrier communications services" provided by telephone companies, and "enhanced services are not."[4] More specifically, the Commission observed that basic service constitutes "the common carrier offering of transmission capacity for the movement of information."[5] In contrast, an enhanced service must meet one of three criteria: it must (1) employ computer processing applications that act on the format, content, protocol, or similar aspects of the subscriber's transmitted information; (2) provide the subscriber additional, different, or restructured information; or (3) involve subscriber interaction with stored information.[6] In all cases, an enhanced service by definition is "offered over common carrier transmission facilities used in interstate communications;" in other words, a basic communications component underlies every enhanced service, so that an enhanced service essentially "rides" on a basic service. Because enhanced services are provided in a competitive marketplace, the FCC decided to leave them unregulated.[7]

While the *Computer Inquiry* rules are remembered largely for the creation of these important definitional distinctions between regulated basic services and unregulated enhanced services, perhaps an even more critical decision followed. The FCC had the then-uncommon insight that because basic communications service constitutes "the building block" upon which enhanced services are offered, "enhanced services are dependent upon the common carrier offering of basic services…"[8] The Commission expressed concern that then-AT&T would have the motive and opportunity to provide unregulated enhanced services in a way that used its own underlying communications facilities and services in a discriminatory and anticompetitive manner. In order to protect against the potential for carriers to commit anticompetitive acts against enhanced service providers (ESPs), the Commission required such carriers to unbundle and provide the underlying basic transmission services to all ESPs on a nondiscriminatory basis. The thrust of this requirement, the Commission explained, is "to establish a structure under which common carrier transmission facilities are offered by them to all providers of enhanced services (including their own enhanced subsidiary) on an equal basis." This requirement "provides a structural constraint on the potential for abuse of the parent's market power through controlling access to and use of the underlying transmission facilities in a discriminatory and anticompetitive manner."[9]

Much deservedly has been made of the crucial role that the FCC's basic/enhanced distinction, and concomitant ESP "equal access" requirement, played in the ultimate birth and development of the Internet. Robert Cannon, for example, claims that the *Computer Inquiry* rules were "a necessary precondition for the success of the Internet" because they involved "affirmative and aggressive regulation of communications networks, specifically for the benefit of the computer networks."[10] Jonathan Weinberg states that the approach taken in the *Computer Inquiry* proceeding "was wildly successful in spurring innovation and competition in the enhanced-services marketplace," because "government maintained its control of the underlying transport, sold primarily by regulated monopolies, while eschewing any control over the newfangled, competitive 'enhancements.'"[11] In the same vein, Philip Weiser notes that the FCC's insistence on non-discriminatory access obligations would "ensure that the telecommunications network could be used for a variety of services (*e.g.*, Internet access) and that rival companies could market equipment like modems that could connect to the network."[12]

Vint Cerf, widely acknowledged as a "father of the Internet," also has pointed out how the *Computer Inquiry* decisions allowed thousands of players to "unleash their creative, innovative, and inspired product and service ideas in the competitive information services marketplace, without artificial barriers erected by the local telephone companies." In Cerf's judgment, "the Commission's foresight in this area contributed strongly towards the commercial introduction, rise, and incredible success of the Internet."[13]

Perhaps overlooked in this justifiable praise is the fact that the FCC had adopted what one could call a horizontal layered regulatory approach, at odds with the vertical silos of the Communications Act. As mentioned previously, the *Computer Inquiry* orders determined that online information services were one type of thing essentially "riding on top of" basic telecommunications services. Cannon has indicated that the basic versus enhanced dichotomy "established a transformation in the conceptual framework, migrating from attempts to determine differences between technologies [Computer I] to an examination of differences between services experienced by edge users." While not necessarily overtly, Cannon indicates, the *Computer Inquiry* orders adopted a horizontal layered model of regulation. Douglas Sicker writes that the *Computer Inquiry* orders "set out the original layered model; separation of the basic transport network from that of the services."[14] Kevin Werbach also believes that the FCC's basic/enhanced distinction can be viewed as a partial implementation of an appropriately layered approach. "The binary distinction embodied in the *Computer II* and *Computer III* decisions … is not sufficiently fine-grained to address the issues in today's data-centric networks, but it has proven quite resilient given the technological and competitive changes since it was first developed."[15] Wittingly or otherwise, the notion of differentiated regulation of the horizontal layers of an electronic communications system was born.

THE NETWORK ENGINEERING CONCEPT OF LAYERED ARCHITECTURE

Of course, even as the FCC first began looking at the definitional issues in its *Computer Inquiry* docket, the various online networks that eventually would comprise the commercial Internet already were being organized around fundamental engineering principles. Key to that organization was the concept of horizontally layered and vertically stacked network architecture, which together with application of the "end-to-end" principle have formed the basis for modern telecommunications architecture standards.[16]

The Layering and End-to-End Principles

One significant point in the development of the modern communications network came in 1969, while the Network Working Group (NWG) of graduate students was working on the U.S. Department of Defense Advanced Research Project Agency (ARPA) network's host-to-host communications system. Among other achievements, the group adopted the word "protocol" (then in widespread use in the medical and political fields to mean "agreed procedures") to denote the set of rules created to enable communications via the ARPANET.[17] In addition, the NWG wrestled with the question of how to construct the foundational protocol in relation to application protocols. As Katie Hafner and Matthew Lyon described it:

> Whatever structure they chose, they knew they wanted it to be as open, adaptable, and accessible to inventiveness as possible. The general view was that any protocol was a potential building block, and so the best approach was to define simple protocols, each limited in scope, with the expectation that any of them might someday be joined or modified in various unanticipated ways. The protocol design philosophy adopted by the NWG broke new ground for what came to be widely accepted as the "layered" approach to protocols.[18]

Five years later, Vint Cerf and Robert Kahn issued their seminal paper on the TCP/IP protocol suite, in which the authors "present a protocol design and philosophy that supports the sharing of resources that exist in different packet switching networks."[19]

Simply put, it is difficult and undesirable to write a single protocol (a set of standardized rules governing the format and conventions of data transmissions between two devices) to handle every operation in a network. As a result, engineers use multiple protocols that partition a communication problem into disparate sub-problems and organize the software into modules that handle the sub-problems. Functions are allocated to different protocol layers or levels, with standardized interfaces between layers. The flexibility offered through the layering approach allows products and services to evolve, by accommodating changes made at the appropriate layer rather than having to rework the entire set of protocols. In other words, layering allows changes to implementation of one layer without affecting others, as long as the interfaces between the layers remain constant.[20]   Figures 3 and 4 show the major advantage of a layered engineering approach.

Given the obvious benefits of protocol layering in terms of simplifying network design and management issues, telecommunications

Figure 3

Without Layers

In the absence of layering, each individual application must
be reconfigured to accommodate every type of network

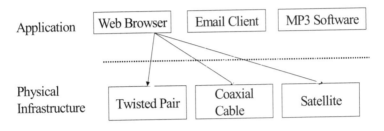

Figure 4

With Layers

Using an intervening protocol layer provides a level of abstraction
that makes the architecture easier to manage

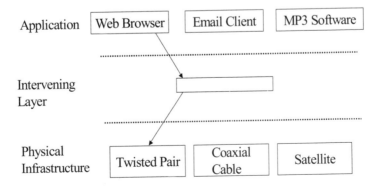

network architectures historically have been broken into various protocol-derived layers. Almost by definition, layers create a degree of "modularity," which allows for ease of maintenance within the network. This modularity, or independence, of each layer creates a useful level of abstraction as one moves through the layered stack. As shown above, applications or protocols at higher layers can be developed or modified with little or no impact on lower layers. This can result in tremendous efficiencies when one seeks to upgrade an existing application (higher layer) that makes use of extensive existing plant (lower layer). Additionally, layers facilitate communications between disparate communications networks.[21]

Moreover, the concept of "end-to-end" network design is closely related to, and provides substantial support for, the concept of protocol layering. Timothy Wu, one of the first scholars to analyze the layered approach with relation to Internet legal analysis, points out that the decision to adopt a layered network architecture does not answer the subsequent question: where exactly to place network functions within this architecture.[22] By itself, the architecture is an empty shell, without specifications on how what Wu calls "the duty to code function" (the ability to delineate specific network functions) will be delegated among layers. In essence, the end-to-end argument states that a class of functions can only be completely and correctly implemented by the applications at each end of a network communication.[23]

As related to the Internet, the end-to-end argument is transformed into a principle to make the basic Internet protocols simple, general, and open, leaving the power and functionality in the hands of the application.[24] Weiser indicates that the end-to-end network design "allows for diversity of the modes of physical access as well as a plethora of applications and content developed to work with the TCP/IP standard."[25] The resulting explosion of innovative applications on the Internet likely would never have happened but for the incorporation of the end-to-end design into the network.[26] In Wu's words, "the Internet's layered architecture and embedded end-to-end design have created an Internet where coding power resides among the designers of applications."[27]

Protocol Layer Models

Since the early 1970s, engineers have developed various network design models incorporating protocols in a layered manner. While sharing a common overall structure and philosophy, these protocol layers models have been organized in somewhat different ways to serve different purposes. Two models in particular stand out.

The justly famous Internet Protocol Suite, introduced in 1974,[28] involves multiple layers riding on separate physical infrastructure. The IP Suite has become the de facto name for a family of over 100 data communications protocols used to organize computer and data communications equipment into practical computer networks. It has been noted that there is no standard, universally accepted way to describe the relevant layers of Internet architecture;[29] Figure 5 shows one typical layer schematic.

Notably, the data received from the applications at the upper layers is broken up into data packets to be handed to the TCP/IP layers; conversely,

Figure 5

Layers Model of the TCP/IP Protocol Suite

Utility Layer	HTTP, FTP, DNS …
Transport Layer	TCP, UDP
Network (Internet Protocol) Layer	IP, ICMP, IGMP
Link Layer	Interface to the Physical Layer
Physical Layer	Ethernet, Modem, DSL, Cable, T1, Fiber Optics, Satellite, Bluetooth, Wi-Fi …

the data packets received from the TCP/IP layers are assembled into a data stream to be delivered to the upper layers. In the encapsulation of data, lower layers treat data passed from upper layers as structureless pure data ("payload"), and place headers and/or trailers around the payload. As Ashish Shah and others state: "Modularity promotes fair and open competition between and among providers of the different layers by allowing competitors to compete with products that will interoperate. The modularity/stratification coupled with openness facilitates the introduction of new transmission technologies and new applications thereby stimulating innovation."[30]

Another example of a protocol layers model is the Open System Interconnection (OSI) Reference Model, which was first developed in 1978 by the International Organization for Standardization and provided a conceptual basis for international protocol development and implementation.[31] The OSI Model includes seven embedded layers:

Application Layer – Semantics — application programs such as electronic mail
Presentation Layer – Syntax — includes functions for basic encoding rules
Session Layer – Dialog Coordination — handles application functionalities
Transport Layer – Reliable Data Transfer — breaks data into packets for transport
Network Layer – Routing and Relaying — handles network flow of data packets
Data Link Layer – Technology-Specific Transfer – interface with physical layer
Physical Layer – Physical Connections — specifies electrical/photonic characteristics

Like the TCP/IP suite, the OSI Model is layered to segment discrete functional responsibilities. Each layer represents a function performed when data is transferred between cooperating applications across the network. In the resulting vertical hierarchy, the content begins at the top layer and works down to the lower physical layer for transport to the ultimate destination, where it then ascends to the top layer again.[32]

From these two standardized industry models (of which the IP Suite has achieved much more universal acceptance and prominence),[33] others have attempted to glean a common model that incorporates the key functions of the different layers.[34] One of the more recent layering models has been suggested by Professor Yochai Benkler of New York University, whom Larry Lessig has described as "perhaps the best communications theorist of our generation."[35] The Benkler model of **Communications System Layers** incorporates the TCP/IP protocol suite as part of three distinct layers: the physical infrastructure, the logical/code/applications layer, and the content layer.[36] Figure 6 shows how these three layers of the Benkler model relate to one another.

In all of these engineering-based models, the fundamental point is that the horizontal layers, defined by code or software, serve as the functional components of an end-to-end communications system.[37] Each layer operates on its own terms, with its own unique rules and constraints, and interfaces with other layers in carefully defined ways.

Figure 6

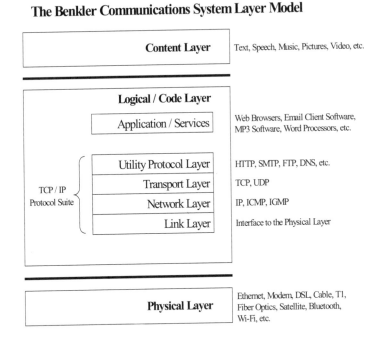

The Benkler Communications System Layer Model

The Internet Era: Legal Walls Stay Up As Logical Walls Come Down

The Communications World

As the 1990s unfolded, political interest in adopting a modern telecommunications law increased. In 1994, while the outline of a new federal statute was beginning to take shape, the Clinton Administration proposed adding another title to the Communications Act. Title VII would have established a new overarching regulatory paradigm governing all "two-way, broadband, interactive, switched, digital transmission services," regardless of the underlying technology.[38] Some subsequently have labeled the Title VII initiative "tremendously ambitious,"[39] while others see it as merely another example of "incremental adaptation of past rules."[40] With concerted industry opposition, however, the end result was a stalled effort on the Title VII approach,[41] and eventual adoption two years later of the Telecommunications Act.

The Telecommunications Act of 1996, while largely sticking to the legacy regulatory "silo" regime, took a small step towards the horizontally layered engineering world in several respects. Most importantly, the 1996 Act largely adopted the basic/enhanced services split, in the guise of "telecommunications service" and "information service,"[42] thereby affirming the rich legacy of the *Computer Inquiry* decisions. In addition, new Section 706 (adopted only as a footnote to the U.S. Code, and not as a separate title unto itself) focused on encouraging the deployment of what Congress called "advanced telecommunications capability."[43] This capability supports a panoply of "voice, data, graphics, and video telecommunications," but "using any technology" and "without regard to any transmission media or technology."[44] The apparent separation between the wide range of services and applications, and the agnostic physical networks involved, appears to be informed in part by the brief legislative battle over the Title VII proposal.

In a slightly different bent, Section 251 of the 1996 Act created a new unbundling regime that focused both on the physical infrastructure that comprise monopoly local exchange networks (local loops, local switches, transport facilities), and all the vertical capabilities that come with those "unbundled network elements" (UNEs).[45] Under Section 271 of the 1996 Act, the Bell Operating Companies (BOCs) were allowed to provide a previously-barred category of services (voice and data in-region long distance service) in exchange for allowing competitors to access and utilize underlying local network functionalities.[46]

Despite these uncharacteristic variations, however, the 1996 Act largely retained the pre-existing vertical legal walls separating various services and applications/networks from each other.[47] A recent report by the National Research Council opines that the 1996 Act for the most part "assumes the continued existence of a number of distinct services that run over distinct communications technologies and separate infrastructure," and thus "does not fully reflect the converged nature of broadband (different communications infrastructure are able to deliver a similar set of services using a common platform, the Internet)."[48] As attorney John Nakahata puts it, "the 1996 Act only started the work of reforming our communications laws to truly harmonize the diversity of regulation among information platforms."[49]

Meanwhile, the FCC retains its basic/enhanced dichotomy and fundamental nondiscriminatory unbundling requirement through the various *Computer Inquiry* proceedings. Even when the Commission replaced the Bell Operating Companies' structural separation requirements with nonstructural safeguards, it affirmed and strengthened the requirement that the BOCs acquire transmission capacity for their own enhanced services operations under the same tariffed terms and conditions as competitive ESPs.[50] Following passage of the Telecommunications Act, the FCC found that the preexisting *Computer Inquiry* requirements are consistent with the statute, and continue to govern BOC provision of information services.[51] The Commission explained that the *Computer Inquiry*-based rules are "the only regulatory means by which certain independent ISPs are guaranteed nondiscriminatory access to BOC local exchange services used in the provision of intraLATA information services."[52]

In 2001, the FCC emphasized the continued retention of the "fundamental provisions" contained in the *Computer Inquiry* decisions "that facilities-based carriers continue to offer the underlying transmission service on nondiscriminatory terms, and that competitive enhanced service providers should therefore continue to have access to this critical input."[53] In particular, the Commission stressed, "the separate availability of the transmission service is fundamental to ensuring that dominant carriers cannot discriminate against customers who do not purchase all the components of a bundle from the carriers, themselves."[54] Thus, the FCC repeatedly and forcefully has acknowledged the "fundamental provisions" of the *Computer Inquiry* decisions that protect an ESP's ability to access lower level transmission services as a "critical input." As will be seen below, that position is now under severe challenge by the very same agency that originally promulgated and defended it.[55]

The Internet World

Meanwhile, on the supposedly unregulated Internet side of the basic/enhanced services divide, vertically-inclined legal precedent was being established by Congress, the courts, and the states. Since the rise of the commercial Internet in the early 1990s, ISPs have found themselves being held legally responsible for the actions of third parties utilizing their networks. Under this new concept of "ISP liability," providers of wholesale and retail network connectivity are deemed responsible for the content exchanged and applications provided by end user customers and unaffiliated third parties.

Congress first addressed the issue squarely in the Digital Millennium Copyright Act (DMCA) of 1998, where ISPs were granted limited legal immunity in exchange for removing infringing material that resides on their networks once an appropriate notice is received from the copyright holder or his legitimate agent. This regime, commonly referred to as a "notice and takedown" requirement, seeks to balance the interests of the ISPs as information conduits, while protecting the owners of copyrighted material from continual infringement. The DMCA further attempts to balance competing interests by giving the alleged infringers an opportunity to challenge the claim of the assumed copyright holder.[56]

Since enactment of the DMCA, however, ISPs increasingly have been under legal, financial, and political pressure to account for the actions of users of the Internet over whom they have little or no control.[57] Some recent examples include: (1) the Recording Industry Association of America's efforts to obtain private customer information from Verizon, without an appropriate judicial subpoena to track down supposed users of peer-to-peer networks; (2) demands from the Attorney General of Pennsylvania for ISPs to block access to users throughout North America to numerous websites, including countless legitimate ones, so that a site allegedly involving child pornography would not be accessible by residents of Pennsylvania; and (3) a French court's holding that a U.S.-based ISP is legally liable under French law for third parties selling Nazi memorabilia via its website.[58]

A NEW CONCEPT: REGULATION ALONG HORIZONTAL LAYERS

The concept of separating out that which needs to be regulated, and that which needs little or no regulation, is a sound one. In MCI's view, the fundamental organizing principles themselves must be reexamined in light of the coming IP-centric world. Werbach insists that the nation's communications policy needs to be reformulated with the Internet at the center, because communications policy inevitably will become a mere subset of Internet policy.[59] Of course, even if it were not premised on the engineering protocols established by the TCP/IP suite, the layering concept would have considerable relevance with regard to any kind of electronic communications network.[60] Nonetheless, given the self-evident dynamics of digital transformation and a networked world,[61] and the market reality of companies and individuals converging to common IP platforms, the discussion below is focused on drawing public policy lessons from Internet topology and experience.

SKETCHING OUT THE LAYERS FRAMEWORK

Given the growing number of complex legal problems that have developed concerning IP-based networks, services, and applications, it is not surprising that a small but well-respected cadre of academics and expert analysts has begun suggesting the creation of a new legal regime. This approach is informed by the horizontal protocol layers first formulated by network engineers over thirty years ago, as well as the partial layered regulatory scheme adopted by the FCC in its *Computer Inquiry* decisions. This section briefly discusses many of the major problems with the current legal system, weighs the pros and cons of a layered framework, and suggests the outline of a new layered model.

Why Adopt A Layers Approach?

Initially, commentators have pointed out some of the obvious intrinsic flaws in the current U.S. "silos"-based legal and regulatory regime.

Werbach puts it succinctly when he observes that "The basic problem is that the hermetically-sealed categories at the core of the [vertical] approach are foreign to the Internet."[62] More precisely, he identifies four fundamental problems with the current regulatory approach: it assumes distinctions between individual services are clear (in the IP world any network can carry virtually any kind of traffic); it applies most rules in an all-or-nothing fashion (many IP services bear indicia of more than one regulatory category); it looks at each service category in isolation (increasingly all networks are interconnected, and the critical policy issues concern the terms of such interconnection); and it concentrates on the services ultimately provided to end users (competitive dynamics are increasingly driven by behind-the-scenes network architectures).[63]

Sicker finds no fewer than nine separate problems created by the current legal and regulatory regime when applied to the IP world, including: (1) interconnection distortions (ISPs have no carrier rights to interconnect with incumbent local exchange carriers [ILECs]); (2) universal service concerns (current model conflates the network with the applications); (3) bundling discriminations (certain players can restrict access to content); (4) content discrimination (certain players can dictate the terms of content and conduit delivery); (5) accessibility concerns (only traditional voice service providers are obligated to facilitate accessibility for individuals with disabilities); (6) security concerns (wiretapping applies only to traditional voice services); (7) safety concerns (only certain players are required to support emergency service); (8) market distortion (price does not reflect cost of service); and (9) investment and deployment distortion (providers make investment choices based on policy).[64]

Rob Frieden adds that U.S. telecom law and policy historically has been based on fixed service definitions and "relatively static assumptions about the industrial organization of telecommunications and information processing." Technological innovations and industry developments jeopardize the non-convergent "Old World Order" dichotomies.[65]

On the flip-side, commentators over the past several years have presented compelling arguments in favor of the wholesale adoption of a public policy paradigm that relies on the network layers model. In general terms, as Canadian Craig McTaggart indicates, "The analysis of Internet legal issues can be aided by an understanding of the Internet's unique layered architecture."[66] Robert Entman summed up the consensus at Aspen's Institute Conference on Telecommunications Policy in August 2000 with the observation that "conceptually distinguishing the technical layers of the system offers a new paradigm that can clarify regulatory problems and point to their solutions."[67] Sicker offers that the model "does not necessarily provide the policy answers, but it provides a framework for better resolving policy issues."[68]

Entman goes on to explain that the power of making conceptual layers distinctions lies in the insights they generate about public policy towards telecommunications. In particular, (1) applications should be separated conceptually from transport and from content; (2) higher degrees of competition may be more feasible and desirable at some layers than others, so that encouraging robust competition at the applications level may yield more consumer benefits than trying to stimulate multiple competitive transport networks; and (3) policymakers can choose their battles more selectively, targeting those points in the layers where promoting competitiveness will yield the most efficient result.[69]

Werbach makes four points about the benefits of what he calls the vertical (and others call the horizontal) approach: it removes the assumption that service boundaries are clear and are tied to physical network boundaries; implies a more granular analysis within each layer; brings to the forefront the issue of interconnection between networks, and between functional layers within those networks; and recognizes the significance of network architecture as a determining factor in shaping business dynamics.[70] As a result, he calls for regulation to track the architectural model of the Internet itself, both its end-to-end nature and its layered protocol stack.[71]

Cannon explains that looking at the layers separately allows policymakers to focus on the different issues in each.[72]

Sicker observes that dividing the model horizontally allows us to "separate service aspects of the network in a manner consistent with the design of the network." The real value is that "regulation can be minimized or compartmentalized by considering the role of regulation on each layer distinct from the layer above or below it."[73] Frieden believes that "a horizontal orientation would trigger a substantial revamping of regulatory treatment as it would possibly free some ventures that have historically operated under extensive regulation, even as it imposes new regulatory burdens on ventures historically exempt from regulation." Such a horizontal orientation also "would establish a regulatory regime based on how technologies function and would foreclose the need to make semantic distinctions between such converging concepts as telecommunications used in the provision of information services and telecommunications services provided directly to users."[74]

Commentators focus in particular on the valuable ways that a layered approach can help uncover and deal with market power issues. Sicker states, for example, that providers at the lower layer should be regulated differently from each other, not on the basis of network type, but rather on the basis of market power.[75] Entman reports that participants at the Aspen Institute's 2000 telecommunications conference found the use of the four-layer framework "an invaluable tool for crafting more calibrated pro-competition policies."[76]   In particular, the multi-layered approach allows policymakers to shift their focus, which traditionally is on regulation of the voice application, to regulation of transport. The primary public policy goal is to encourage efficiency in innovation, by ensuring a lack of artificial barriers to entry of innovative technologies and services. Competition itself is not a policy goal, Entman states, but rather merely a means to stimulate and direct market forces that help attain the primary goals. Recognizing the distinctions among layers will help achieve optimal levels of competition. Each layer needs to be analyzed separately in terms of bottlenecks that exist or might arise to stymie competition, given the fact that each layer has different economies of scale, and economies of scope may cross layers.[77]

As with any analytical tool, the layers principle is not without its drawbacks. However, to date most of the concerns raised in the academic literature come from otherwise committed supporters of the principle, and go more to process and political issues than to any significant substantive reservations. Lingering questions include developing the optimal way to translate valuable insights into concrete and effective policy rules;[78] devising empirically-based tests for market power and monopoly abuses, and tough enforcement mechanisms to minimize delays and gaming of the process;[79] defining and implementing a realistic transition strategy to a comprehensive new framework;[80] and needing to grant policymakers broad authority to make the necessary comprehensive statutory and regulatory changes.[81] While challenging and deserving of careful attention, none of these concerns appears insurmountable.

A more straightforward objection is a political one, namely that a layered approach is simply too extreme a change to garner the political support to make the necessary legal and regulatory revisions.[82]   However, as has been shown, the layered approach is not that different in concept from the FCC's basic/enhanced distinction, or the impetus behind the failed Title VII regime. Sicker insists that "one of the strongest motivations for moving toward the proposed framework is that there exists significant precedence. It is not a radical departure from the basic regulatory structure and precedent of the last four decades."[83]

Moreover, several far-sighted regulators already have acknowledged the compelling need for a new regulatory paradigm that reflects the reality of the IP world. In recent months, FCC Chairman Michael Powell has expressed the desire to embrace "Internet-premised, Internet-based IP type communications" and "tailor a set of regulatory clothing uniquely for it."[84] More explicitly, Powell discusses the need to "build from a blank slate up as opposed to from the myriad of telecommunications regulation down," so that one can "make each regulatory judgment as the consequence of forethought and judgment and understanding about this specific technology."[85] In contrast, he notes, "there is no clear answer in the statute, the statute is in little buckets, and the buckets don't make sense."[86] Powell invokes the imperative to "establish a rational policy environment for IP-based services to continue to evolve," informed by "the recognition that the Internet is inherently a global network that does not acknowledge narrow, artificial boundaries."[87]

Robert Pepper, Chief of Policy Development at the FCC, explains in a recent interview how the network layered concept represents a different approach in Washington, but one that may require only some further education of policymakers.[88]

Some leading regulators have publicly advocated adoption of a layers model. As one example, Brett Perlman, then-Commissioner of the Public Utility Commission of Texas, told FCC Commissioner Kevin Martin in January 2003 that the FCC could meet its goals of encouraging broadband competition and network investment "if it were to apply a 'layered model' to broadband infrastructure."[89]

Thus, while the political, institutional, and educational challenges cannot be underestimated, the layers model represents a shift in thinking that successfully mirrors the way that networks and markets actually operate. Adoption of a layering framework would be but a logical extension of recent technology and policy insights to the broader areas of telecommunications and Internet law.[90]

What Kind of Layers Model to Adopt?

While there are obvious commonalities among them, different layers models have been proposed by a number of commentators.[91] As Sicker aptly points out, the goal of adopting a layers model is to create a framework that logically divides a network (and services provided over that network) so that policy can then be applied in a more consistent manner.[92] Thus, public policy considerations should be taken into account when deciding where and how to divide up the protocol layers. Sicker warns us in particular not to be too tightly wedded to the specifics of any particular protocols model. The specifications of the TCP/IP suite deal with the technical characteristics of the protocol, not necessarily the business or policy characteristics. "We should not confuse the technical implementation of the Internet with the policy goals of a layered model. What we should take away from the protocol design is its design philosophy; including things like decentralized control, autonomy, efficiency, etc."[93]

A number of useful observations can be gleaned from the various commentators. First and foremost, there is an obvious separation between the upper applications layer and the lower physical layer. Economist Michael Katz calls this fundamental separation of applications from transport "de-lamination."[94] Second, we should identify separate layers for content and for applications, per Entman and Sicker, to better help analyze e-commerce and ISP liability issues. Third, as Werbach points out, even though the physical and logical layers are tightly coupled in the voice public switched telephone network (PSTN), they remain distinct and separated as engineering concepts.[95] Fourth, it is useful to separate out the software that routes network traffic (the logical layer) from the software that is exposed to end users (the application layer).[96] Fifth, McTaggart suggests a further refinement of the content layer, where he includes the notion of "transactions" in order to encompass the full range of activities possible on the Internet.[97] He views content as information available on, or obtainable by means of, the Internet, while transactions are the dynamic interactions carried out over the Internet.

Finally, Sicker observes the need to identify two different Physical Layer networks, the Access and the Transport. Sicker believes that it is critical to separate the access network (the physical "edge" of the communications network, typically thought of as last-mile telephone facilities provided by local exchange carriers) from the transport network (the physical "core" of the network, typically thought of as long-haul telecommunications provided by interexchange carriers) for a horizontal public policy model to succeed. Through regulation or economic incentive, the proper means can be introduced to encourage providers of various services to interconnect on reasonable terms. Where a provider owns multiple layers, Sicker explains, regulation might be imposed to ensure that this player provides reasonable interconnection. Although other models tend not to consider the issues of interconnection, market power, or the transition to such a layered model, each of these issues is critical in creating a workable model. In short, the separation described between the access and transport providers maps to the actual design of communications networks.[98]

Thus, incorporating many of these important public policy-related insights, we adopt the Network Layers Model as shown in Figure 7.

Figure 7

MCI's Proposed Layers Model

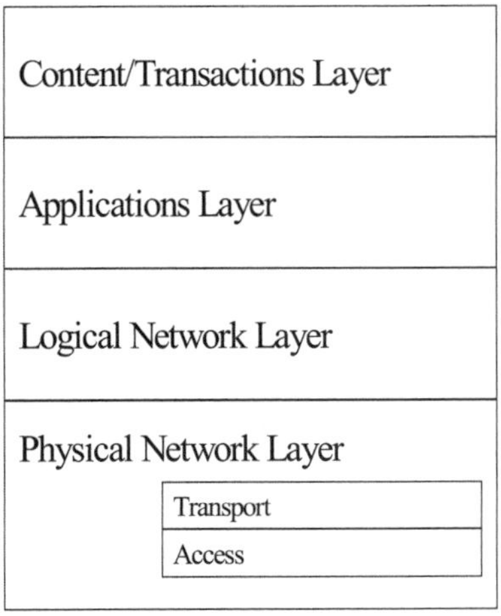

| Content/Transactions Layer |
| Applications Layer |
| Logical Network Layer |
| Physical Network Layer |

Within the Physical Network Layer:

| Transport |
| Access |

SOLUM'S "LAYERS PRINCIPLE"

Next we need to consider some of the primary analytical elements of our network layers model. Professor Lawrence Solum of Loyola Marymount University recently published an extensive paper that lays out some of the fundamental concepts to support a proposed new public policy framework.[99] After describing Solum's approach in some detail, we adopt and supplement his key principles, and then extend them to apply to specific examples in the public policy world of IP-based services and applications.

Solum relies in part on the leading work of Professor Larry Lessig and his so-called "code thesis," which in its essence describes how code is the prime regulator of the Internet.[100] Lessig explains that the architecture of the Internet has profound implications for its legal regulation. Under the "end-to-end" principle described earlier, the Internet is viewed as a combination of a stupid network and smart applications. As Lessig makes clear, the Internet is transparent to applications (e.g., does not associate data packets with application file types), and this transparency is a built-in characteristic of the layered architecture of the Internet.[101]

Solum calls his key concept the "layers principle," which amounts to the general exhortation to "**Respect the integrity of the layers.**" Solum's layers principle is defined by the following statement: **Public regulators should not adopt legal regulations of the Internet (including statutes, regulations, common law rules, or interpretations of any of these) that violate the integrity of the layered nature of Internet architecture, absent a compelling regulatory interest and consideration of layer respecting alternatives.**[102]

In his paper, Solum describes two interrelated corollaries in support of his layers principle:

• Corollary One: The principle of layers separation

Regulation should not violate or compromise the separation between layers designed into the basic infrastructure of the Internet, so that one layer of the Internet would differentiate the handling of data on the basis of information available only at another layer, absent a compelling regulatory interest.

• Corollary Two: The principle of minimizing layer crossing

If compelling regulatory interests require a layer-crossing regulation, that regulation should minimize the distance between the layer at which the law aims to produce an effect, and the layer directly targeted by legal regulation.[103]

Solum indicates that two theses form the supporting pillars that provide a compelling justification for the layers principle and its two foundational corollaries:

The transparency thesis: The fact that layer-violating regulations inherently damage the transparency of the Internet, combined with the fact that Internet transparency lowers the barriers to innovation, provides compelling support for the principle of layer separation.

The fit thesis: The fact that layer-crossing regulations result in an inherent mismatch between the ends such regulations seek to promote and the means employed implies that layer-crossing regulations suffer from problems of overbreadth and underinclusion. Avoidance of these problems requires Internet regulators to abide by the principle of minimizing layer crossing regulations.[104]

Solum explains that the layers principle rests on a solid foundation of engineering facts and norms: namely, that the layers are separated for sound reasons of network engineering. As we have seen previously, each layer depends on lower ones; to avoid replicating functions in higher layers, one should put in a lower layer to serve all higher layers. As a result, functions normally should not cross layers unless there is an exceptional reason to do so. In Solum's view, horizontal communication requires vertical transparency. The lower layer, by design, cannot or is not supposed to discriminate the payload from the upper layer based on its content, or modify the content. Hence, the lower layer is transparent with respect to the upper layer. Transparency means the Internet is a neutral platform; anyone can develop network applications with or on top of the TCP/IP protocol, with no permission necessary.[105]

Solum's proposed six-layer model includes the Content, Application, Transport, Network (IP), Link, and Physical layers. In his model, the public conduit function of the Internet operates mainly at the IP Layer and the Physical Layer below it. The IP Layer is the greatest common denominator of the publicly shared resources on the Internet. It is the function of the IP Layer, along with the "stupid" hop-by-hop routing design, that fuses multitudes of disparate networks into an apparently single unified, seamless network.[106]

THE LAYERS PRINCIPLE AND INFORMED DECISIONMAKING

In Solum's view, applying the layers analysis (by identifying the layer of the problem conduct and the layer where the regulation operates) provides a more concrete analysis of the issues by placing the disputed function at a proper layer and providing a correct focus on the relevant operation of the Internet. In essence, the legal regulation can only be as effective as is permitted by the architecture of the Internet. And, in turn, the nature and limitations of the legal regulation will be determined by the nature of the code being implemented.[107]

Solum discusses the proper role of policymakers and regulators in determining whether or not to adopt and enforce a regulation that affects the Internet. Initially he defends the need for regulators to utilize the layers principle, as opposed to a more case-by-case, incremental approach to fashioning public policy. In a nutshell, his case against "incrementalism" revolves around: (1) the tyranny of small decisions; (2) ignorance of unforeseen and unintended consequences; (3) layers-violating regulations inherently damaging the transparency of the Internet; (4) Kenneth Arrow's information paradox (i.e., we cannot know the innovation costs of damaging the transparency of the Internet, but we must consider those costs when formulating Internet regulatory policy); and (5) institutional capacity (regulators are ill-prepared to understand Internet architecture).[108]

Solum also states that the layers principle and its corollaries should be treated by prospective regulators as presumptive rules of decisions. Before adopting a layer-violating rule or regulation, a regulator must articulate a compelling regulatory justification. At minimum, decisionmakers should be required to consider the availability of layer respecting alternatives.[109]

The layers principle also can be employed as an aid to statutory interpretation. For example, as part of explicating the meaning of "the public interest" standard in the Communications Act,[110] the layers principle can give more particular and concrete meaning to the ambiguous statutory command. The layers principle can also be used to fill statutory gaps, and to narrow or broaden legal text where appropriate.[111]

Finally, Solum recognizes that the layers principle is only as valid as the network engineering concepts that inform it and can be expected to change with the underlying technology.[112]

ANOTHER PUBLIC INTEREST ASPECT: CREATING AND PRESERVING THE "INNOVATION ENGINE"

Commentators also draw interesting public policy lessons from the robust innovation that currently is evident on the Internet. To many, policymakers must ensure that the upper layers of content and applications remain competitive and free from any untoward influence, from either public (government) or private (corporate) actors. As one example, Professor Solum discusses how nearly all user functions are implemented at the upper application layer. Thus, innovation is decentralized and placed in the hands of individual innovators, and the Internet can become an "innovation commons."[113]

The work of Professor Yochai Benkler expands on the idea of the Internet as an innovation commons. Benkler describes how the Internet helps disrupt the traditional producer/consumer model by empowering the rise of end users who can play both roles as part of a continuing conversation and exchange of information. The "Great Shopping Mall" can be transformed into the "Great Agora," featuring unmediated conversation of the many with the many.[114]

Benkler addresses the network layers concept in his conception of the proper role of regulation:

> We are making regulatory choices at all layers of the information environment – the physical infrastructure, logical infrastructure, and content layers — that threaten to concentrate the digital environment as it becomes more central to our social conversation.... At all these layers, the wrong decisions could enable a reproduction of the mass media model, with all its shortcomings, in the digitally networked environment. Avoiding making these mistakes

should be the focus of the efforts we have traditionally focused on structural media regulation.[115]

Regulatory choices that assume a producer/consumer model often perpetuate this model by regulating in a manner that increases the costs of becoming a producer of information. Benkler asserts that this scenario leads inevitably to: (1) Concentration (because the cost of becoming a professional provider of the type whose activity is facilitated by the regulation creates an entry barrier); (2) Commercialization (because of the high cost, providers must adopt a strategy that relies on sale of their information and cultural products); and (3) Homogenization (because most producers must be commercial, their reasons to produce are similar, and their need to attract wide audiences leads to convergence of the content towards the mainstream and the inoffensive).[116]

Other commentators have observed the strong correlation between robust, ends-oriented innovation and the architecture of the Internet. Lee McKnight notes that innovation is the key factor enabling growth and change in capitalist economies, and that in turn "the Internet works its magic through rapid development and diffusion of innovations."[117] The Internet Protocol acts as a "bearer service" – the general purpose platform technology linking technologies, software, services, customers, firms, and markets – so that the Internet is "an innovation engine that enables creation of a remarkable range of new products and services."[118] McKnight argues that an open communications infrastructure policy framework is best suited to foster innovation and growth, although "legal and political forces may intentionally or inadvertently foster innovation – or suppress it."[119] Katz believes that "the hourglass architecture allows innovations to take place at the application and transport layers separately. This ability for independent innovation speeds the rate of innovation and increases the ability of entrepreneurs to take advantage of new opportunities."[120]

Lessig describes how the end-to-end principle renders the Internet an innovation commons, where innovators can develop and deploy new applications or content without the permission of anyone else.[121] Others demonstrate how the benefits of the end-to-end design include the way it facilitates user control and power, innovation, flexibility, competition, and reliability.[122] Lessig also claims that "to those who argue that control is necessary if innovation is to occur, and that more control will yield more innovation, the Internet is the simplest and most direct reply."[123]

The very uncertainty stemming from the potential of future innovation is yet another reason for policymakers to refrain from direct regulation of the upper layers. Lessig states that "the network is open to adopting applications not originally foreseen by the designer."[124] When the future is uncertain (when future uses of a technology cannot be predicted), leaving the technology uncontrolled is a better way of helping it find the right sort of innovation. Plasticity – the ability of a system to evolve easily in a number of ways – is optimal in a world of uncertainty.[125] Sicker observes that new applications can quickly enter this space and radically change the landscape. "It is the dynamic and innovative nature of the application space that suggests that the government use prudence when considering policy."[126]

There is also considerable support for linking technological innovation to evolutionary theories. In August 2003, Wu and Lessig compared the FCC's "competitive model of innovation" to "survival-of-the-fittest competition" that results in the emergence of a best innovation that a planned approach might not have predicted.[127]

Innovation and the Internet also are closely aligned with proponents of the school of "creative destruction." McKnight claims that "the seeming chaos of rapid market rises to prominence of new firms, new technologies, and new business models is not a passing phenomenon, but rather is a permanent feature of an Internet economy." Because of this, he writes, "the Internet enables creative destruction as usual."[128]

Of course, innovations are not limited to the content and applications layers, or to consumer-facing retail offerings. Innovation also happens deep in the logical and physical infrastructure of the network. Indeed, layering with IP at the center allows for network innovation below, as well as above, the IP layer. Recent history shows that much of that innovation comes not from established incumbents guarding legacy market power positions, but from hungry, eager competitors. For example, it is well-established that data CLECs [Competitive Local Exchange Carriers] such as Covad, Rhythms, and Northpoint were the early adopters of Digital Subscriber Line (DSL) as a broadband platform, and not the ILECs, because the incumbents feared cannibalization of their profitable T-1 services.[129] So the purpose of competition at the lower layers is not merely to hold in check market power that could damage innovation at the upper layers. In itself, competition within the logical and physical layers provides a valuable spur to infrastructure innovation and investment, which in turn provides significant benefits to the upper layers, and also reduces the need for regulation overall as the market becomes more competitive.

DEFINING AND GUARDING AGAINST MARKET POWER ABUSE IN THE LAYERS

As McTaggart puts it, "one of the most difficult questions of telecommunications and information technology law in the 21st century [is] whether competition law is capable of protecting the public interest in the Internet environment."[130] In a world where policymakers would begin to look to the horizontal network layers model to guide the development of public policy, a well-developed theory of market power abuse, coupled with strong and effective enforcement tools, is a must. While this paper is not intended to provide a nuanced and detailed economic analysis suitable for a robust layers framework, a few general points are raised below.

In the United States, antitrust laws broadly define the scope of unacceptable market power and abuses of such power. The case-by-case determinations of market power, and any possible remedies for abuse of that power, are left to the U.S. Department of Justice (an arm of the Executive Branch) and the Federal Trade Commission (an independent regulatory agency). The joint DOJ/FTC "Horizontal Merger Guidelines" establish the methodological tools that the two agencies will employ in reviewing mergers between companies in the same or related industries.[131] Relevant product markets are defined, and market concentration measured with the assistance of the Herfindal-Hirschman Index (HHI), which assesses the market shares of each entity. The HHI measures relative concentration within a market, anywhere from approaching zero (numerous small competitors) up to 10,000 (completely monopolized). HHI factors above 1,800 signify potentially significant competitive concerns.[132] On the other hand, where the FCC is involved in reviewing a proposed merger between regulated entities, the touchstone is whether the transaction would be in the "public interest."[133]

In 2002, the European Union took a major step towards combining competition law and a regulatory framework guided by the horizontal layers principle.[134] As Frieden explains it, the European Commission (the executive branch of the EU) considered whether a horizontal regulatory and policy orientation would provide a better outcome — by attempting to use a harmonized regulatory approach that makes a functional assessment of what a company currently provides and whether it possesses market power — rather than who provides a service and that provider's "legacy" regulatory status.[135] The market power assessment revolves around the concept of Significant Market Power (SMP), as developed by the European Commission.[136]

The European Union's new regulatory framework presents an interesting case of an explicit endorsement and adoption of the horizontal way of thinking about regulatory policies and market power. Rather than apply regulation based on specific service definitions, the EU's framework establishes a neutral process for determining whether to apply regulation and when to remove it.[137]

In the United States, the economic literature on layering rightly focuses on the appropriate exercise of the government's authority to curb anticompetitive activity at different levels. Katz has explained that the "de-lamination" of transport and applications layers should be taken into account in assessing market power and determining the appropriate treatment of firms under merger policy, price regulation, and interconnection obligations.[138] As de-lamination continues, the assessment of market power should largely take place at each layer separately.[139]

Sicker states that there is sound reason to treat providers with market dominance at a given layer differently from providers without. "While similar policy would be applied to all service providers, those determined as having significant market power will have additional obligations. When a player is determined to have significant market power, a pricing condition will be invoked. This condition will vary depending on power exerted; whether the player controls multiple layers or significantly controls a particular layer."[140]

Looking in particular at the transport layer, Katz writes that it is useful to focus on "bottleneck assets" or "network choke points" as sources of market power, as long as networks remain interconnected. A bottleneck is created when one or very few providers possess an asset (for example, transport facilities) that is critical to competitive success and cannot readily be obtained by rivals. In the case of local access networks, economies of density and scale, coupled with the sunk-cost nature of network investments, have created a system in which incumbents may have preempted additional entry to serve most end users, including single-family residences, small businesses, as well as large businesses in less densely populated areas. Of course, as Weiser observes, one cannot assume that the exclusive gatekeeper will only exist at the physical layer.[141] The analysis of market power at the applications layer is likely to focus on somewhat different factors, such as intellectual property rights, first-mover advantages resulting from large fixed and sunk development costs, and network effects.[142] McKnight adds that as entities seek to obtain market power through establishment of a controlling position in access markets, a new information and communication policy architecture is necessary, built on four principles: open architecture, open access, universal access, and flexible access.[143] Finally, Weisman cautions that a strong antitrust-type enforcement role, while difficult in practice, is necessary in theory.[144]

In short, unregulated market power is counter-innovation. Monopoly essentially acts as the worst form of "regulation" by inhibiting activities in otherwise competitive markets. Policymakers must use the network layers concept to develop a more sophisticated understanding of the deleterious effects of unconstrained market power.

APPLYING THE LAYERS PRINCIPLE: TRADITIONAL COMMON CARRIER REGULATION

In general, so-called "regulation of the Internet" comes in two different guises: (1) common carrier-type entry, exit, and service regulation by federal and state regulatory bodies (primarily the Federal Communications Commission and state public utility commissions); and (2) legal liability imposed on ISPs by statute or regulation (primarily the U.S. Congress, Federal Trade Commission, and state legislatures). Telecommunications regulators in other countries, and international bodies such as the Internet Corporation for Assigned Names and Numbers (ICANN) and the Organization for Economic Cooperation and Development, also play roles in Internet-related matters. By way of example, the FCC adopting rules concerning VoIP could be considered to constitute the first kind of Internet regulation, while the European Commission adopting rules governing spam could constitute the second kind of Internet regulation. Generally speaking, traditional communications regulation should focus on the lower (physical and network) layers, while Internet content-related regulation should focus on higher (applications and content) layers.

Solum emphasizes employing the layers principle in situations where policymakers must be dissuaded from imposing legal or regulatory burdens on the upper layers of the end-to-end Internet (in other words, e-commerce issues involving potential ISP liability). The key implications of Solum's approach, which are laid out in admirable detail in his paper. This paper provides a separate, more extensive analysis focused on employing the layers principle in the telecommunications regulatory context. In particular, the paper focuses on situations where policymakers must be persuaded to impose legal or regulatory burdens on the lower layers of the last-mile facilities leading to and from Internet, and not on the actual IP services or applications themselves.

The remaining portion of the paper expands on the layers principles suggested by Solum by adopting two additional corollaries, and then applying those corollaries to a variety of real-life public policy issues involving the regulation of telecommunications and Internet markets. These applications should be considered preliminary in nature, and can be revised or supplemented as part of further development and refinement of a viable horizontal layering framework.

As Solum notes, the severity of the layers violation is greater when the regulation is attempted at a lower or deeper layer in the layer hierarchy in order to address the problems at an upper or higher layer. One can also take the related position, as will be shown, that the severity of the layers violation is greater when non-regulation by a public actor (the government) allows a private actor's behavior at a lower or deeper layer of the network to disrupt transparency and harms innovation and innocent use at an upper or higher layer. This behavior would harm competition by reinforcing abuse of market power or monopoly control over lower layer facilities.

Lower Layer Control

The addition of two corollaries to Solum's list, aimed specifically at traditional communications regulators, appears to flow naturally from his first two corollaries. The third corollary concerns the logical and economic link between an entity's control over unique elements of the Physical Layer and its resulting control over higher layers in the protocol stack. The fourth corollary builds on that point to recommend carefully-targeted regulatory attention to those specific horizontal layers where providers abuse market power, while leaving the remaining horizontal layers free from unnecessary regulatory constraints.

- ## • Corollary Three: The principle of leveraging lower layer control

The ability of a private actor to employ market power at the lower Physical Layer allows that same entity to leverage market power into the higher layers that depend on the Physical Layer. In essence, he who controls the lower layers also can control the dependent upper layers.

This reality of leveraged market power from the lower to upper layers ("monopoly leveraging" in antitrust terms) raises the stakes considerably in the current telecom regulatory battles over local competition, last-mile regulation, and broadband regulation. In the IP world, the preponderance of innovative applications, services, and content depends on the ability of producers and end users at the "edge" (upper layers) of the network to freely access the lower layers at the network core, including the Physical Layer. If, for example, a Physical Access provider, such as an incumbent local exchange carrier or a cable services company, is able to exert disproportionate market power over a last-mile conduit — based on traditional monopoly-derived advantages – that market power then can be leveraged unfairly into the Applications Layer, with detrimental impact on the levels of competition, innovation, and consumer choices otherwise prevalent at that level. Further, given the expanding scope of applications and services that are and seek to be provided on the Applications Layer in the IP-based environment, the degree of market power control over the Physical Layer is proportional to the degree of damage that can be caused as a result of inequitable market power control over the higher layers. In short, understanding the basis for employing horizontal regulation is all the more critical in an era of vertical integration, especially where that integration involves control over essential Physical Access Layer facilities and infrastructure.

Last-Mile Regulation and Competition Policy

Under the proposed third corollary, the need for regulation rests largely on the need to deter and limit the adverse effects of market power, which in turn resides largely in certain last-mile physical infrastructure and connections with other networks. In the United States, such market power tends to be concentrated in two discrete areas: local communications transport facilities (ILECs and cable companies) and certain exclusive use of radio spectrum frequencies (wireless service providers; broadcast radio and television stations). Utilization of the horizontal layers framework allows policymakers to focus on retaining regulation at the Physical Access Layer, where historic scarcity of public resources (radio and television spectrum) or monopoly-derived advantages (local telephony and cable plant) remain in place. Of course, to the extent that competition (such as the increased availability of robust intramodal and intermodal platform alternatives) and/or technology gains (such as the use of spread-spectrum modulation techniques) can fully remove these non-market-based advantages, the need for continuing regulation of these facilities is eliminated as well.[145]

Local Competition and Unbundled Network Elements

The validity of the layers principle, and the proposed third corollary above, only highlights the need to create as much competition as possible at the last-mile network level. Indeed, given the enormous stakes involved at the higher Applications and Content Layers, U.S. regulators have a duty to engender competition both between different physical platforms (intermodal) and within those particular platforms that display market power (intramodal). Section 251(c) of the Telecommunications Act, which requires the ILECs to provide unbundled network elements, can be an important legal mechanism in service of the layers principle.[146] In particular, UNEs can help foster intramodal competition within the entrenched local exchange network, both in terms of near-term UNE platform competition and longer-term facilities-based competition.

As mentioned previously, the concept of a UNE is an interesting blend of horizontal and vertical thinking. Horizontal framing can help unlock some of the public policy confusion surrounding the appropriate use of UNEs to foster local competition. For example, application of a horizontal layers framework helps raise significant doubts about several factual conclusions adopted by the FCC in its recent *UNE Triennial Review Order*.[147] There the FCC created a regulatory distinction between a circuit-switched environment,[148] and what it calls "packet-switching capability," for purposes of defining what UNEs should be provided to CLECs. The FCC further devised a regulatory distinction between fiber-based local loops and copper-based local loops. In both cases, the Commission appears to believe (without any supporting empirical evidence) that the particular access medium employed at the various layers is a more salient factor in determining which UNEs to unbundle than the market power and other characteristics of the network provider that employs it.

FOCUSED REGULATORY ATTENTION

Many people unfamiliar with the role of regulation have an almost instinctive negative reaction without fully understanding or appreciating its utility. As Sicker writes, "regulations are applied to promote certain desirable goals, such as ubiquity of service, efficiency of commerce, public safety, national security, innovation, and education. The problem is that regulation is a difficult balancing act, where the goals may stand in opposition to each other."[149]

When cast in terms of the horizontal layers framework, the traditional telecom regulator's chief objective is to prevent the exercise of market power at lower network layers from impinging upon the otherwise robustly competitive and innovative upper service layers, and to limit/ eliminate unnecessary regulation of upper layers. In this way, policymakers can help foster a "deregulatory commons," where innovation can flourish. Thus, the fourth proposed corollary calls on regulators to employ their regulatory tools and attention only where necessary, and no further.

• **Corollary Four: The principle of focusing regulatory attention**

Regulators should target necessary legal and regulatory resources only to those specific horizontal layers where market power resides, or where regulatory attention otherwise is necessary in the public interest, and leave the remaining horizontal layers free from unnecessary regulatory constraints.

This deregulatory corollary is well-supported in the economic literature. As just one example, Professor Reza Dibadji of the University of Miami has written about the proper way to exert regulatory authority. Dibadji's central thesis is that regulators must move away from industry definitions based on historical distinctions, and towards a regulatory framework based on economics, with a goal of maximizing both efficiency and equity. Under this approach, the decisionmaker must: (1) identify the scarce resource (or "bottleneck" input) in question; (2) determine whether a market participant is exerting monopoly power over the input to the detriment of competition or public policy; and (3) regulate the resource based on empirical economic models. The fundamental idea is to confine regulation to "bottleneck inputs" (portions of existing networks that are vestiges of monopoly and/or prohibitively expensive for new entrants to build), and let competition flourish for the services and applications that utilize those networks. Simple economics dictates that competitive entities be allowed to access these inputs. As Dibadji succinctly puts it, "without access to these bottlenecks, competition is a farce."[150]

The Basic/Enhanced Dichotomy

While the FCC's concept of separating out the basic telecommunications services that should remain subject to common carriage regulation from those enhanced features and functionalities that should remain outside such regulation,[151] it is obvious from continuing debates over the proper classification of broadband and VoIP services that the purported "bright-line" that once separated these two classes of service increasingly is becoming blurred and subject to confusion.

The horizontal layers framework offers a significantly more refined, engineering-based update to the FCC's basic/enhanced dichotomy (which mirrors the 1996 Act's telecommunications service/information service definitions). In general, the FCC should be receptive to finding better empirical footing in the actual network and code topology employed in the telecommunications and Internet sectors, rather than continuing to rely on the relatively rough-hewn concepts employed more or less unchanged for several decades. In addition, the basic/enhanced distinction was born within the confines of the telephone network and telephony regulation, and to date has not been expressly extended to other types of transmission networks. By incorporating the horizontal layers framework, the FCC can expand the scope of the concept beyond telephony to all types of two-way networks, regardless of the particular technologies used (copper, fiber, coaxial cable, radio signals, power lines) to construct and operate them.

The ILECs frequently make the argument that they should be freed from regulation on their data services because these markets are competitive. But Werbach notes that this analysis misses the importance of interfaces between layers. Under the layered model, ILEC data services should be deregulated if and when the FCC can assure itself that the ILECs will not be able to leverage lower-level control into other layers. This could happen in one of two ways: if the physical and logical infrastructure layers in the relevant markets were sufficiently competitive, or if the FCC or Congress adopt rules that prevent ILECs from closing the interfaces between layers or otherwise constraining higher-level competition. To Werbach, "the Computer II structural separation requirements and the Computer III non-structural safeguards are in effect such rules."[152]

Broadband Regulation

The layers principle also assists telecom policymakers in assessing the viability of arguments raised with regard to broadband services regulation. For example, several commentators have written about how proposals to allow the incumbent cable and telephone companies to establish "closed" broadband networks, thereby denying access to independent ISPs, are contrary to the "end-to-end" engineering principle. Werbach, for example, says that the layers model, more than reframing existing debates, brings to the surface important issues of competition and consumer choice that tend to become lost under the existing regulatory model.[153]

David Clark and Marjory Blumenthal opine that the "open access" debate is not just about choice in ISPs; rather, if access to alternative ISPs is constrained or blocked, user access to content would be similarly compromised. There is a presumed linkage between lack of choice in access to the Internet and a loss of the open, end-to-end nature of the Internet.[154] François Bar and Christian Sandvig urge the adoption of a new policy bargain between "control" and "access," that allows the non-discriminatory ability to design the architecture of a communication platform, not only for those who own and control network infrastructures, but also for end-users or third parties. Clark and Blumenthal see a policy interest in safeguarding this ability to design, for at least two reasons: fairness and innovation promotion.[155]

The layers approach also supports the current definitional scheme employed by the FCC for DSL-based broadband services. At present, the FCC views the DSL transmission component as a telecommunications service, while the Internet access typically bundled with ("riding on top of") that service is an unregulated information service.[156] However, in its wireline broadband proceeding, the FCC has proposed doing away with this distinction, and instead treat the entire service as one unregulated information service, with no underlying DSL transmission component.[157] The upshot of this proposed reclassification is that independent ISPs no longer would have access to DSL inputs, as mandated by the nondiscrimination rules first fashioned in the *Computer Inquiry* docket.

A careful understanding of the horizontal layers framework exposes the technical fallacy of the FCC's proposal. In short, the FCC's broadband redefinition would violate the layers concept by collapsing the various layers into a single information service defined by its upper layers, and allowing the Physical Access Layer (DSL) to control/discriminate against those layers. Through an understanding of the layers principle and its corollaries, the Commission should be led to abandon the mistaken conflation of upper-level Application Layer services such as Internet access with lower-level Physical Access Layer services such as DSL, and instead retain its original correct classification of DSL-based transport as a telecommunications service (see Figure 8).

Figure 8

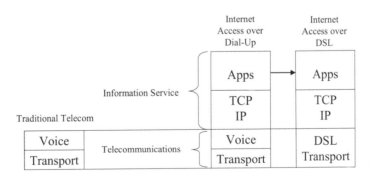

Layers Analysis Supports DSL As Telecommunications Service

Others have picked up on this fatal flaw in the FCC's tentative thinking. Cerf cautions that "this [DSL] transmission path should not in any way be confused with one of the more common applications of DSL: Internet access."[158] Frieden observes that the unclear legal status of broadband service evidences "significant confusion in determining the length and breadth of what constitutes a telecommunications service, particularly when coupled with either a cable service or an information service."[159] Frieden sees dubious motivations at work, believing that the FCC seeks to eliminate the application of longstanding common carrier regulatory burdens on telephone companies when they bundle or blend broadband telecommunications services with information services. In order to carry out its claimed "functional" approach, however, the Commission "has to subordinate the telecommunications transport function relative to the information services provided and also to dismiss the previously recognized legal, marketplace and technological differences between the two carriers."[160] Frieden states that "in its chosen deregulatory quest, the FCC has engaged in a flawed and disingenuous strategy to combine previously different regulatory models based on new functional similarity. Suddenly a telecommunications service can become stripped of its common carrier regulatory triggers if and when the FCC chooses to emphasize the content or enhancements carried via the telecommunications conduit."[161]

The FCC's proposed policy also could unleash some enormously anticompetitive consequences. Frieden observes that:

> In the Commission's view telecommunications services can lose their identity and regulatory trigger when they become packaged with an information service and the content and other functionality contained in information services. Rather than narrow a regulatory loophole the FCC has created an incredibly larger one [whereby telecommunications service providers would have] the ability to free themselves of any and all common carrier burdens that otherwise would apply to broadband telecommunications service simply by characterizing those offerings as information services.[162]

Sicker notes the hazy thought process behind the FCC's stated desire to create broadband deployment incentives for the incumbent DSL facilities providers. In particular, "some believe that the only way to create an incentive for broadband deployment is vertical integration. We view this as an invitation for abuse. While we believe that physical network providers need a return on investment, we do not believe that this should come at the expense of eliminating competition in a higher layer to create that incentive. There is no just reason to destroy the competitive application market that has developed in the name of broadband deployment."[163] Cerf has expressed puzzlement at the idea that the ILECs require additional incentives to deploy DSL-based broadband facilities. In addition to the fact that such facilities largely are available now, he writes, "competition is its own incentive." In the supposed battle between the ILECs and cable companies, "no company can afford to sit on the sidelines ands watch its competitors take the market. To the extent the ILECs believe they can do so, of course, it is yet another sign that they have market power in providing broadband services."[164]

Werbach gives the lie to the so-called need for "regulatory parity:"

> The layered model makes many of the conflicts that today bedevil regulators more tractable. For example, the inconsistency between the treatment of DSL, which is subject to federal open interconnection requirements (under Title II), and cable modem services, which currently are not, turns out to be a figment of the [vertical] model. Both cases involve the possibility that service providers with control over the physical and logical layers of networks will extend that control into applications and content. Looking at the issue in this way doesn't compel one outcome or the other. It may be that the FCC concludes open access is the right policy result, but that in the cable situation market forces will be sufficient to arrive at that result. The important shift is that the focus is now on the key policy issue at stake, rather than the almost accidental context that defines the issue today.[165]

Moreover, contrary to ILEC claims, the advent of Digital Subscriber Line technology constitutes only an evolution of the Physical Access Layer, not a top-to-bottom vertical revolution. DSL utilizes existing physical links already connected to most homes: the twisted-pair copper telephone lines. While the higher modem speeds, "always on" feature, and ability simultaneously to use the telephone and the Internet are superior aspects of DSL vis-à-vis ISDN or traditional narrowband dial-up service, in every other way the DSL service provided to consumers (the bundled retail marriage of Internet access and DSL platform) represents merely a network upgrade from the point of view of the Physical Layer. From the Internet's perspective, "broadband" and "narrowband" (however defined) essentially are one and the same. As Cerf puts it, "DSL technology is merely the latest in a continuing stream of incremental improvements to the use of the existing telephone network."[166]

In addition, the horizontal layers framework shows the deep nature of ISPs' dependency on DSL, at least for the present time. Cerf and others have shown that there are no viable near-term alternatives to the two dominant broadband platforms of cable modem and DSL service.[167] At the same time, the very existence and flourishing of the Applications Layer obviously relies on the lower Physical Access Layer – there is no such thing as a stand-alone application without the means of conveying that application between different points in a network. As a result, the failure to appropriately regulate last-mile broadband facilities will allow those providers to extend their market power into the higher layers, including applications and content; this form of vertical integration would cause undue harm to the Internet.

The layers principle also offers a well-founded basis for disproving the BOCs' claim that Internet access and DSL constitute one unified thing that would be difficult and costly to untangle, somehow resulting in a loss of innovation. In fact, as ISPs have argued repeatedly in the FCC's wireline broadband proceeding, innovation is the hallmark of the Internet, and the FCC's proposed redefinition of DSL would wreck havoc on that innovation.[168] Benkler points out that "competing ISPs can compete [with cable modem operators] precisely by offering users different types of capacities over the same system. These ISPs are the primary potential separating agent between the ownership of the carriage medium and control of the content." Without that separation, the underlying provider can seize control over the upper layers as well, to the detriment of innovation and other consumer welfare benefits. As Solum remarks, "the nature of ISP service is not inherently fixed, and they can and do provide a wide range of diverse services. In short, the independent ISPs are engines for innovation in markets we do not yet imagine."[169]

Solum also discusses the danger of vertical integration in the cable modem services context, where "the same company sells products at the

Content Layer as a media company, owns the cable wires at the Physical Layer as a cable company, and has the ability to impose controls at the code layers as an ISP." Such vertical integration of functions across the layers raise anti-competition and antitrust concerns, especially when considering the cable companies' monopolies in the high-speed Internet access market – "perhaps the most important segment of the market because that is where the future lies."[170] The same lesson applies to the ILECs' DSL offerings. For example, it is not in the ILECs' interest to allow end users to utilize VoIP services and applications, which would tend to cannibalize the ILECs' long distance and exchange access services. In these instances and others, innovation clashes with legacy revenue streams, and the latter wins out if the underlying platform provider is allowed to control what the customer can and cannot do.[171]

Policymakers generally have two choices: restrict (quarantine) the upstream dominant firm, or regulate that firm to some degree (which requires regulation of wholesale price and quality of access). While a restriction on vertical integration would more directly address the market dominance concerns, appropriate regulation designed to facilitate nondiscriminatory access at various layers appears sufficient in most cases to largely negate those concerns. Many forms of vertical integration can bring efficiency benefits, and a relatively small likelihood of harming competition. At the same time, layers analysis helps reveal those instances where powerful firms at one level should not be allowed to leverage that power unfairly into adjacent levels, causing significant damage to competition and innovation. Broadband transport by the incumbent LECs is one such instance meriting careful regulatory scrutiny.

In sum, it is important to allow effective "vertical competition" in the broadband space, primarily through engendering robust intermodal and intramodal competition at the Physical Access Layer. The Internet market generally has been characterized by massive shifts in the competitive center, with competition coming from other layers (hardware companies versus operating system companies versus browser companies versus open source platform companies). Cerf sees no logical reason to adopt the FCC's recommended view that "open nondiscriminatory telecommunications platforms no longer serve the public interest when they are used to provide so-called broadband services."[172] As Solum notes, the "vertical integration of content, ISP, and access market threatens to stifle the innovative future of the Internet by eliminating this strategic competitive factor in the critically important residential broadband market."

IP Communications (VoIP)

Providers of so-called Voice over Internet Protocol services and other IP communications, such as MCI, Vonage, and AT&T, have argued against common carrier-style federal and state regulation of competitive VoIP services. The typical argument is that VoIP is an information service that by definition cannot be classified and treated as a telecommunications service.[173] This particular view faces stiff political challenges on several fronts. State regulators already have begun to insist that providers of VoIP services look just like ordinary telephone companies, and so must seek state approval as common carriers to provide such services to the public.[174] With that carrier certification would come other public interest obligations, such as the payment of federal and state universal service charges, the provisioning of 911 emergency services, and submission to wiretapping requirements under CALEA and related statutes. In a similar vein, the incumbent LECs have argued that providers of VoIP service must comply with many existing carrier regulations, particularly with regard to the payment of intercarrier compensation (interstate carrier access charges) to the ILECs.[175] At this juncture it is unclear whether and when this legal issue ultimately will be resolved at the FCC or elsewhere.[176]

Moreover, when the FCC first was compelled to take a look at the regulatory classification of VoIP in 1998, it fell back on familiar territory: the notion that one should regulate based on what type of service one can discern.[177] Employing its so-called "functional approach," the FCC tentatively divided up the world of "IP telephony" services into three buckets: phone-to-phone, computer-to-computer, and computer-to-phone. Based on four non-dispositive factors (the provider holds itself out as providing voice telephony service; does not require the customer to use different CPE; allows the customer to call ordinary telephone numbers; and transmits customer information without net change in form or content), the Commission indicated that certain types of phone-to-phone service lack the characteristic of an "information service."[178] However, the FCC declined to make definitive pronouncements in the absence of a more complete record.[179]

As Chairman Powell already recognizes, the FCC desperately needs a new theory to encompass all forms of IP-based services and applications. The layers approach offers a compelling way to frame the issue. In the coming IP world, voice service becomes just another application – in this case, audio bits – that "ride on top of" the IP protocol. So, too, data bits and video bits and any other bits would be treated from an engineering perspective as any other element of the Applications Layer. There no longer is any necessary tie between the service being offered – two-way interactive voice service – and the underlying network used to provide the service – IP transport (see Figure 9).[180] In point of fact, regulation of the upper layer application simply makes no sense where there is no automatic correlation to a fixed lower layer platform technology.

Moreover, in a market where any and all such applications are offered on a competitive basis, there simply is no need for common carrier-

Figure 9

Layers Analysis Supports Non-Telecom Regulation of VoIP

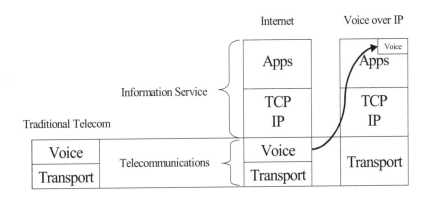

style regulation. Employing new Corollary Four, any lingering concerns about the need for government oversight of the retail voice services market largely are negated when those services are shifted to an IP platform. While regulation of last-mile Physical Access Layer facilities that carry the VoIP services continues to be necessary in the presence of considerable market power, such pro-competition regulation need not and should not extend upward to the Application Layer.

> Of course, VoIP is not a monolith, and not every mingling of voice service with IP automatically constitutes an Application Layer functionality. Sicker acknowledges that voice services running over packet networks brings up many difficult issues.[181] Policymakers initially must consider distinctions between (1) voice services running over the Internet and those services running over Internet protocols, (2) self-provisioned services and those obtained from a service provider, (3) whether there is a "holding out of a service," and (3) whether IP-based services should be viewed as in their infancy, and therefore should be free from burdensome regulations. Fundamentally, because voice is becoming an application, however, and not coterminous with the network on which it operates, voice as a service generally should not be subject to the same regulatory conditions as the physical network.[182]

CONCLUSION

Layers analysis offers a fresh and compelling way to look at legacy U.S. legal and regulatory policies. In the e-commerce world, where ISPs face the prospects of legal liability for the actions of third parties using their network, a horizontal layers framework exposes the very real dangers of overzealous and ill-reasoned regulation at disparate layers. In the world of telecommunications regulation, the framework provides a valuable new mechanism for assessing harm from the exercise of undue market power, and suggesting practical alternatives. In particular, the MCI Layers Model can assist policymakers in targeting regulation to foster needed competition at the core (or lower layers) of the network, while preserving and enhancing innovation at the edge (or upper layers). Well-founded on fundamental engineering principles, and buttressed by economic analysis, the layers principle, as expressed in this paper's notion of a horizontal layers framework, should be adopted by policymakers as a necessary and productive public policy tool.

ENDNOTES

[*] The author would like to thank Vint Cerf for first recommending that I review Professor Lawrence Solum's cogent paper on the layers principle, as well as for Vint's unflagging enthusiasm and patient prodding in seeing this white paper to completion. MCI attorneys Dennis Guard and Karen Johnson also provided invaluable research, drafting, and editing contributions. Any residual dubious thinking contained in the paper is solely my own.

[1] *See, e.g.*, Kevin Werbach, *A Layered Model for Internet Policy*, 1 J. ON TELECOMM. & HIGH TECH. L. 37, 39-40 (2002) (Communications policy traditionally has been organized around horizontal divisions between service categories and between geographic regions.); Douglas Sicker, *Further Defining a Layered Model for Telecommunications Policy*, Telecommunications Policy Research Conference ("TPRC") Paper, at 4 (2002) (Traditionally "regulatory conditions are based on the type of infrastructure on which a telecommunications service is offered.... This regulatory structure is often referred to as the 'silo model' in that each network and service is regulated separately from the other."); Jonathan Weinberg, *The Internet and "Telecommunications Services," Universal Service Mechanisms, Access Charges, and Other Flotsam of the Regulatory System*, 16 YALE J. ON REG. 211, 213 ("American communications law has developed along service-specific lines, with complex and distinct regulatory structures covering telephony (wired and wireless), broadcasting, cable television, and satellites."); François Bar & Christian Sandvig, *Rules From Truth: Post-Convergence Policy for Access*, TPRC Paper, at 3 (2000) ("Modern communication policy in most of the world has evolved to treat different media as islands.").

[2] 47 U.S.C. Title II, Title III, and Title VI (2003). *See* Sicker, *supra* note 1, at 4 (in the U.S. silo model, each network and service is regulated separately from the other, and "the top defines the regulatory Title."). Attorney John Nakahata calls this arrangement "regulation by service 'pigeonhole.'" John T. Nakahata, *Regulating Information Platforms: The Challenge of Rewriting Communications Regulation From the Bottom Up*, 1 J. ON TELECOMM. & HIGH TECH. L. 95, 100 (2002).

[3] *In re Regulatory and Policy Problems Presented by the Interdependence of Computer and Communication Services and Facilities)*, Notice of Inquiry, 7 F.C.C.2d 11, 11 (1966) (hereinafter "*Computer I*").

[4] *In re Amendment of Section 64.702 of the Commission's Rules and Regulations* (Second Computer Inquiry), Final Decision, 77 F.C.C.2d 384, 430 (1980) (hereinafter "*Computer II*").

[5] *Id.* at 419.

[6] 47 C.F.R. § 64.702(a) (2003).

[7] *Computer II*, 77 F.C.C. 2d at 422-23.

[8] *Id.* at 475.

[9] *Id.* at 474.

[10] Robert Cannon, *The Legacy of the Federal Communications Commission's Computer Inquiries*, 55 FED. COMM. L.J. 167, 169, 180 (2003).

[11] Weinberg, *supra* note 1, at 222.

[12] Philip J. Weiser, *Law and Information Platforms,* 1 J. ON TELECOMM. & HIGH TECH. L. 1, 12 (2002).

[13] Letter from Vinton G. Cerf, Senior Vice-President, WorldCom, Inc., to The Honorable Donald Evans, Secretary, U.S. Department of Commerce, and The Honorable Michael Powell, Chairman, Federal Communications Commission, CC Docket Nos. 02-33, 01-338 (May 20, 2002) (hereinafter "Cerf Letter to Evans/Powell").

[14] Sicker, *supra* note 1, at 5.

[15] Werbach, *supra* note 1, at 65. At the same time, Werbach questions whether the *Computer Inquiry* orders merely added a new category of services carved out of the existing Title II rules. *Id.* Werbach's references to "vertical" and "horizontal" regulation in his paper essentially invert the terminology employed by other commentators, and in this paper, likely because he is referring to the "vertical" protocol stacks that are made up of "horizontal" layers.

[16] *See, e.g,,* Werbach, *supra* note 1, at 58 (Internet architecture is based on end-to-end design and a layered protocol stack).

[17] Additionally, in a private communication Vint Cerf reports that the ancient Greek root "protokollon" referred to the bit of papyrus affixed to the beginning of a scroll to describe its contents – much like the header of an Internet packet.

[18] Katie Hafner & Matthew Lyon, Where Wizards Stay Up Late: The Origins of the Internet, at 147 (1996).

[19] *See* Vinton G. Cerf and Robert E. Kahn, *A Protocol for Packet Network Intercommunication*, IEEE Trans. On Comms, Vol Com-22, No. 5 (May 1974) (hereinafter "Cerf/Kahn TCP Paper").

[20] As Shah, Sicker, and Hatfield put it: "Protocol layering is a common technique to simplify networking designs by dividing them into functional layers, and assigning protocols to perform each layer's task…. The concept of layering relies on breaking a complex task into smaller subsets, each of which addresses a specific issue. Each layer provides a well-defined set of services to the layers above it and depends on lower layers for its own foundation." Ashish Shah, Douglas Sicker, and Dale Hatfield, *Thinking About Openness in the Telecommunications Policy Context,* TPRC Paper, at 13 (2003).

[21] *See* RICHARD W. STEVENS, TCP/IP ILLUSTRATED, VOLUME 1: THE PROTOCOLS, at 4-5 (1994).

[22] Timothy Wu, *Application-Centered Internet Analysis,* 85 VA. L. REV. 1163, 1192 (1999).

[23] Clark and Blumenthal explain that the end-to-end arguments are a set of design principles concerning how application requirements should be met in a communications system. The end-to-end arguments suggest that specific application-level functions usually cannot, and preferably should not, be built into the lower levels of the system – the core of the network. David D. Clark & Marjory S. Blumenthal, *Rethinking the Design of the Internet: The End to End Arguments vs. the Brave New World,* at 1 (2000).

[24] *See* Wu, *supra* note 22, at 1164-65.

[25] Weiser, *supra* note 12, at 4-5.

[26] *See, e.g.,* Mark A. Lemley & Lawrence Lessig, *The End of End-to-End: Preserving the Architecture of the Internet in the Broadband Era,* at 304 (Stanford Law School,

Working Paper No. 207) (2000) (explaining role of "e2e" design in producing the "extraordinary innovation" of the Internet).

[27] Wu, *supra* note 22, at 1193.

[28] *See generally* Cerf/Kahn TCP Paper, *supra* note 19.

[29] *See, e.g.,* CRAIG HUNT, TCP/IP NETWORK ADMINISTRATION, at 8 (1992) (with no universal agreement about how to describe the layers of the TCP/IP model, it is generally viewed as composed of fewer than seven layers); LAWRENCE LESSIG, CODE AND OTHER LAWS OF CYBERSPACE, at 101 (2000) (most descriptions of the TCP/IP suite define three to five functional layers); Shah et al., *supra* note 20, at 15 (the TCP/IP protocols map to a four-layer conceptual model).

[30] Shah, et al., *supra* note 20, at 13; the authors also state:

> The Internet protocols are arranged in essentially independent, unbundled layers with the Internet Protocol itself at the "waist" of the stack. The protocol stack broadens above the waist to support a wide range of transport and application layers including email, the World Wide Web, file transfer protocols, remote login, etc. The protocol stack broadens below the waist to ride on a wide range of underlying networks using a variety of technologies including frame relay, ATM, ADSL, fiber optic systems, and so on.

[31] *See* JOHN D. SPRAGINS ET AL., TELECOMMUNICATIONS PROTOCOLS AND DESIGN, at 14-15, 118-27 (1991).

[32] Various principles were applied to arrive at the seven layers: a layer should be created where a different level of abstraction is needed; each layer should perform a well-defined function; the layer boundaries should be chosen to minimize the information flow across the interfaces; and the number of layers should be large enough that distinct functions need not be thrown together in the same layer out of necessity, and small enough that the architecture does not become unwieldy. Shah, et al., *supra* note 20, at 9.

[33] Werbach, *supra* note 1, at 59 n.87 (TCP/IP, not OSI, has become the dominant protocols model).

[34] *See, e.g.,* COMPUTER SCIENCE AND TELECOMMUNICATIONS BOARD, NATIONAL RESEARCH COUNCIL, REALIZING THE INFORMATION FUTURE: THE INTERNET AND BEYOND, at 47-51 (1994) (proposing an "open data network architecture," with Network Technology Substrate, ODN Bearer Service, Transportation Services and Representation Standards, Middleware Services, and Applications layers).

[35] LAWRENCE LESSIG, THE FUTURE OF IDEAS: THE FATE OF THE COMMONS IN A CONNECTED WORLD, at 23 (2002).

[36] Yochai Benkler, *From Consumers to Users: Shifting the Deeper Structures of Regulation Toward Sustainable Commons and User Access,* 52 FED. COMM. L.J. 561, 562 (2000).

[37] It must be noted that these various models are somewhat oversimplified for cases where IP layers over Frame Relay, Asynchronous Transfer Mode (ATM), Multi Protocol Label Switching (MPLS), and other types of networks.

[38] THE WHITE HOUSE, *Administration White Paper on Communications Act Reforms,* at 7 (1994).

[39] Nakahata, *supra* note 2, at 129.

[40] Bar & Sandvig, *supra* note 1, at 2 n.3. Indeed, the authors criticize both the FCC's *Computer Inquiry* rules and the failed Title VII proposal as inherently flawed. They argue that both approaches to the crisis of convergence – fitting new communication services into existing categories (the *Computer Inquiries*) and establishing new categories for new services (the ill-fated Title VII approach in 1994) – suffer from the same shortcomings of proposing "marginal adjustments to a system anchored in particular technological implementations of communications services, rather than starting from any fundamental purpose of communication policy." *Id.* at 19.

[41] As Bar and Sandvig report, "the attempt was quickly killed by telcos and cable operators who feared losing the advantages each saw in the established regimes." Bar & Sandvig, *supra* note 1, at 2 n.3. *See also* Nakahata, *supra* note 2, at 129 (the Title VII proposal "had something for everyone to hate").

[42] 47 U.S.C. § 153(46), (20) (2003). *In re Implementation of the Non-Accounting Safeguards of Sections 271 and 272 of the Communications Act of 1934, as amended,* 11 F.C.C.R. 21905, 21955-58 (1996) (hereinafter "*Non-Accounting Safeguards Order*").

[43] 47 U.S.C. § 157 nt (2003).

[44] *Id.*

[45] 47 U.S.C. § 251 (2003). Werbach reports that the 1996 Act's unbundling regime was founded on the FCC's earlier concept of Open Network Architecture (ONA), intended originally as a form of modular network unbundling to benefit enhanced service providers. Werbach, *supra* note 1, at 61.

[46] 47 U.S.C. § 271 (2003).

[47] *See* Werbach, *supra* note 1, at 42 (the Telecommunications Act of 1996 retained the silo model of communications policy); Weiser, *supra* note 12, at 11 (the 1996 Act did not disturb a category-based regulatory strategy).

[48] COMMITTEE ON BROADBAND LAST MILE TECHNOLOGY, NATIONAL RESEARCH COUNCIL, BROADBAND: BRINGING HOME THE BITS, at 32 (2002).

[49] Nakahata, *supra* note 2, at 97. As will be discussed later, in contrast the European Union had adopted a comprehensive regulatory framework that encompasses a technology-neutral model relying in part on the horizontal network layers concept.

[50] In re Policy and Rules Concerning The Interstate, Interexchange Marketplace, Implementation of Section 254(g) of the Communications Act of 1934, as amended, 1998 Biennial Regulatory Review — Review of Customer Premises Equipment And Enhanced Services Unbundling Rules In the Interexchange, Exchange Access And Local Exchange Markets, CC Docket No. 96-61, CC Docket No. 98-183, Report and Order, 16 F.C.C.R. 7418, 7420-7421, (2001) (hereinafter "CPE/Enhanced Services Bundling Order"); see Cannon, supra note 10, at 200.

[51] *Non-Accounting Safeguards Order,* 11 F.C.C.R. at 21969-71.

[52] *Id.* at 21970-71. *In re Federal-State Joint Board on Universal Service*, Report to Congress, 11 F.C.C.R. 11501, 11546 (1998) (hereinafter "*FCC Report to Congress*"), the FCC summarized its regulatory philosophy (apparently informed by layers thinking) in this regard:

> Communications networks function as overlapping layers, with multiple providers often leveraging a common infrastructure. As long as the underlying market for provision of transmission facilities

is competitive or is subject to sufficient pro-competitive safeguards, we see no need to regulate the enhanced functionalities that can be built on top of those facilities.... As an empirical matter, the level of competition, innovation, investment, and growth in the enhanced services industry over the past two decades provides a strong endorsement for such an approach."
The FCC also has acknowledged that the Internet is an global information system that "provides, uses, or makes accessible, either publicly or privately, high level services layered on the communications and related infrastructure...." *In re Inquiry Concerning High-Speed Access to the Internet over Cable and Other Facilities*, Declaratory Ruling and Notice of Proposed Rulemaking, GN Docket No. 00-185, CS Docket No. 02-521, 17 F.C.C.R. 4798, 4799 at n.1 (2002).

[53] *CPE/Enhanced Services Bundling Order*, 16 F.C.C.R. at 7425.

[54] *Id.* at 7444.

[55] *See infra* Section III.B.2.b.

[56] 17 U.S.C. § 512(c) (2003).

[57] For a detailed account of this subject, *see generally* TIMOTHY D. CASEY, ISP LIABILITY SURVIVAL GUIDE: STRATEGIES FOR MANAGING COPYRIGHT, SPAM, CACHE, AND PRIVACY REGULATIONS, at xix (2000) (a practical guide for "understanding, complying, or otherwise dealing with existing and ongoing efforts to control or regulate the Internet").

[58] *See infra* Section III.A. for a further discussion of these and other recent examples.

[59] Werbach, *supra* note 1, at 38, 46.

[60] Indeed, as Craig McTaggart reminds, us, "telephone and Internet traffic are often carried over the same physical wires and cables. They are simply encoded using different technical protocols at the logical layer." Craig McTaggart, *A Layered Approach to Internet Legal Analysis* (Dec. 21, 2002), at 5 (unpublished article available at http://www.innovationlaw.org/cm/ilg2002/reading/layered1.pdf).

[61] Weiser, *supra* note 12, at 10 (there are two fundamental dynamics of the Information Age: digital transformation and a networked world).

[62] Werbach, *supra* note 1, at 47.

[63] *Id.* at 58.

[64] Sicker, *supra* note 1, at 6-8.

[65] Rob Frieden, Adjusting the Horizontal and Vertical in Telecommunications Regulation: A Comparison of the Traditional and a New Layered Approach, 55 FED. COMM. L.J. 207, 209 (2003). See also Bar & Sandvig, supra note 1, at 17 ("A single infrastructure, the internet, now offers the range of applications that once existed in distinct domains, governed by different policies reflecting different compromises between control and access. In addition, the Internet also brings about new applications that defy classification....").

[66] McTaggart, *supra* note 60, at 1.

[67] Robert M. Entman, in TRANSITION TO AN IP ENVIRONMENT: A REPORT OF THE FIFTEENTH ANNUAL ASPEN INSTITUTE CONFERENCE ON TELECOMMUNICATIONS POLICY, at 1 (2001).

[68] Sicker, *supra* note 1, at 9.

[69] Entman, *supra* note 67, at 2-3.

[70] Werbach, *supra* note 1, at 67.

[71] *Id.*

[72] Cannon, *supra* note 10, at 195:

> Differing layers demarcate natural boundaries between markets. These market boundaries permit communications regulation, where necessary, to be particularly successful. By conceptualizing the policy as layers, the analyst is capable of grouping and segregating issues. Issues related to the physical network layer (i.e., common carrier regulation, spectrum policy, cable franchises) are different from those of the logical layer (i.e., open access, peering) and are different from those in the content layer (i.e., intellectual property, gambling, taxation, libel). Thus, by conceptualizing the policy as layers, the analyst is enabled to identify markets, clarify issues, create boundary regulations that are effective, and, in so doing, target solutions where issues reside without interfering with other industries and opportunities. The Layered Model is a market policy mapped onto a technical conception

[73] Sicker, *supra* note 1, at 9.

[74] Frieden, *supra* note 65, at 213-14.

[75] Sicker, *supra* note 1, at 9.

[76] Entman, *supra* note 67, at 6.

[77] *Id.* at 13-14.

[78] *Id.* at 16.

[79] *Id. See also* Michael J. Weisman, *The Regulation of a Layered Regulatory Approach to E-Mail, Internet Radio and IP Telephony,* at 30 (March 2002) (unpublished essay submitted to Professor Toshiko Takanaka, University of Washington School of Law), available at http://www.law.washington.edu/Casrip/classes/Layeredregulationpaper.pdf (changes proposed by advocates of the layered model "would only be possible in an atmosphere of aggressive antitrust enforcement.").

[80] Werbach, supra note 1, at 54-64; Douglas C. Sicker and Joshua L. Mindel, *Refinements of a Layered Model for Telecommunications Policy,* 1 J. ON TELECOMM. & HIGH TECH. L. 69, 71, 85, 92-93.

[81] See J. Scott Marcus, The Potential Relevance to the United States of the European Union's Newly Adopted Regulatory Framework for Telecommunications, at 28 (FCC, OPP Working Paper Series No. 36) (2002); Nakahata, supra note 2, at 97; Frieden, supra note 65, at 249.

[82] Nakahata, *supra* note 2, at 130, Nakahata, otherwise a proponent of the concept, opines that from an institutional perspective, a "bottoms-up" statutory overhaul focused on a functional layers approach is "a fundamental, radical change."

[83] Douglas C. Sicker, *Applying a Layered Policy Model to IP Based Voice Services,* IEEE Computer Society, Proceedings of the 36th Hawaii International Conference on Systems Sciences (HICSS '03), at 8 (2002).

[84] Michael K. Powell, Chairman, Federal Communications Commission, Remarks on Voice over IP at Meeting of the Technology Advisory Council, at 1 (Oct. 20, 2003), available at www.fcc.gov .

[85] *Id.* at 2.

406   A HORIZONTAL LEAP FORWARD

[86] *Id.*

[87] Michael K. Powell, Chairman, Federal Communications Commission, Opening Remarks at the FCC Voice over Internet Protocol Forum, at 1 (Dec. 1, 2003), available at www.fcc.gov .

[88] Jeff Pulver, *VON Pioneers: Robert Pepper of the FCC*, VON MAGAZINE, Nov.-Dec. 2003, at 13-14:

> We're seeing a significant shift in the telecom industry's underlying technology as we move from circuits to packets and from a traditional architecture to one where all forms of traffic ultimately ride over IP.... Now, there are people in Washington who don't understand a great deal about technology or even the concept of the layered approach to communications networks and services. The idea that you could have a transport link that is independent of sound or analog waves is new to them.... It's a completely different way of thinking about our networks. In many respects it all really comes down to an issue of educating people

[89] Letter from Brett Perlman, Commissioner, Public Utility Commission of Texas, to The Honorable Kevin Martin, Commissioner, Federal Communications Commission, at 3-4 (January 28, 2003), available at http://www.puc.state.tx.us/about/commissioners/perlman/news/news_bb.cfm?comname=2. Perlman went on to note that the layered model "has been discussed in several recent legal and technical articles and is consistent with the underlying protocols governing the Internet." *Id.* at 4. After discussing the model in some detail, Perlman observes that application of the model would allow regulation based on a market power test, not on types of networks or services, so that network access and unbundling requirements would apply to any broadband provider with market power. *Id.*

[90] Sicker, *supra* note 1, at 12.

[91] *See, e.g.,* TIM BERNERS-LEE, WEAVING THE WEB: THE ORIGINAL DESIGN AND ULTIMATE DESTINY OF THE WORLD WIDE WEB BY ITS INVENTOR, at 129-30 (1999). He sees four horizontal layers in the Web's infrastructure: the transmission medium, the computer hardware, the software, and the content. LESSIG, *supra* note 29, at 101, discusses four layers (applications, transport, network, and data-link, with content layer included in what others call the application layer)). Werbach, *supra* note 1, at 59, uses a four layers model (content, applications or services, logical infrastructure, physical infrastructure. Entman, *supra* note 67, at 2, indicates that for purposes of public policy, it might suffice to distinguish four layers: content, which describes the actual information transmitted (voice conversation, e-commerce transactions, video streams); applications, which describes the nature of the service provided (voice, video); network; and data link (interconnection point), for routing protocols and packet structure, fiber and copper, and coaxial cable. McTaggart, *supra* note 60, at 1, also finds four readily-separable layers: content/transaction layer, application layer, logical layer, and physical layer. Others see only three layers necessary for a viable model.Bar and Sandvig see a "fundamental separability" between three network components: physical hardware, control software, and communications applications." Bar and Sandvig, *supra* note 1, at 21. As discussed earlier, the Benkler model adopts a three layers approach (content, logical or code, and

physical). Benkler, *supra* note 36, at 562. Sicker, *supra* note 1, at 10-11, concludes that the generalized horizontal policy model has either three or four layers: Content, Applications, Transport, and Access. Still others go up to six layers, see Lawrence B. Solum and Minn Chung, *The Layers Principle: Internet Architecture and the Law,* at 32-33 (University of San Diego School of Law, Public Law and Legal Theory Research Paper No. 55) (2003), *downloaded from* the Social Science Research Network (SSRN) electronic library at: http://ssrn.com/abstract=416263 (the six layers are Content, Application, Transport, IP, Link, and Physical). Shah, Sicker, and Hatfield propose a model that closely resembles a traditional protocol stack, but adds a Layer 0 to represent the physical and power related issues not generally captured in Layer 1, and a Layer 6 to include issues beyond the layered model and other non-conforming topics (process issues such as standards participation and interconnection negotiations). Shah, et al., *supra* note 20, at 16.

[92] Sicker, *supra* note 1, at 12.

[93] *Id.* at 10.

[94] Michael L. Katz, *Thoughts on the Implications of Technological Change for Telecommunications Policy*, in TRANSITION TO AN IP ENVIRONMENT, A REPORT OF THE FIFTEENTH ANNUAL ASPEN INSTITUTE CONFERENCE ON TELECOMMUNICATIONS POLICY (2001), at 25-26.

[95] Werbach, *supra* note 1, at 61 n.91.

[96] *Id.* at 60 n.89.

[97] McTaggart, *supra* note 60, at 5, 9.

[98] Sicker, *supra* note 1, at 10-12.

[99] Solum and Chung, *supra* note 91.

[100] LESSIG, *supra* note 29, at 30-60.

[101] LESSIG, *supra* note 35, at 34-37. For example, the TCP/IP protocol is independent from the underlying computer hardware or operating system. *See* STEVENS, *supra* note 21, at 5.

[102] Solum and Chung, *supra* note 98, at 29.

[103] *Id.* at 29-32, 42-43.

[104] *Id.* at 51-53.

[105] *Id.* at 25-27.

[106] *Id.* at 27-28.

[107] *Id.* at 28-29.

[108] *Id.* at 33-38.

[109] *Id.* at 38-41.

[110] *See* 47 U.S.C. § 214(a), § 310(d) (2003).

[111] Solum and Chung, *supra* note 91, at 45-46.

[112] The layers principle is supported by sound considerations of network engineering. But there is no reason to believe that these principles of network design are written in stone for all time. As the Internet evolves, it is possible that superior architectures may be conceived. Moreover, just as the Internet changed the total electronic communications system, there may be similar revolutionary innovations in the future

Id. at 42.

[113] *Id.* at 27.

[114] Benkler, *supra* note 36, at 565.

[115] *Id.* at 568.

[116] *Id.* at 569-70, 575-76. In a related observation, Philip Weiser points out that 70 percent of the three billion or so web pages are built by individuals from their desire to share ideas, rather than to make money. Weiser, *supra* note 12, at 33 n.147.

[117] Lee McKnight, *Internet Business Models: Creative Destruction As Usual,* in CREATIVE DESTRUCTION: BUSINESS SURVIVAL STRATEGIES IN THE GLOBAL INTERNET ECONOMY, at 39, 40-41 (Lee McKnight, et al., eds., 2002).

[118] *Id.* at 45.

[119] *Id.* at 42.

[120] Katz, *supra* note 102, at 26. Weiser also sees the Internet as "a uniquely suitable platform for innovation." Weiser, *supra* note 12, at 22.

[121] LESSIG, *supra* note 35, at 40.

[122] Shah, et al., *supra* note 20, at 6.

[123] LESSIG, *supra* note 35, at 14, In particular, "rather than relying upon the creativity of a small group of innovators who might work for the companies that control the network, the end-to-end design enables anyone with an Internet connection to design and implement a better way to use the Internet.".

[124] *Id.* at 37.

[125] *Id.* at 37, 39.

[126] Sicker, *supra* note 83, at 8.

[127] In the academic literature, the Commission has endorsed the evolutionary, or competitive model of innovation. It holds that the process of technological innovation proceeds most rapidly through a survival-of-the-fittest competition between new technologies, and it encourages policies to ensure a fair fight among competing innovations. If this 'Darwinian evolution' is the best path of innovation, it follows that the most promising path of development will be difficult to predict in advance. Hence, despite the 'waste' generated by a competitive process, the results will be superior to planned innovation directed by a single prospect holder, however well-intentioned. That entity will suffer from cognitive biases (such as a predisposition to continue with current ways of doing business) that makes it unlikely to come to the right decisions, even if it means well.

Letter from Timothy Wu, Associate Professor, University of Virginia Law School, and Lawrence Lessig, Professor, Stanford Law School, to Marlene H. Dortch, Secretary, Federal Communications Commission, CS Docket No. 02-52, at 5 (Aug. 22, 2003) (hereinafter "Wu & Lessig Letter"). *See also* Timothy Wu, *Network Neutrality & Broadband Discrimination,* 2 J. TELECOMM. & HIGH TECH. L. 5 (2003). Adherents to this evolutionary model view the innovation process as a survival-of-the-fittest competition among developers of new technologies. "They are suspicious of models of development that might vest control in any initial prospect-holder, private or public, who is expected to direct the optimal path of innovation, minimizing the excesses of innovative competition." The most promising path of development is difficult to predict in advance.

Some evolutionary theorists view a communications network like the Internet as a platform for a competition among application developers. "It is therefore important that the platform be neutral to ensure the competition remains meritocratic." Backers of an evolutionary approach to innovation take the Internet as evidence of the superiority of a network designed along evolutionary principles. *Id.* at 5-6.

[128] McKnight, *supra* note 117, at 40.

[129] *See, e.g.,* Todd Spangler, *Initiatives Underscore DSL Future. (UUNET Technologies, Cisco Systems' Digital Subscriber Line Strategies) (Company Business and Marketing),* Internet World, March 16, 1998, available at http://www.findarticles.com/cf_dls/m0DXS/n10_v4/21049642/p1/article.jhtml (Analysts suggest that "telcos are reluctant to bring to market DSL service on the order of 1 to 1.5 Mbps… because doing so would cannibalize the lucrative business of selling dedicated circuits, such as T-1 lines, for access.").

[130] McTaggart, *supra* note 60, at 1.

[131] U.S. Department of Justice and Federal Trade Commission, Horizontal Merger Guidelines, 57 Fed. Reg. 41,552 (1992, as revised in 1997) ("Horizontal Merger Guidelines"); *see also* Marcus, *supra* note 81, at 7-9 (providing an overview of U.S. antitrust law, agencies, and methodologies).

[132] Horizontal Merger Guidelines, Section 1.5 (Concentration and Market Shares).

[133] Pursuant to sections 214(a) and 310(d) of the Communications Act, the Commission must determine whether proposed transfers of control of licenses and authorizations will serve the public interest. 47 U.S.C. § 214(a), § 310(d) (2003). The FCC's public interest standard includes an evaluation of the effect of the proposed transaction on competition, consistency with specific provisions of the Act, other applicable statutes, and the Commission's rules and policies, and in some cases, a consideration of the impact on program and viewpoint diversity. *See, e.g., In re Application of EchoStar Communications Corporation, General Motors Corporation, and Hughes Electronics Corporation, Transferors, and EchoStar Communications Corporation, Transferee,* CS Docket No. 01-348, 17 F.C.C.R. 20559, 20574-76 (2002).

[134] Directive 2002/21/EC of the European Parliament and of the Council of 7 March 2002 on a Common Regulatory Framework for Electronic Communications Networks and Services (Framework Directive), 2002 O.J. (L. 108).

[135] Frieden, 5note 66, at 7.

[136] Commission Guidelines on Market Analysis and the Assessment of Significant Market Power Under the Community Regulatory Framework for Electronic Communications Networks and Services, 2002 O.J. (C 165).

[137] The EU approach separates content from conduits and subjects either horizontal layer to regulation only where market distortions have occurred, or potentially may occur in view of the market power exercised by one or more stakeholders. The primary regulatory oversight model derives from general antitrust/competition policy rather than an industry or service specific predicate. Regulation occurs if and only if competition does not exist in a particular geographic or specific market, and existing regulatory obligations may be withdrawn on the basis of market analysis.

Frieden, *supra* note 65, at 51.

[138] Katz, *supra* note 94, at 28-29.

[139] *Id.* at 37.

[140] Sicker, *supra* note 83, at 6.

[141] Weiser, *supra* note 12, at 13.

[142] Katz, *supra* note 94, at 37-38. *See also* Sicker, *supra* note 83, at 6 ("Many cable and LECs would be viewed as significantly controlling the access layer.")

[143] McKnight, *supra* note 117, at 55.

[144] Weisman, *supra* note 79, at 30. "Although the Internet may be a layered network, corporate business plans in the United States often focus on vertical integration.... In practice, companies will do almost anything to avoid competition. They will gladly surrender markets and products lines to avoid the 'ruinous' price competition that strips monopoly rents out of the revenue stream." *Id.* at 25, 27.

[145] Nor does the layers principle apply only to the IP-based world of data packets. Given the reality of layered telecom networks, with ready technical distinctions between services provided and underlying facilities utilized, many of the concepts and principles associated with layering can be invoked in the analog and circuit-switched world as well. For example, even the traditional voice network employs layered protocols. Data networks also utilize layering models based on different protocols, including Frame Relay, ATM, MPLS, and Ethernet networks. *See, e.g.*, http://www-comm.itsi.disa.mil/atm/atm_pr.html (showing layers of ATM protocol); http://www.ieee802.org/17/documents/presentations/jan2002/hp_phy_02.pdf (showing layers of Ethernet protocol).

[146] 47 U.S.C. § 251(c)(3) (2003).

[147] *In re Review of the Section 251 Unbundling Obligations of Incumbent Local Exchange Carriers,* CC Docket No. 01-338, Report and Order, 16 F.C.C.R. 22, 781 (2002) ("*UNE Triennial Review Order*").

[148] More precisely, a 64-kilobits per second transmission path established via the Time Division Multiplexing of interleaved voice signals.

[149] Sicker, *supra* note 83, at 2.

[150] *See* Reza Dibadji, *Deregulation: A Tragedy in Three Acts*, THE WASHINGTON POST, Sept. 13, 2003, at A21.

[151] For example, Robert Cannon concludes that the FCC implicitly found that within the different layers are different markets and different regulatory concerns: the physical network layers (OSI layers 1 and 2) is "basic services" provisioned by telephone carriers regulated under Title II; the logical network layers (OSI layers 3 and 4) is TCP/IP or Internet access provisioned by ISPs, directly and intentionally benefiting from the *Computer Inquiry* safeguards; and the services, applications, and content provisioned by many providers, all generally removed from communication regulation. This layered approach to the *Computer Inquiries* means clear segregation between basic and enhanced services: basic is never enhanced, and enhanced is never basic. "Identifying something as an enhanced service does not alter the underlying transmission capacity as basic." Cannon, *supra* note 10, at 196-98.

[152] Werbach, *supra* note 1, at 67.

[153] Perhaps the most significant of these is the question of interfaces between layers. A key element of the Internet model is that these interfaces are open.

This allows competitors to circumvent a bottleneck at one layer by deploying services over another layer, and prevents companies that have control of lower-level services to prejudice or preclude certain services at higher layers. Cable open access can thus be understood as a debate over whether cable operators can use their control of the physical layers (cable distribution plan) to restrict choice and competition at the three higher levels.... Open interfaces are increasingly critical to an innovative, competitive model

Id. at 65-66.

[154] Clark & Blumenthal, *supra* note 23, at 19. Others agree about the negative consequences of allowing the cable company to bundle ISP service and access facilities, and that "giving such power to discriminate to the owner of the actual network infrastructure may be viewed as inconsistent with the end-to-end philosophy of the Internet." Shah, et al., *supra* note 20, at 5 n.9.

[155] Bar & Sandvig, *supra* note 1, at 22.

[156] *See Deployment of Wireline Services Offering Advanced Telecommunications Capability*, Memorandum Opinion and Order and Notice of Proposed Rulemaking, 13 F.C.C.R. 24012, 24029 (1998) (xDSL constitutes telecommunications service when offered to the public directly or on a stand-alone basis).

[157] *In re Appropriate Framework for Broadband Access to the Internet over Wireline Facilities*, CC Docket Nos. 02-33, 95-20 and 98-10, Notice of Proposed Rulemaking, 67 Fed. Reg. 9232, 9233 (2002) (hereinafter "*Broadband Framework NPRM*").

[158] Cerf Letter to Evans/Powell, *supra* note 13, at 3.

[159] Frieden, *supra* note 65, at 27.

[160] *Id.* at 27, 29-30.

[161] *Id.*

[162] *Id.* at 34. *see also id.* at 36 ("Much of this ad hoc rethinking of how definitions apply stems from the vertical regulatory models the Commission has erected and seeks to maintain. While new technologies do force regulatory agencies to determine into which categories innovative new services fit, the predominant trigger for trouble lies in the Commission's perceived need to make all or nothing assignments...")*and id.* at 42-43 ("The Commission cannot achieve the twin goal of sustaining service classifications and the vertical regulatory regimes while also creating novel ways to ignore the telecommunication services aspect of a convergent, blended and hybrid service that clearly has a horizontal layer of telecommunications delivered to consumers.... Instead the Commission pulls telecommunications capabilities out from the telecommunications service classification...."); Katz, *supra* note 94, at 35-36 (Manifestly a broadband policy that did not break out the telecommunications component from the vertically bundled package of information services "would fail to recognize de-lamination and would be subject to gaming and raising the possibility of competitive distortions.").

[163] Sicker, *supra* note 1, at 14.

[164] Cerf Letter to Evans/Powell, *supra* note 13, at 4.

[165] Werbach, *supra* note 1, at 64-65.

[166] Cerf Letter to Evans/Powell, *supra* note 13, at 3.

[167] *See Id.* at 4 ("Physics gets in the way of the supposed competition" in providing broadband transmission services. As a result, "at best, the residential market is a duopoly

– and in the worst case, consumers have only one choice or, in poorly served areas, *no* choice at all."); Dr. Vinton G. Cerf, *Broadband Policy and Delivery Options*, International Engineering Consortium, at 3 (hereinafter "Cerf IEC Paper") (brochure containing Cerf's June 3, 2002 keynote address at SUPERCOMM 2002) (Different broadband platforms "are indeed technologically competitive," but "whether they effectively compete is another story.").

[168] *See generally* The BroadNet Alliance, *The Importance of a Broad Net: The Significant Role of Online Service Providers in the Development and Success of the Information Age*, CC Docket No. 02-33 (July 1, 2002), available at www.broadnetalliance.org).

[169] Solum and Chung, *supra* note 91, at 95.

[170] *Id.*

[171] As the Supreme Court found in *Turner Broadcasting v. FCC*, 512 U.S. 622, 657 (1994), the First Amendment authorizes the U.S. Government to take steps "to ensure that private interests not restrict, through physical control of a critical pathway of communications, the free flow of information and ideas."

[172] Cerf IEC Paper, *supra* note 197, at 4.

[173] *See, e.g.*, Joint Comments of MCI and CompTel, WC Docket No. 03-211, October 27, 2003, at 5-13 (Vonage's VoIP service is an interstate information service under pertinent law and regulations).

[174] One example is a recent order from the Minnesota Public Utilities Commission concluding that it possesses jurisdiction over Vonage "as a company providing telephone service in Minnesota," and ordering Vonage to acquire a carrier certification and comply with 911 service and fee requirements. *In re Complaint of the Minnesota Department of Commerce Against Vonage Holding Corp. Regarding Lack of Authority to Operate in Minnesota*, Docket No. P-6214/C-03-108, 2003 Minn. PUC LEXIS 94 (Minn. Pub. Utils. Comm'n, Sept. 11, 2003). A federal district court subsequently overturned the PUC decision as contrary to federal law and issued a permanent injunction against its enforcement. *Vonage Holdings Corp. v. Minn. Pub. Utils. Comm'n*, 2003 WL 225676345, 2003 Minn. PUC LEXIS 106 (D. Minn. Oct. 13, 2003).

[175] *See, e.g.*, Comments of Verizon, WC Docket No. 03-211, October 27, 2003, at 13-15 (Vonage provides a telecommunications service and must pay interstate access charges); Comments of SBC Communications, Inc., WC Docket No. 03-211, October 27, 2003, at 8 (all IP telephony services are subject to paying terminating interstate access charges).

[176] The FCC has announced its intention to initiate a rulemaking proceeding in early 2004 to examine the various legal and regulatory issues surrounding VoIP and other IP-based applications. FCC Public Notice, *FCC to Begin Internet Telephony Proceeding*, November 6, 2003.

[177] *FCC Report to Congress, supra* note 52, at 11543 ("the classification of a service under the 1996 Act depends on the functional nature of the end-user offering.").

[178] *Id.* at 11543-44.

[179] *Id.* at 11544.

[180] Figure 9 (and the format for Figure 8) is derived from a slide contained in the following: Ray Gifford, President, The Progress & Freedom Foundation, *VoIP – Creative*

Destruction of Regulation, SEARUC, June 9, 2003, available at http://198.87.232.130/issues/communications/testimony/060903voip.ppt.

[181] Sicker, *supra* note 1, at 22.

[182] Sicker, *supra* note 83, at 7.

BIBLIOGRAPHY

@Home Corp., *@Home Acceptable Use Policy*, *at* http://www.home.com/support/aup/ (last modified May 8, 2000).

@Home Corp., *@Home Frequently Asked Questions*, *at* http://www.home.com/qa.html (last visited Jan. 9, 2001).

A New Model for AOL May Influence Cable's Future, NEW YORK TIMES, August 26, 2002, at C.1.

Abbate, Janet, INVENTING THE INTERNET (1999).

Adelphia FAQ, Home Networking, *at* http://www.adelphia.com/high_speed_internet/faqs.cfm (last visited Mar. 13, 2003).

AdHoc Telecommunications Users, *Comments of Ad Hoc Telecommunications Users Committee*, IN THE MATTER OF REVIEW OF REGULATORY REQUIREMENTS FOR INCUMBENT LEC BROADBAND TELECOMMUNICATIONS SERVICES, Federal Communications Commission, CC Docket No. 01-337, March 1, 2002.

Advisory Concerning VeriSign's Deployment of DNS Wildcard Service, ICANN, September 19, 2003.

Allot Communications Netenforcer® Data Sheet, *at* http://www.allot.com/html/ products_netenforcer_sp.shtml (last visited Mar. 13, 2003).

Amalgamated Transit Union v. Skinner, 894 F.2d 1362, 1364 (D.C. Cir. 1990).

Amazon.com *Ex Parte Letter*, CS DOCKET NO. 02-52, Appendix B, Dec. 10, 2002.

America Online Inc., *Open Access Comments of America Online, Inc.*, before the Department of Telecommunications and Information Services, San Francisco, October 27, 1999 (on file with author).

America Online, Inc., *Comments, Transfer of Control of FCC Licenses of MediaOne Group Inc., to AT&T Corp.,* CS Docket 99-251 (filed Aug. 23, 1999).

American Cable Association, Comments, In Re Implementation of the Cable Television Consumer Protection & Competition Act of 1992, Development of Competition in Video Programming Distribution: Section 628(c)(5) of the Communications Act: Sunset of Exclusive Contract Prohibition, CS Docket No. 01-290 (filed Dec. 3, 2001) *available at* http://gullfoss2.fcc.gov/prod/ecfs/comsrch_v2.cgi.

Antiwar Protests Reverse Satellite Company's Decision to Cut Internet Service to Yugoslavia, Antiwar.com, May 15, 1999, available at http://www.antiwar.com/satellite1.html.

AOL Inc., *Open Access Comments of America Online, Inc.,* before the Department of Telecommunications and Information Services of San Francisco, Cal., Oct. 27, 1999.

AOL Seen Unlikely to Remain Advocate of Open Access Rules, Comm. Daily, Jan. 12, 2001.

AOL, Time Warner Vow on ISP Access to Broadband Cable Seen as Positive Step, 5 Electronic Comm. & L. Rep. (2000).

Areeda, Philip & Herbert Hovenkamp, Antitrust Law (vol. 3A, 1996).

Arizona Consumer Council, et al., *Comments,* In the Matter of Appropriate Framework for Broadband Access to the Internet Over Wireline Facilities Universal Service Obligations of Broadband Providers Computer III Further Remand Proceedings: Bell Operating Company Provision of Enhanced Services; 1998 Biennial Regulatory Review – Review of Computer III and ONA Safeguards And Requirements, Federal Communications Commission, CC Dockets Nos. 95-20, 98-10, May 3, 2002; Reply Comments, July 1, 2002.

Arlen, Jennifer, *The Future of Behavioral Economic Analysis of Law,* 51 Vand. L. Rev. (1998).

Arora, Ashish, Andrea Fosfuri and Alfonso Gamardella, Markets for Technology: The Economics of Innovation and Corporate Strategy (2001),

Arrow, Kenneth J., *Economic Welfare and the Allocation of Resources for Invention*, in THE RATE AND DIRECTION OF INVENTIVE ACTIVITY (Nat'l Bureau of Econ. Research, ed., 1962), *reprinted in* 5 Kenneth J. Arrow, COLLECTED PAPERS OF KENNETH J. ARROW: PRODUCTION AND CAPITAL (1985).

Arthur, W. Brian, *Competing Technologies, Increasing Returns and Lock-in by Historical Events*, 99 ECON. J. (1989).

Arthur, W. Brian, INCREASING RETURNS AND PATH DEPENDENCY IN THE ECONOMY (1994).

Arthur, W. Brian, *Positive Feedbacks in the Economy*, 262 SCIENTIFIC AM. (Feb. 1990).

Associated Press v. United States, 326 U.S. 1, 20 (1945).

AT&T Broadband Internet Acceptable Use Policy, ¶ xiv, *available at* http://help.broadband.att.com/faq.jsp?content_id=1107&category_id=34 (revised July 25, 2002).

AT&T Broadband Internet Subscriber Agreement, § 6(g), *at* http://www.attbi.com/ general-info/bb_terms.html (last visited Mar. 13, 2003).

AT&T Broadband, December, 2002 Acceptable Internet Use Agreement, then available at http://help.broadband.att.com/faq.jsp?content_id=1107&category_id=34.

AT&T Canada Long Distance Services, *Comments of AT&T Canada Long Distance Services Company*, before the Canadian Radio-television and Telecommunications Commission, Telecom Public Notice CRTC 96-36: Regulation of Certain Telecommunications Service Offered by Broadcast Carriers (1997).

AT&T Corp. v. City of Portland, 216 F.3d 871 (9th Cir. 2000).

AT&T Corp. v. City of Portland, 43 F. Supp.2d 1146,1154 (D. Ore 1999).

AT&T Corp., *Reply Comments*, DEPLOYMENT OF WIRELINE SERVS. OFFERING ADVANCED TELECOMMS. CAPABILITY, CC Docket No. 98-147 (1998).

AT&T Corp., *Reply Comments,* OPPOSITION TO SOUTHWESTERN BELL TEL. CO. SECTION 271 APPLICATION FOR TEX., APPLICATION OF SBC COMMUNICATIONS INC., SOUTHWESTERN BELL TEL. CO., &

SOUTHWESTERN BELL COMMUNICATIONS SERVS., INC. D/B/A SOUTHWESTERN BELL LONG DISTANCE FOR PROVISION OF IN-REGION INTERLATA SERVS. IN TEX. (2000), *at* http://gullfoss2.fcc.gov/ prod/ ecfs/comsrch_v2.cgi.

Atchison, Topeka & Santa Fe Ry. v. Wichita Bd. of Trade, 412 U.S. 800, 807-08 (1973).

Audretsch, David B. & Charles F. Bonser, *Regional Policy in the New Economy*, in THE NEW ECONOMY AND ECONOMIC GROWTH IN EUROPE AND THE US (David B. Audretsch & Paul J.J. Welfens, eds., 2002).

Audretsch, David B. & Paul J.J. Welfens, *Introduction*, in THE NEW ECONOMY AND ECONOMIC GROWTH IN EUROPE AND THE US (David B. Audretsch & Paul J.J. Welfens, eds., 2002).

Audretsch, David B. & Paul J.J. Welfens, (eds.) THE NEW ECONOMY AND ECONOMIC GROWTH IN EUROPE AND THE US (2002).

Baase, Sara, A GIFT OF FIRE: SOCIAL, LEGAL AND ETHICAL ISSUES IN COMPUTING (1997)

Baker, C. Edwin, MEDIA, MARKET AND DEMOCRACY (2001).

Baker, David N., Vice President, Legal & Regulatory Affairs, Mindspring Enterprises, Inc., James W. Cicconi, General Council and Executive Vice President, AT&T Corp., and Kenneth S. Fellman, Esq., Chairman, FCC Local & State Government Advisory Committee, Letter to William E. Kennard, Chairman of FCC (Dec. 6, 1999), *available at* http://www.fcc.gov/mb/attmindspringletter.txt.

Banerjee, Anupam & Marvin Sirvu, "Towards Technologically and Competitively Neutral Fiber to the Home (FTTH) Infrastructure," paper presented at *Telecommunications Policy Research Conference, 2003.*

Bar, François & Christian Sandvig, *Rules From Truth: Post-Convergence Policy for Access*, paper presented at the Telecommunications Policy Research Conference (2002).

Bar, François, et al., *Defending the Internet Revolution in the Broadband Era: When Doing Nothing is Doing Harm* (1999), *at* http://e-conomy.berkeley.edu/publications/ wp/ewp12.pdf.

Barabasi, Albert-Laszlo, Linked (2002).

Baran, P., et al., "On Distributed Communications", Volumes I-XI, RAND Corporation Research Documents, August 1964.

Barrett, Randy, *Cable, Phone Lines in Battle for Supremacy*, Inter@ctive Week, Jan. 25, 1999.

Barthold, Jim, *Allot looks to help servers with bandwidth congestion problems*, Telephony.Online.com, *available at* http://telephonyonline.com/ar/telecom_allot_looks_help/index.htm (Dec. 3, 2002).

Baseman, Kenneth, Fredrick R. Warren-Boulton, & Susan Woodward, *Depreciation and Capital Recovery Issues: A Response to Professor Hausman,* submitted as *ex parte* filing by MCI in CC Docket No. 96-98, July 24, 1996.

Beard, T. Randolph, George S. Ford & Lawrence J. Spiwak, *Why ADCo? Why Now: An Economic Exploration into the Future of Industry Structure for the "Last Mile" in Local Telecommunications Markets* (Phoenix Center, November 2001).

Bell Atlantic Tel. Cos. v. F.C.C., 206 F.3d 1, 9 (D.C. Cir. 2000).

Bell, Tom W., *The Common Law in Cyberspace*, 97 Mich. L. Rev. 1746 (1999).

Belleflamme, Paul, *Stable Coalition Structures with Open Membership and Asymmetric Firms*, 30 Games & Econ. Behavior (2000).

BellSouth Internet Service, *Acceptable Use Policies, available at* http://home.bellsouth.net/csbellsouth/s/editorial.dll?fromspage=cg/legal/legal_homepage.htm&categoryid=

&bfromind=354&eeid=376138&eetype=article&render=y5ck= (last visited Oct. 8, 2003).

Benjamin, Stuart Minor, *Proactive Legislation and the First Amendment*, 99 Mich. L. Rev. (2000).

Benkler, Yochai, *Coase's Penguin, or Linux and the Nature of the Firm* (paper presented at the *Conference on the Public Domain,* Duke University Law School, Nov. 9-11, 2001), *at* http://

www.law.duke.edu/pd/papers/ Coase's_Penguin.pdf (last visited Jan. 24, 2003).

Benkler, Yochai, *From Consumers to Users: Shifting the Deeper Structures of Regulation Toward Sustainable Commons and User Access,* 52 FED. COMM. L.J. (2000).

Benkler, Yochai, *Intellectual Property and the Organization of Information Production,* 22 INT'L REV. L. & ECON. 81 (2002), *available at* http://www.law.nyu.edu/benklery/IP&Organization.pdf, (last visited Jan. 24, 2003).

Benkler, Yochai, *Property Commons and the First Amendment: Toward a Core Common Infrastructure,* BRENNAN CENTER FOR JUSTICE, NEW YORK UNIVERSITY LAW SCHOOL, March 2000.

Berners-Lee, Tim, WEAVING THE WEB: THE ORIGINAL DESIGN AND ULTIMATE DESTINY OF THE WORLD WIDE WEB BY ITS INVENTOR (1999).

Bernstein, Sanford C. and McKinsey and Company, *Broadband!*, January, 2000.

Besen, Stanley M. and Robert W. Crandall, *The Deregulation of Cable Television,* 4 LAW & CONTEMP. PROBS. 77, 81-91 (1981)

Beverly Enters., Inc. v. Herman, 119 F. Supp.2d 1, 11 (D.D.C. 2000).

Bhagwat, Ashutosh, *Unnatural Competition?: Applying the New Antitrust Learning to Foster Competition in the Local Exchange,* 50 HASTINGS L.J. (1999).

Bickerstaff, Steve, *Shackles on the Giant: How the Federal Government Created Microsoft, Personal Computers, and the Internet,* 78 TEX. L. REV. 1 (1999).

Big Planet Inc., *Comments of Big Planet, Inc.,* IN THE MATTER OF APPROPRIATE FRAMEWORK FOR BROADBAND ACCESS TO THE INTERNET OVER WIRELINE FACILITIES, UNIVERSAL SERVICE OBLIGATIONS OF BROADBAND PROVIDERS, COMPUTER III REMAND PROCEEDINGS: BELL OPERATING COMPANY PROVISION OF ENHANCED SERVICES; 1998 BIENNIAL REGULATORY REVIEW – REVIEW OF COMPUTER II AND ONA SAFEGUARDS AND REQUIREMENTS, Federal Communications Commission, CC Docket NO. 02-33, 95-20, 98-10, May 3, 2002.

BITNET charter, (available at http://www.geocities.com/SiliconValley/ 2260/bitchart.html)

Bluestone, Barry & Bennett Harrison, GROWING PROSPERITY: THE BATTLE FOR GROWTH WITH EQUITY IN THE TWENTY-FIRST CENTURY (2001).

BOARDWATCH MAGAZINE, *North American ISPS*.

Bode, Karl, *Defining Gluttony: Cox Cable Gets Specific*, *at* http:// www.dslreports.com/shownews/23465 (Nov. 12, 2002).

Bork, Robert H., THE ANTITRUST PARADOX: A POLICY AT WAR WITH ITSELF (1978).

Borland, John, *ISP download caps to slow swapping?* CNET NEWS.COM, *at* http://news.com.com/2100-1023-975320.html (Nov. 26, 2002).

Brand X Internet Services v FCC, 345 F.3d 1120 (9th Cir. 2003).

Brand X Internet Services Inc., Comments *of Brand X.,* IN THE MATTER OF APPROPRIATE FRAMEWORK FOR BROADBAND ACCESS TO THE INTERNET OVER WIRELINE FACILITIES, UNIVERSAL SERVICE OBLIGATIONS OF BROADBAND PROVIDERS, COMPUTER III REMAND PROCEEDINGS: BELL OPERATING COMPANY PROVISION OF ENHANCED SERVICES; 1998 BIENNIAL REGULATORY REVIEW – REVIEW OF COMPUTER II AND ONA SAFEGUARDS AND REQUIREMENTS, Federal Communications Commission, CC Docket NO. 02-33, 95-20, 98-10, May 3, 2002.

Braunstein, Yale, MARKET POWER AND PRICE INCREASES IN THE DSL MARKET (July 2001).

Bresnahan, Timothy F., New Modes of Competition: Implications for the Future Structure of the Computer Industry, at http://www.pff.org/ microsoft/bresnahan.html (June 1998).

Bresnahan, Timothy, THE ECONOMICS OF THE MICROSOFT CASE *(*unpublished manuscript).

Bresnahan, Timothy F. & Shane Greenstein, *Technological Competition and the Structure of the Computer Industry*, 47 J. INDUSTRIAL ECON. (1999).

BRIE-IGCC E-conomy Project, Tracking a Transformation: E-commerce and the Terms of Competition in Industries (2001).

Broadband Reports, *at* http://www.dslreports.com/forum/remark,3775421;mode=flat;root=sware (July, 2002).

BROADBAND REPORTS.COM, *at* http://www.dslreports.com (Mar. 2002).

Brodsky, Ira, *Telecom Carriers Need to Smarter Up their Pipes*, NETWORK WORLD, Jan. 15, 2001.

Brynjolfsson, Erik and Brian Kahin, *Introduction*, in UNDERSTANDING THE DIGITAL ECONOMY (Erik Brynjolfsson and Brian Kahin, eds., 2000).

Buchanan, Mark, NEXUS: SMALL WORLDS AND THE GROUNDBREAKING THEORY OF NETWORKS (2002).

Cable Act of 1984, § 2, 98 Stat. 2779, 2781.

Cable Carried Incentive for AOL Merger, WASH. POST, Jan. 18, 2000.

Cable Modem Service Subscription Agreement, Time Warner Cable, *at* http://help.twcable.com/html/twc_sub_agreement.html (last visited Mar. 12, 2003).

Cable Modem/DOCSIS^{TM}, CABLELABS, *at* http://www.cablemodem.com/faq (last visited Mar. 13, 2003).

Cable Operators Finding Success in Local Phone Service, COMM. DAILY, June 17, 1999.

Cable Takes the Early Lead, INDUSTRY STANDARD, Oct. 11, 1999.

California ISP Association, *Reply Comments of the California ISP Association, Inc., FURTHER NOTICE OF PROPOSED RULEMAKING IN THE MATTER OF THE COMPUTER III REMAND PROCEEDINGS: BELL OPERATING COMPANY PROVISION OF ENHANCED SERVICES; 1998 BIENNIAL REGULATORY REVIEW – REVIEW OF COMPUTER II AND ONA SAFEGUARDS AND REQUIREMENTS*, Federal Communications Commission, CC Docket NO. 95-20, 98-10, April 30, 2000.

Campbell, Angela J., *Publish or Carriage: Approaches to Analyzing the First Amendment Rights of Telephone Companies*, 70 N.C. L. REV. (1992).

Cannon, Robert, *The Legacy of the Federal Communications Commission's Computer Inquiries,* 55 FED. COMM. L.J. (2003).

Cargill, Inc. v. Monfort of Colo., Inc., 479 U.S. 104, 124–25 (1986) (Stevens, J., dissenting).

Carree, Mark A., *The Effect of Restructuring the Organization of Production on Economic Growth*, in THE NEW ECONOMY AND ECONOMIC GROWTH IN EUROPE AND THE US (David B. Audretsch & Paul J.J. Welfens, eds., 2002).

Carterfone, 13 F.C.C.2d 420 (1968)

Casey, Timothy D., ISP LIABILITY SURVIVAL GUIDE: STRATEGIES FOR MANAGING COPYRIGHT, SPAM, CACHE, AND PRIVACY REGULATIONS (2000).

Castells, Manuel, THE INTERNET GALAXY – REFLECTIONS ON THE INTERNET, BUSINESS, AND SOCIETY (2001).

Castells, Manuel, THE RISE OF NETWORK SOCIETY (1996).

Cbeyond, "Response of Cbeyond, Inc.," *Ten Questions to Begin the Committee's Inquiry Into State Broadband Policy*, Committee on State Affairs, April 3, 2002.

Cbeyond, *Joint Comments of Cbeyond and Nuvox*, IN THE MATTER OF REVIEW OF REGULATORY REQUIREMENTS FOR INCUMBENT LEC BROADBAND TELECOMMUNICATIONS SERVICES, Federal Communications Commission, CC Docket No. 01-337, March 1, 2002.

CDT, et al., Motion and Brief *Amici Curiae* in Support of Yahoo! Inc.'s Motion for Summary Judgment, No. 00-21275 JF.

Center for Democracy & Technology, *French Court Rules in Favor of Yahoo! in Internet Free Speech Case*, INTERNATIONAL JURISDICTION NEWS, January 14, 2003, available at http://www.cdt.org/jurisdiction.

Center for Media Education, et al., *Reply Comments*, INQUIRY CONCERNING THE DEPLOYMENT OF ADVANCED TELECOMMUNICATIONS CAPABILITY TO AMERICA AMERICANS IN A REASONABLE AND TIMELY FASHION, AND POSSIBLE STEPS TO ACCELERATE SUCH DEPLOYMENT PURSUANT TO SECTION 706 OF THE TELECOMMUNICATIONS ACT OF 1996, Federal Communications Commission, CC Docket No. 98-146, October 10, 1998.

Cerf, Vinton G. & Robert E. Kahn, *A Protocol for Packet Network Intercommunication*, COM-22 IEEE Transactions on Communications (May 1974).

Cerf, Vinton G., Broadband Policy and Delivery Options, International Engineering Consortium.

Cerf, Vinton G., Senior Vice-President, WorldCom, Inc., Letter to The Honorable Donald Evans, Secretary, U.S. Department of Commerce, and The Honorable Michael Powell, Chairman, Federal Communications Commission, CC Docket Nos. 02-33, 01-338 (May 20, 2002).

Charter Communications Pipeline, *Acceptable Use Policy* § 1(A), *available at* http://www.chartercom.com/site/rules.asp#aup (last checked Oct. 8, 2003).

Chazen, Leonard and Leonard Ross, Federal Regulation of Cable Television, the Visible Hand, 83 Harv. L. Rev. 1820, 1820 (1970);

Chen, Jim, *Standing in the Shadows of Giants: The Role of Intergenerational Equity in Telecommunications Reform*, 71 U. Colo. L. Rev. (2000).

Chen, Jim, *The Authority to Regulate Broadband Internet Access Over Cable*, 16 Berkeley Tech. L.J. (2001).

Chen, Jim, *The Magnificent Seven: American Telephony's Deregulatory Shootout*, 50 HASTINGS L.J. (1999).

Chen, Jim, *Titanic Telecommunications*, 25 SW. U. L. Rev. (1996).

Chien-fu, Chou & Oz Shy, *Network Effects Without Network Externalities*, 8 Int'l J. Indus. Org. (1990).

Choi, Jay Pil, *Network Externalities, Compatibility Choice and Planned Obsolescence*, 42 J. Indus. Econ. (1994).

Christiansen, Clay, The Innovators Dilemma (1997).

Church, Jeffrey & Neil Gandal, *Complementary Network Externalities and Technological Adoption*, 11 Int'l J. Indus. Org. (1993).

Church, Jeffrey & Neil Gandal, *Systems Competition, Vertical Merger, and Foreclosure*, 9 J. Econ. & Mgmt. Strategy (2000).

Cisco, WHITE PAPER: CISCO CONTENT DELIVERY NETWORK SOLUTION FOR THE ENTERPRISE, (Apr. 2002), available at http://www.cisco.com/warp/public/cc/so/neso/ienesv/cxne/cdnen_wp.htm.

City of Dallas, Texas v. FCC, 165 F.3d 341, 354 (5th Cir. 1999).

California ISP Association, Inc., *Reply Comments of the California ISP Association, Inc., FURTHER NOTICE OF PROPOSED RULEMAKING IN THE MATTER OF THE COMPUTER III REMAND PROCEEDINGS: BELL OPERATING COMPANY PROVISION OF ENHANCED SERVICES; 1998 BIENNIAL REGULATORY REVIEW – REVIEW OF COMPUTER II AND ONA SAFEGUARDS AND REQUIREMENTS*, Federal Communications Commission, CC Docket NO. 95-20, 98-10, April 30, 2000.

Commercial Internet Exchange Association, *Reply Comments of the Commercial Internet Exchange Association, FURTHER NOTICE OF PROPOSED RULEMAKING IN THE MATTER OF THE COMPUTER III REMAND PROCEEDINGS: BELL OPERATING COMPANY PROVISION OF ENHANCED SERVICES; 1998 BIENNIAL REGULATORY REVIEW – REVIEW OF COMPUTER II AND ONA SAFEGUARDS AND REQUIREMENTS*, FEDERAL COMMUNICATIONS COMMISSION, CC DOCKET NO. 95-20, 98-10, April 30, 2000.

Clark, David D. & Marjory S. Blumenthal, *Rethinking the Design of the Internet: The End-to-End Arguments vs. the Brave New World,* ACM TRANSACTIONS ON INTERNET TECHNOLOGY (2001).

Clayton Act, Pub. L. No. 98-443, § 7, 98 Stat. 1708 (1984) (codified at 15 U.S.C. § 18 (1994)).

Coalition of Broadband Users and Innovators Ex Parte Letter, CS DOCKET NO. 02-52, Nov. 18, 2002.

Coalition Of Utah Independent Internet Service Providers, *Comments of the New York State Department of Public Service,* IN THE MATTER OF REVIEW OF REGULATORY REQUIREMENTS FOR INCUMBENT LEC BROADBAND TELECOMMUNICATIONS SERVICES, Federal Communications Commission, CC Docket No. 01-337, March 1, 2002.

Cockburn, Alexander & Jeffrey St. Clair, ed., *US Shuts Down Yugoslav Internet,* CounterPunch, May 12, 1999, available at http://www.counterpunch.org/beograd.html.

Comcast Cablevision v. Broward County, 124 F. Supp. 2d 685 (S.D. Fla. 2000).

Comcast Corp., *FCC Ex Parte Letter*, CS Docket NO. 02-52, May 9, 2002.

Comcast Corporation, Ex Parte Notice, CS Docket NO. 02-52, May 15, 2003.

Comcast VPN letter, Practically Networked, *at* http://www.practically networked.com/news/comcast.htm (last visited Mar. 12, 2003).

Comcast, Acceptable Use policy and subscriber agreements, available at http://www.comcast.net/terms.

Commercial Internet Exchange Association, *Reply Comments of the Commercial Internet Exchange Association, Further Notice of Proposed Rulemaking in the matter of the Computer III Remand Proceedings: Bell Operating Company Provision of Enhanced Services; 1998 Biennial Regulatory Review – Review of Computer II and ONA Safeguards and Requirements*, Federal Communications Commission, CC Docket NO. 95-20, 98-10, April 30, 2000.

Committee on Broadband Last Mile Technology, National Research Council, Broadband: Bringing Home the Bits (2002).

Communications Act of 1934, Ch. 652, 48 Stat. 1064 (codified as amended at 47 U.S.C. §§ 151–613 (1994)).

Competitive Broadband Coalition, Comments, *Implementation of the Cable Television Consumer Protection & Competition Act of 1992*, Cable Services Bureau Dkt. No. 01-290 (Dec. 3, 2001).

Computer Science and Telecommunications Board, National Research Council, Broadband, Bringing Home the Bits (2002).

Computer Science and Telecommunications Board, National Research Council, Realizing the Information Future: The Internet and Beyond (1994).

Comstock, Earl W. & John Butler, *Access Denied: The FCC's Failure to Implement Open Access as Required by the Communications Act*, J. of Comm. L. & Pol. (Winter 2000).

Conference Report, Telecommunications Act of 1996, Senate, No, 104-230

Congressional Record, 142 (1996).

Console Wars: Video Games Grow Up, THE ECONOMIST, June 22, 2002.

Consumer Federation of America, Texas Office of Public Utility Counsel, Consumers Union, and Center For Digital Democracy, *Comments and Reply Comments*, IN THE MATTER OF REVIEW OF THE SECTION 251 UNBUNDLING, OBLIGATIONS OF INCUMBENT LOCAL EXCHANGE CARRIERS, IMPLEMENTATION OF THE LOCAL COMPETITION PROVISIONS OF THE TELECOMMUNICATIONS ACT OF 1996, DEPLOYMENT OF WIRELINE SERVICES OFFERING ADVANCED TELECOMMUNICATIONS CAPABILITY, Federal Communications Commission, CC Dockets Nos. 01-338, 96-98, 98-147, April 5, 2002; Reply Comments, July 1, 2002.

Consumers Union, et al., *Comments*, INQUIRY CONCERNING HIGH-SPEED ACCESS TO THE INTERNET OVER CABLE AND OTHER FACILITIES, GN Docket No. 00-185 (filed December 1, 2001).

Cooper, Mark, *Antitrust as Consumer Protection in the New Economy: Lessons from the Microsoft Case*, 52 HASTINGS L.J. (2001).

Cooper, Mark, "Breaking the Rules," attached to Petition to Deny of Consumers Union, Consumer Federation of America and Media Access Project, Applications for Consent to Transfer of Control of Licenses, MediaOne Group, Inc. Transferor to AT&T Corp., Transferee, CS 99-251 (filed August 23, 1999) (on file with author).

Cooper, Mark, *Delivering the Information Age Now*, in Telecom *Infrastructure*: 1993, Telecommunications Reports, 1993.

Cooper, Mark, DEVELOPING THE INFORMATION AGE IN THE 1990S: A PRAGMATIC CONSUMER VIEW (June 8, 1992).

Cooper, Mark, EXPANDING THE INFORMATION AGE FOR THE 1990S: A PRAGMATIC CONSUMER VIEW (January 11, 1990).

Cooper, Mark, *Inequality in Digital Society: Why the Digital Divide Deserves All the Attention it Gets*, CARDOZO ARTS & ENTERTAINMENT LAW J., 20 (2002).

Cooper, Mark, *Open Access to the Broadband Internet: Technical and Economic Discrimination in Closed, Proprietary Networks*, 71 U. COLO. L. REV. (2000).

Cooper, Mark, *Open Communications Platforms: The Physical Infrastructure as the Bedrock of Innovation and Democratic Discourse in the Internet Age*, 2 J. ON TELECOMM. & HIGH TECH. L. 1 (2003).

Cooper, Mark, *Protecting the Public Interest Against Monopoly Abuse by Cable Companies: Strategies for Local Franchising Authorities in the AT&T Comcast License Transfer Process,* STATEMENT TO THE CITY OF CHICAGO, May 22, 2002.

Cooper, Mark, THE FAILURE OF 'INTERMODAL' COMPETITION IN CABLE MARKETS, April 2002.

Cooper, Mark, *The Importance of ISPs in The Growth of The Commercial Internet: Why Reliance on Facility-Based Competition Will Not Preserve Vibrant Competition and Dynamic Innovation on the High-Speed Internet, Attachment A to "Comments of the Texas Office of People's Council, et al.*," APPROPRIATE FRAMEWORK FOR BROADBAND ACCESS TO THE INTERNET OVER WIRELINE FACILITIES UNIVERSAL SERVICE OBLIGATIONS OF BROADBAND PROVIDERS COMPUTER III FURTHER REMAND PROCEEDINGS: BELL OPERATING COMPANY PROVISION OF ENHANCED SERVICES; 1998 BIENNIAL REGULATORY REVIEW – REVIEW OF COMPUTER III AND ONA SAFEGUARDS AND REQUIREMENTS, Federal Communications Commission, CC Dockets Nos. 02-33, 98-10. 95-20 (July 1, 2002).

Cooper, Mark, THE MEANING OF THE WORD INFRASTRUCTURE (June 30, 1994).

Cooper, Mark, TRANSFORMING THE INFORMATION SUPER HIGHWAY INTO A PRIVATE TOLL ROAD (October, 1999).

Copps, Michael, J., THE BEGINNING OF THE END OF THE INTERNET? DISCRIMINATION, CLOSED NETWORKS, AND THE FUTURE OF CYBERSPACE, New America Foundation, Washington, October 9, 2003.

Cosine Communications, DIGITAL SUBSCRIBER LINES AND MANAGED NETWORK-BASED SERVICES: A PERFECT—AND PROFITABLE—MARRIAGE,

White Paper, available at http://cnscenter.future.co.kr/ resource/rsc-center/vendor-wp/cosine/dslwp.pdf.

Cowan, Robin, *Tortoises and Hares: Choice Among Technologies of Unknown Merit*, 101 ECON. J. (1991).

Cox Communications, Ex Parte Letter, CS DOCKET NO. 02-52, April 7, 2003.

Cox Enterprises Inc., FCC Ex Parte Letter, CS DOCKET NO. 02-52, May 1, 2003.

Cox Communications, Policies, *Acceptable Use Policy*, Cox Communications, Inc., *at* http://support.cox.net/custsup/policies/acceptableuse.shtml (revised Feb. 3, 2003).

Cox Communications Inc., *Comments of Cox Communications, Inc.,* IN THE MATTER OF APPROPRIATE FRAMEWORK FOR BROADBAND ACCESS TO THE INTERNET OVER WIRELINE FACILITIES, UNIVERSAL SERVICE OBLIGATIONS OF BROADBAND PROVIDERS, COMPUTER III REMAND PROCEEDINGS: BELL OPERATING COMPANY PROVISION OF ENHANCED SERVICES; 1998 BIENNIAL REGULATORY REVIEW – REVIEW OF COMPUTER II AND ONA SAFEGUARDS AND REQUIREMENTS, Federal Communications Commission, CC Docket NO. 02-33, 95-20, 98-10, May 3, 2002 (Hereafter Cox, 2002).

Cox Systems, *Acceptable Use Policy* § 6, *available at* http://www.cox.com/iNetIncludes/policy/acceptable.asp (updated Apr. 28, 2003).

Cox, Kenneth, The Problem of Television Service for Smaller Communities. Staff Report to the Senate Committee on Interstate and Foreign Commerce, 26 December 1958.

Cremer, J., P. Rey & J. Tirole, *Connectivity in the Commercial Internet*, 84 J. INDUS. ECON. (2000).

Cutting Off Internet, Diaspora, May 13, 1999, available at http://www.diaspora-net.org/food4thought/cutting_off_internet.htm.

Daly, James, *101 Ways to Save Apple*, WIRED (June 1997), *available at* http://www.wired.com/wired/archive/5.06/apple.html.

Dansby, Robert E. & Cecilia Conrad, *Commodity Bundling*, 74 AM. ECON. REV. (1984).

Davies, D.W., K.A. Bartlett, R.A. Scantlebury, and P. T. Wilkinson, "A Digital Communication Network for Computers Giving Rapid Response at Remote Terminals," *Proceedings of the ACM Symposium on Operating System Principles,* Association for Computing Machinery, New York, 1967.

Davis, D., *Shine Your Light on Me,* December 23, 2002 (http://D-squareddiest.blogpost.org/2002_12_22_d-squareddigest_archives.html#86435321)

DeFontenay, Allaine, WHY INEFFICIENT INCUMBENTS CAN PREVAIL IN THE MARKETPLACE OVER MORE EFFICIENT ENTRANT: AN ANALYSIS OF ECONOMIES OF SCALE AND SCOPE, TRANSACTION COSTS AND THE MISUSE OF DATA, (2003).

Desert Citizens Against Pollution v. Bisson, 231 F.3d 1172, 1180 (9th Cir. 2000).

Dibadji, Reza, *Deregulation: A Tragedy in Three Acts,* THE WASHINGTON POST, Sept. 13, 2003, at A21.

Directive 2002/21/EC of the European Parliament and of the Council of 7 March 2002 on a Common Regulatory Framework for Electronic Communications Networks and Services (Framework Directive), 2002 O.J. (L. 108).

Earthlink, Inc., *Comments,* IN THE MATTER OF APPROPRIATE FRAMEWORK FOR BROADBAND ACCESS TO THE INTERNET OVER WIRELINE FACILITIES, UNIVERSAL SERVICE OBLIGATIONS OF BROADBAND PROVIDERS, COMPUTER III REMAND PROCEEDINGS: BELL OPERATING COMPANY PROVISION OF ENHANCED SERVICES; 1998 BIENNIAL REGULATORY REVIEW – REVIEW OF COMPUTER II AND ONA SAFEGUARDS AND REQUIREMENTS, Federal Communications Commission, CC Docket NO. 02-33, 95-20, 98-10, May 3, 2002.

Earthlink, *Notice of Ex Parte, Presentation* REGARDING THE APPLICATIONS OF AMERICA ONLINE, INC. & TIME WARNER INC. FOR TRANSFERS OF CONTROL CS Docket No 00-30 (filed Oct. 18, 2000), *available at* http://gullfoss2.fcc.gov/prod/ecfs/comsrch_v2.cgi.

Easterbrook, Frank, *The Law of the Horse,* 1996 U. CHI. LEGAL F. 207, 212-213 (1996).

Eastman Kodak Co. v. Image Technical Servs., Inc., 504 U.S. 451 (1992).

Eatwell, John, et al., eds., THE NEW PALGRAVE: A DICTIONARY OF ECONOMICS (1987).

Eddings, Joshua, HOW THE INTERNET WORKS (1994).

Ellison, Glenn & Drew Fudenberg, *The Neo-Luddite's Lament: Excessive Upgrades in the Software Industry*, 31 RAND J. ECON. (2000).

Entman, Robert M., TRANSITION TO AN IP ENVIRONMENT: A REPORT OF THE FIFTEENTH ANNUAL ASPEN INSTITUTE CONFERENCE ON TELECOMMUNICATIONS POLICY (2001).

Esbin, Barbara, *Internet Over Cable: Defining the Future in Terms of the Past,* 7 COMMLAW CONSPECTUS 37, 98 (1998)

European Commission, Commission GUIDELINES ON MARKET ANALYSIS AND THE ASSESSMENT OF SIGNIFICANT MARKET POWER UNDER THE COMMUNITY REGULATORY FRAMEWORK FOR ELECTRONIC COMMUNICATIONS NETWORKS AND SERVICES, 2002 O.J. (C 165).

Evans, George, et al., *Growth Cycles*, 88 AM. ECON. REV. (1998).

Evans, Harold, THE AMERICAN CENTURY (1998).

Evans, Philip & Thomas S. Wurster, BLOWN TO BITS: HOW THE NEW ECONOMICS OF INFORMATION TRANSFORMS STRATEGY (2000).

Fagerberg, Jan, A LAYMAN'S GUIDE TO EVOLUTIONARY ECONOMICS 15 (2002).

Fano, Robert M., *On the Social Role of Computer Communications*, PROC. IEEE, Nov. 1972, *reprinted in* PROC. IEEE, Dec. 1999.

Farrell, Joseph, *Creating Local Competition*, 49 FED. COMM. L.J. (1996).

Farrell, Joseph & Garth Saloner, *Installed Base and Compatibility: Innovation, Product Preannouncements, and Predation*, 76 AM. ECON. REV. (1986).

Farrell, Joseph & Garth Saloner, *Standardization, Compatibility, and Innovation*, 16 RAND J. ECON. (1985).

Farrell, Joseph & Michael L. Katz, *The Effect of Antitrust and Intellectual Property Law on Compatibility and Innovation*, 43 ANTITRUST BULL. (1998).

Farrell, Joseph & Philip J. Weiser, *Modularity, Vertical Integration, and Open Access Policies: Towards a Convergence of Antitrust and Regulation in the Internet Age*, 17 HARV. J.L. & TECH. (forthcoming 2003), available at http://repositories. cdlib.org/iber/cpc/CPC02-035 (last visited Sept. 24, 2003).

FCC v. Midwest Video Corp., 440 U.S. 689 (1979).

Federal Communications Commission, *Amicus Curiae Brief of the Federal Communications Commission*, AT&T CORP. V. CITY OF PORTLAND, No.99-35609 (9th Cir. Aug. 16, 1999).

Federal Communications Commission, *CPE/Enhanced Services Bundling Order*, 16 F.C.C.R. at 7425.

Federal Communications Commission, *Final Decision,* IN RE AMENDMENT OF SECTION 64.702 OF THE COMMISSION'S RULES AND REGULATIONS (Second Computer Inquiry), 77 F.C.C.2d 384 (1980).

Federal Communications Commission, IMPLEMENTATION OF SECTION 11 OF THE CABLE TELEVISION CONSUMER PROTECTION AND COMPETITION ACT OF 1992, Further Notice of Proposed Rulemaking, 16 F.C.C.R. 17,312, (2001).

Federal Communications Commission, INQUIRY CONCERNING HIGH-SPEED ACCESS TO THE INTERNET OVER CABLE AND OTHER FACILITIES, GN Docket No. 00-185, Notice of Inquiry, 15 FCC Rcd 19287 (2000).

Federal Communications Commission, INQUIRY CONCERNING HIGH-SPEED ACCESS TO THE INTERNET OVER CABLE AND OTHER FACILITIES, INTERNET OVER CABLE DECLARATORY RULING, APPROPRIATE REGULATORY TREATMENT FOR BROADBAND ACCESS TO THE INTERNET OVER CABLE FACILITIES, CS Docket No. 02-52, Declaratory Notice and Notice of Proposed Rulemaking, (rel. Mar. 15, 2002).

Federal Communications Commission, INQUIRY CONCERNING THE DEPLOYMENT OF ADVANCED TELECOMMUNICATIONS CAPABILITY TO ALL AMERICANS IN A REASONABLE AND TIMELY FASHION, AND POSSIBLE STEPS TO ACCELERATE SUCH DEPLOYMENT PURSUANT TO SECTION 706 OF THE TELECOMMUNICATIONS ACT OF 1996, CC Docket No. 98-146, 15 FCC Rcd 20913 (2000).

Federal Communications Commission, In re Annual Assessment of the Status of Competition in the Markets for Delivery of Video Programming, Sixth Annual Report, CB Dkt. No.99-230, FCC 99-418, (released Jan. 14, 2000).

Federal Communications Commission, In re Appropriate Framework for Broadband Access to the Internet over Wireline Facilities, CC Docket Nos. 02-33, 95-20 and 98-10, Notice of Proposed Rulemaking, 67 Fed. Reg. 9232 (2002).

Federal Communications Commission, In re Applications for Consent to the Transfer of Control of Licenses and Section 214 Authorizations from TCI to AT&T Corp., Application, Description of Transaction, Public Interest Showing and Related Demonstrations, CS Dkt. No. 98-178, at 20 n.36 (Sept. 14, 1998).

Federal Communications Commission, In re Applications for Consent to the Transfer of Control of Licenses and Section 214 Authorizations from TCI to AT&T, Memorandum opinion and Order, 14 FCC Rcd. 3160, 3195, (1999).

Federal Communications Commission, In re Application of EchoStar Communications Corporation, General Motors Corporation, and Hughes Electronics Corporation, Transferors, and EchoStar Communications Corporation, Transferee, CS Docket No. 01-348, 17 F.C.C.R. 20559 (2002).

Federal Communications Commission, In re: Deployment of Wireline Services Offering Advanced Telecommunications Capability, Memorandum Opinion and Order and Notice of Proposed Rulemaking, 13 F.C.C.R. 24012 (1998).

Federal Communications Commission, In re Deployment of Wireline Services Offering Advanced Telecommunications Capability, Order on Remand, FCC 99-413 (Dec. 23, 1999).

Federal Communications Commission, In re Federal-State Joint Board on Universal Service, Report to Congress, 11 F.C.C.R. 11501 (1998).

Federal Communications Commission, IN RE FILING AND REVIEW OF OPEN NETWORK ARCHITECTURE PLANS, Memorandum and Order, 4 F.C.C.R. 1, 141 (1988).

Federal Communications Commission, IN RE IMPLEMENTATION OF THE NON-ACCOUNTING SAFEGUARDS OF SECTIONS 271 AND 272 OF THE COMMUNICATIONS ACT OF 1934, AS AMENDED, 11 F.C.C.R. 21905 (1996).

Federal Communications Commission, IN RE INDEPENDENT DATA COMMUNICATIONS MFRS. ASS'N. PETITION FOR DECLARATORY RULING THAT AT&T'S INTERSPAN FRAME RELAY SERVICE IS A BASIC SERVICE; AND AM. TEL. AND TEL. CO. PETITION FOR DECLARATORY RULING THAT ALL IXC'S BE SUBJECT TO THE COMMISSION'S DECISION ON THE IDCMA PETITION, Memorandum Opinion and Order, 10 F.C.C.R. 13717, 13723 (October 18, 1995).

Federal Communications Commission, IN RE INQUIRY CONCERNING HIGH-SPEED ACCESS TO THE INTERNET OVER CABLE AND OTHER FACILITIES, GN Docket No. 00-185 (March 15, 2002)

Federal Communications Commission, IN RE INQUIRY CONCERNING HIGH-SPEED ACCESS TO THE INTERNET OVER CABLE AND OTHER FACILITIES, Declaratory Ruling and Notice of Proposed Rulemaking, GN Docket No. 00-185, CS Docket No. 02-521, 17 F.C.C.R. 4798 (2002).

Federal Communications Commission, IN RE JOINT APPLICATION OF AT&T CORP. AND TELECOMMUNICATIONS, INC., AT&T's and TCI's Joint Reply to Comments and Joint Opposition to Petitions to Deny or to Impose Conditions, CS Dkt. No.98-178, (Nov. 13, 1998)

Federal Communications Commission, IN RE PETITION OF INTERNET VENTURES, INC. AND INTERNET ON-RAMP, INC., Reply Comments of AT&T Corp., Dkt. No. GSR-5407-L, (Aug. 11, 1999).

Federal Communications Commission, IN RE POLICY & RULE CONCERNING RATES FOR DOMINANT CARRIERS, 4 F.C.C.R. (1989).

Federal Communications Commission, IN RE POLICY AND RULES CONCERNING THE INTERSTATE, INTEREXCHANGE MARKETPLACE, IMPLEMENTATION OF SECTION 254(G) OF THE COMMUNICATIONS ACT OF 1934, AS AMENDED,

1998 BIENNIAL REGULATORY REVIEW — REVIEW OF CUSTOMER PREMISES EQUIPMENT AND ENHANCED SERVICES UNBUNDLING RULES IN THE INTEREXCHANGE, EXCHANGE ACCESS AND LOCAL EXCHANGE MARKETS, CC Docket No. 96-61, CC Docket No. 98-183, Report and Order, 16 F.C.C.R. 7418 (2001).

Federal Communications Commission, *IN RE REGULATORY AND POLICY PROBLEMS PRESENTED BY THE INTERDEPENDENCE OF COMPUTER AND COMMUNICATION SERVICES AND FACILITIES*), Notice of Inquiry, 7 F.C.C.2d 11 (1966).

Federal Communications Commission, *IN RE REVIEW OF THE SECTION 251 UNBUNDLING OBLIGATIONS OF INCUMBENT LOCAL EXCHANGE CARRIERS*, CC Docket No. 01-338, Report and Order, 16 F.C.C.R. 22, 781 (2002).

Federal Communications Commission, *IN RE USE OF THE CARTERFONE DEVICE IN MESSAGE TOLL TEL. SERV.*, 13 F.C.C.2d 420 (1968).

Federal Communications Commission, *IN THE MATTER OF APPROPRIATE FRAMEWORK FOR BROADBAND ACCESS TO THE INTERNET OVER WIRELINE FACILITIES, UNIVERSAL SERVICE OBLIGATIONS OF BROADBAND PROVIDERS, COMPUTER III FURTHER REMAND PROCEEDING: BELL OPERATING COMPANY PROVISION OF ENHANCED SERVICES; 1998 BIENNIAL REGULATORY REVIEW – REVIEW OF COMPUTER III AND ONA SAFEGUARDS AND REQUIREMENTS*, Notice of Proposed Rulemaking, CC Docket No. 02-33; CC Docket Nos. 95-20, 98-10.

Federal Communications Commission, *IN THE MATTER OF FEDERAL-STATE JOINT BOARD ON UNIVERSAL SERVICE*, CC Docket No. 96-45, Report and Order, 12 F.C.C.R. 8776 (1997).

Federal Communications Commission, *In the Matter of Inquiry Concerning High-Speed Access to the Internet Over Cable and Other Facilities, Internet Over Cable Declaratory Ruling, Appropriate Regulatory Treatment for Broadband Access to the Intern t Over Cable Facilities*, "Declaratory Ruling and Notice of Proposed Rulemaking," GN Docket No. 00-185, CS Docket No. 02-52, March 15, 2002.

Federal Communications Commission, *IN THE MATTER OF REVIEW OF SECTION 251 UNBUNDLING OBLIGATIONS OF INCUMBENT LOCAL EXCHANGE*

CARRIERS, IMPLEMENTATION OF THE LOCAL COMPETITION PROVISIONS OF THE TELECOMMUNICATIONS ACT OF 1996, DEPLOYMENT OF WIRELINE SERVICE OFFERING ADVANCED TELECOMMUNICATIONS CAPABILITY, Report and Order on Remand and Further Notice of Proposed Rulemaking, CC Docket Nos. 01-338, 96-98, 98-147.

Federal Communications Commission, IN THE MATTER OF REVIEW OF THE COMMISSION'S RULES REGARDING THE PRICING OF UNBUNDLED NETWORK ELEMENTS AND THE RESALE OF SERVICE BY INCUMBENT LOCAL EXCHANGE CARRIERS, WC Docket No. 03-173, Notice of Proposed Rulemaking, September 15, 2003.

Federal Communications Commission, Public Notice, FCC TO BEGIN INTERNET TELEPHONY PROCEEDING, November 6, 2003.

Federal Communications Commission, STATEMENT OF BROADBAND POLICY, available at http://www.fcc.gov/broadband/.

Federal Communications Commission, Cable Services Bureau, BROADBAND TODAY: INDUSTRY MONITORING SESSIONS 44 (staff report authored by Deborah A. Lathen) (1999).

Federal Communications Commission, Office of Policy Planning, THE FCC AND THE UNREGULATION OF THE INTERNET 25 (authored by Jason Oxman) (1999).

Federal-State Joint Board on Universal Service, CC Docket No. 96-45, REPORT TO CONGRESS, 13 FCC Rcd 1105, 11516 (1998).

Federal Trade Commission, Am. Online, Inc., No. C-3989 (Apr. 17, 2001), at 12, *available at* http://www.ftc.gov/os/2001/04/aoltwdo.pdf.

Federal Trade Commission, *In re* Am. Online, Inc. & Time Warner Inc., No. C-3989, 2000 WL 1843019 (Dec. 14, 2000).

Feld, Harold, *Whose Line Is It Anyway? The First Amendment and Cable Open Access*, 8 COMMLAW CONSPECTUS (2000).

Ferguson, Charles H., HIGH ST@KES, NO PRISONERS: A WINNER'S TALE OF GREED AND GLORY IN THE INTERNET WARS (1999).

Fisher, Franklin M., *Innovation and Monopoly Leveraging,* in DYNAMIC COMPETITION AND PUBLIC POLICY: TECHNOLOGY, INNOVATION, AND ANTITRUST ISSUES 138 (Jerry Ellig, ed., 2001).

Fisher, Franklin M., *The IBM and Microsoft Cases: What's the Difference?*, 90 AM. ECON. REV. (1999).

Foray, Dominique, *The Dynamic Implications of Increasing Returns: Technological Change and Path Dependent Efficiency*, 15 INT. J. INDUSTRIAL ORG. (1997).

Forrester.com/ER/Press/Release/0,1769,655,00.html; ISP-Planet.

France Telecom Intelmatique, SI VOUS ÊTES EN FRANCE, UTILISEZ LE MINITEL NOUVELLE GÉNÉRATION, *at* http://www.minitel.fr (last visited Jan. 29, 2001).

Free Software Foundation, Inc., *GNU'S NOT UNIX!—THE GNU PROJECT AND THE FREE SOFTWARE FOUNDATION (FSF)*, *at* http://www.gnu.org (last modified June 28, 2001).

French Court Holds Yahoo Accountable for U.S. Auction Content, CDT Policy Post, Vol. 6, No. 20, November 21, 2000, available at http://www.cdt.org/publications/pp_6.20.shtml.

Frieden, Rob, *Adjusting the Horizontal and Vertical in Telecommunications Regulation: A Comparison of the Traditional and a New Layered Approach*, 55 FED. COMM. L.J. (2003).

Fudenberg, Drew & Jean Tirole, *Upgrades, Trade-ins, and Buybacks*, 29 RAND J. ECON. (1998).

Fusco, Patricia, *Top U.S. ISPs by Subscriber: Q1 2002*, ISP-PLANET, May 29, 2002.

Gaines, Brian R., *The Learning Curve Underlying Convergence*, TECHNOLOGY FORECASTING AND SOCIAL CHANGE, Jan./Feb. 1998.

Gawer, Annabelle & Michael A. Cusumano, PLATFORM LEADERSHIP: HOW INTEL, MICROSOFT AND CISCO DRIVE INNOVATION (2002).

Gifford, Ray, *VoIP – Creative Destruction of Regulation*, SEARUC, June 9, 2003, available at http://198.87.232.130/issues/communications/testimony/060903voip.ppt.

Gilder, George, TELECOSM: HOW INFINITE BANDWIDTH WILL REVOLUTIONIZE OUR WORLD (2000).

Gilmer v. Interstate/Johnson Lane Corp., 500 U.S. 20, 27 (1991).

Gilmore, Dan, *AOL Capitulates, Gives Up Struggle for 'Open Access'*, SAN JOSE MERCURY NEWS, September 1, 2002.

Gleick, James, FASTER: THE ACCELERATION OF JUST ABOUT EVERYTHING (1999).

Goldman Sachs, AMERICA ONLINE/TIME WARNER: PERFECT TIME-ING, March 10, 2000.

Goodman, Peter S. & Craig Timberg, *AOL Ends Lobbying for Open Access*, WASH. POST, Feb. 12, 2000, at A1.

Goodman, Peter S., *AT&T Puts Open Access to a Test: Competitors Take Issue with Firm's Coveted First-Screen Presence*, WASH. POST, Nov. 23, 2000, at E1.

Google, AltaVista: Resist Chinese Censorship, Human Rights News, September 7, 2002, available at http://www.hrw.org/press/2002/09/china0907.htm.

Greater Boston Tel. Corp. v. F.C.C., 444 F.2d 841, 852 (D.C. Cir. 1970).

Greenstein, Shane *The Evolving Structure of Commercial Internet Markets*, in UNDERSTANDING THE DIGITAL ECONOMY (Erik Brynjolfsson & Brian Kahin, eds., 2000).

Greenstein, Shane, *Building and Delivering the Virtual World: Commercializing Services for Internet Access,* paper written for Competition and Innovation in the Personal Computer Industry (San Diego, March 31, 2000).

Greenstein, Shane, *Commercialization of the Internet: The Interaction of Public Policy and Private Choices, or Why Introducing the Market Worked so Well* (NBER, April 2000).

Greenstein, Shane, *The Evolving Structure of the Internet Market*, in UNDERSTANDING THE DIGITAL ECONOMY (Erik Brynjolfsson and Brian Kahin, eds., 2000).

Guiltinan, Joseph P., *The Price Bundling of Services: A Normative Framework,* 74 J. MKTG. (April 1987).

Hafner, Katie & Matthew Lyon, WHERE WIZARDS STAY UP LATE (1996).

Harbert, Tam, *Broadband Penetration in U.S. Continues*, ELECTRONIC BUSINESS, July 1, 2003.

Hardin, Garrett, *The Tragedy of the Commons*, 162 SCIENCE 1243 (1968).

Hausman, Jerry A. & J. Gregory Sidak, *A Consumer-Welfare Approach to the Mandatory Unbundling of Telecommunications Networks*, 109 YALE L.J. (1999).

Hausman, Jerry A., et al., *Residential Demand for Broadband Telecommunications and Consumer Access to Unaffiliated Internet Content Providers,* 18 YALE J. ON REG. (2001).

Hayes, John B., Jith Jayaratne, & Michael L. Katz, *An Empirical Analysis of the Footprint Effects of Mergers Between Large ILECS*, submitted as an attachment to *Petition to Deny of Spring Communications Company L.P,* in *Ameritech Corp. & SBC Communications, Inc., for Consent to Transfer of Control,* CC Dkt. No. 98-141 (filed Oct. 15, 1998) and *Petition to Deny of Spring Communications Company L.P,* in *GTE Corporation and Bell Atlantic Corp. for Consent to Transfer of Control,* CC Docket. No. 98-184 (filed Nov. 23, 1998).

Hazlett, Thomas W. & George Bittlingmayer, THE POLITICAL ECONOMY OF CABLE "OPEN ACCESS, (2001), *available at* http:// www.aei.brookings.org/publications/working/ working_01_06.pdf.

Hicks, Matt, *VeriSign Rebuffs ICANN on Redirects,* e-week, September 22, 2003, available at http://www.eweek.com/article2/ 0,4149,1276359,00.asp.

High Tech Broadband Coalition, *Comments*, IN RE: INQUIRY CONCERNING HIGH-SPEED ACCESS TO THE INTERNET OVER CABLE AND OTHER FACILITIES (filed June 18, 2002), *available at* http://www.itic.org/ policy/fcc_020618.pdf.

High Tech Broadband Coalition, *Comments*, IN THE MATTER OF APPROPRIATE REGULATORY TREATMENT FOR BROADBAND ACCESS TO THE INTERNET OVER CABLE FACILITIES, CC Docket No. 96-45, June 17, 2002.

High Tech Broadband Coalition, *Reply Comments,* IN THE MATTER OF APPROPRIATE FRAMEWORK FOR BROADBAND ACCESS TO THE INTERNET OVER WIRELINE FACILITIES, CC Docket No. 02-33, July 1, 2002.

High Tech Broadband Coalition, *Ex Parte Letter*, CS DOCKET NO. 02-52, May 1, 2003.

Hockett v. State Indiana, 1886.

Hometown *Communications, Response of Hometown Communications,* TEN QUESTIONS TO BEGIN THE COMMITTEE'S INQUIRY INTO STATE BROADBAND POLICY, Committee on State Affairs, April 3, 2002

Hovenkamp, Herbert, *Antitrust Policy After Chicago*, 84 MICH. L. REV. (1985).

Hovenkamp, Herbert, FEDERAL ANTITRUST POLICY: THE LAW OF COMPETITION AND ITS PRACTICE (1994).

Howe, Peter J., *Earthlink Debuts On AT&T Networks Offers High-Speed Internet Service,* BOSTON GLOBE, Oct. 17, 2002, at C4.

House Cable Act Report, H.R. Rep. No.98-934 (1984).

http://soa.granitecanyon.com/faq.shtml

    http://www.cisco.com/warp/public/779/servpro/solutions/cable (last visited Mar. 13, 2003).

http://www.ieee802.org/17/documents/presentations/jan2002/hp_phy_02.pdf.

http://www-comm.itsi.disa.mil/atm/atm_pr.html

Hu, Jim, *AOL's Unrequited Cable Love,* CNET NEWS.COM, January 26, 2004.

Huber, Peter, LAW AND DISORDER IN CYBERSPACE 62 (1997).

Huber, Peter, et al., FEDERAL BROADBAND LAW §1.2.4 (1995).

Hunt, Craig, TCP/IP NETWORK ADMINISTRATION (1992).

    Hush-A-Phone Corp. v. AT&T, 22 FCC 112, 114 (1957).

    Hush-A-Phone Corp. v. United States, 238 F.2d 266 (D.C. Cir. 1956).

ICANN Throws Down the Gauntlet to VeriSign on SiteFinder, ICANN Watch, October 3, 2003, available at http://www.icannwatch.org/article.pl?sid=03/10/03/1350217.

IETF RFC 826, *available at* http://www.ietf.org/rfc/rfc1027.txt.

Information Infrastructure Task Force, INTELLECTUAL PROPERTY AND THE NATIONAL INFORMATION INFRASTRUCTURE: THE REPORT OF THE WORKING GROUP ON INTELLECTUAL PROPERTY RIGHTS (1995).

Information Technology Association of America, *Comments of the Information Technology Association of America, IN THE MATTER OF REVIEW OF REGULATORY REQUIREMENTS FOR INCUMBENT LEC BROADBAND TELECOMMUNICATIONS SERVICES*, Federal Communications Commission, CC Docket No. 01-337, March 1, 2002.

IP Communications, *Comments of the IP Communications Corporation*, IN THE MATTER OF REVIEW OF REGULATORY REQUIREMENTS FOR INCUMBENT LEC BROADBAND TELECOMMUNICATIONS SERVICES, Federal Communications Commission, CC Docket No. 01-337, March 1, 2002.

IP Communications, *Response of IP Communications*, TEN QUESTIONS TO BEGIN THE COMMITTEE'S INQUIRY INTO STATE BROADBAND POLICY, Committee on State Affairs, April 3, 2002.

Internet Service Providers' Consortium, *Comments,* Federal Communications Commission, IN THE MATTER OF IN THE MATTER OF DEPLOYMENT OF WIRELINE SERVICES OFFERING ADVANCED TELECOMMUNICATIONS CAPABILITY, ETC., CC Docket Nos. 98-147, 98-11, 98-26, 98-32, 98-78, 98-91, CCB/CPD Docket N. 98-15, RM 9244.

Issacharoff, Samuel, *Can There Be a Behavioral Law and Economics?*, 51 VAND. L. REV. (1998).

Indiana Utility Regulatory Commission, *Comments,* Federal Communications Commission, IN THE MATTER OF IN THE MATTER OF DEPLOYMENT OF WIRELINE SERVICES OFFERING ADVANCED TELECOMMUNICATIONS CAPABILITY, ETC., CC Docket Nos. 98-147, 98-11, 98-26, 98-32, 98-78, 98-91, CCB/CPD Docket N. 98-15, RM 9244.

Iyengar, Swaroopa, *Myanmar's Tangled Web,* WIRED NEWS, October 30, 2000, available at http://www.wired.com/news/politics/0,1283,39631,00.html.

Jefferson Parish Hosp. Dist. No. 2 v. Hyde, 466 U.S. 2 (1984).

Johnson, Steven, EMERGENCE: THE CONNECTED LIVES OF ANTS, BRAINS, CITIES AND SOFTWARE (2001).

Joint Comments of MCI and CompTel, WC Docket No. 03-211, October 27, 2003.

Jorde, Thomas M., et al., *Innovation, Investment, and Unbundling*, 17 YALE J. ON REG. (2000).

Kahn, Alfred, THE ECONOMICS OF REGULATION: PRINCIPLES AND INSTITUTIONS (1988).

Kahn, Robert E & Robert Wilensky, A FRAMEWORK FOR DISTRIBUTED DIGITAL OBJECT SERVICES (available at www.cnri.reston.va.us/cstr/arch/k-w.html).

Kamarck, Elaine Ciulla & Joseph S. Nye Jr., eds., GOVERNANCE.COM: DEMOCRACY IN THE INFORMATION AGE (2002).

Kaplow, Louis, *Extension of Monopoly Power Through Leverage*, 85 COLUM. L. REV. (1985).

Kapor, Mitchell, *Where Is the Digital Highway Really Heading*, WIRED, July–Aug. 1993, available at http://www.wired.com/wired/archive/1.03/kapor.on.nii_pr.html.

Katz, Michael & Carl Shapiro, *Antitrust and Software Markets*, in COMPETITION, INNOVATION AND THE MICROSOFT MONOPOLY: ANTITRUST AND THE DIGITAL MARKETPLACE, (Jeffrey A. Eisenach & Thomas M. Lenard, eds., 1999).

Katz, Michael L. & Carl Shapiro, *Network Externalities, Competition, and Compatibility*, 75 AM. ECON. REV. (1985).

Katz, Michael L. & Carl Shapiro, *Product Introduction with Network Externalities*, 40 J. INDUS. ECON. (1992).

Katz, Michael L. & Carl Shapiro, *System Competition and Network Effects*, 8 J. ECON. PERSPECTIVES (1994).

Katz, Michael L., *Thoughts on the Implications of Technological Change for Telecommunications Policy*, in TRANSITION TO AN IP ENVIRONMENT, A REPORT OF THE FIFTEENTH ANNUAL ASPEN INSTITUTE CONFERENCE ON TELECOMMUNICATIONS POLICY (2001).

Kearney, Joseph D. & Thomas W. Merrill, *The Great Transformation of Regulated Industries Law*, 98 COLUM. L. REV. (1998).

Kennard, William, *How to End the Worldwide Wait,* WALL ST. J., Aug. 24, 1999.

Kennard, William, E., *Consumer Choice Through Competition,* Remarks to the NATIONAL ASSOCIATION OF TELECOMMUNICATIONS OFFICERS AND ADVISORS (Sept. 17, 1999).

Kennedy Leonard and Lori Zallaps, *If It Ain't Broke ... The FCC and Internet Regulation,* 7 COMMLAW CONSPECTUS 17, 26 (1999).

Kirikos, George, *Stop Verisign DNS Abuse*, Petition to ICANN, hosted at whois.sc/verisign-dns/.

Kitch, Edmund W., *The Nature and Function of the Patent System*, 20 J.L. & ECON. (1977).

Kleinert, Jorn & Danial Piazolo, *Governing the Cyber Space*, in THE NEW ECONOMY AND ECONOMIC GROWTH IN EUROPE AND THE US (David B. Audretsch & Paul J.J. Welfens, eds., 2002).

Kleinrock, Leonard, COMMUNICATION NETS: STOCHASTIC MESSAGE FLOW AND DELAY (1964).

Korobkin, Russell B. & Thomas S. Ulen, *Law and Behavioral Science: Removing the Rationality Assumption from Law and Economics*, 88 CAL. L. REV. (2000).

Korobkin, Russell, *Inertia and Preference in Contract Negotiation: The Psychological Power of Default Rules and Form Terms*, 51 VAND. L. REV. (1998).

Krattenmaker, Thomas G. & L.A. Powe, Jr., *Converging First Amendment Principles for Converging Communications Media*, 104 YALE L.J. (1995).

Krattenmaker, Thomas G. & Lucas A. Powe, Jr., REGULATING BROADCAST PROGRAMMING (1994).

Krause, Jason & Elizabeth Wasserman, *Switching Teams on Open Access?*, THE INDUSTRY STANDARD (Jan. 24, 2000), *available at* http://www.thestandard.com/article/display/1,1153,8903,00.html.

Krim, Jonathan, *FCC Rules Seek High-Speed Shift; Phone Firms Would Keep Cable Rights*, WASH. POST, Feb. 15, 2002, at E1.

Kruse, Hans, et al., *The InterNAT: Policy Implications of the Internet Architecture Debate*, Proceedings of the 28th Research Conference on Communication, Information and Internet Policy, *at* http://www.csm.ohiou.edu/kruse/publications/InterNAT_v4.pdf (last visited Mar. 16, 2001).

Ku, Raymond Shih Ray, *Open Internet Access and Freedom of Speech: A First Amendment Catch-22*, 75 TUL. L. REV. (2000).

Ladha v. INS, 215 F.3d 889, 896 (9th Cir. 2000).

Laffont, Jean-Jacques & Jean Tirole, COMPETITION IN TELECOMMUNICATIONS (2000).

Lamb's Chapel v. Center Moriches Union Free Sch. Dist., 113 S. Ct. 2141, 2149-50 (1993) (Scalia, J., concurring).

Langlois, Richard N., *Technology Standards, Innovation, and Essential Facilities: Toward a Schumpeterian Post-Chicago Approach*, in DYNAMIC COMPETITION & PUB. POLICY: TECHNOLOGY, INNOVATIONS, AND ANTITRUST ISSUES (Jerry Ellig, ed., 2001), *available at http://papers.ssrn.com/sol3/papers.cfm?abstract_id=204069* (last visited Jan. 24, 2003).

Lathen, Deborah A., Cable Services Bureau, BROADBAND TODAY 43 (1999), *available at* http://www.fcc.gov/Bureaus/Cable/Reports/broadbandtoday.pdf.

Lechmere v. N.L.R.B., 502 U.S. 527, 536-37 (1992); *Neal v. U.S.*, 516 U.S. 284, 295 (1996).

Lee, Chong-Moon, William F. Miller, Marguerite Gong Hancock & Henry S. Rowen, "The Silicon Valley Habitat," in THE SILICON VALLEY EDGE: A HABITAT FOR INNOVATION AND ENTREPRENEURSHIP (Chong-Moon Lee, William F. Miller, Marguerite Gong Hancock & Henry S. Rowen, eds., 2000).

Legal Rights Satellite Org., *Communications Convergence of Broadcasting and Telecommunications Services* (arguing that there were barriers to entry into physical facilities), at http://www.legal-rights.org/Laws/convergence.html (last visited Jan. 17, 2003).

Leiner, Barry M., Vinton G. Cerf, David D. Clark, Robert E. Kahn, Leonard Kleinrock, Daniel C. Lynch, Jon Postel, Larry G. Roberts, Stephen Wolff, A BRIEF HISTORY OF THE INTERNET, available at www.isoc.org/internet/history/brief.shtml.

Lemley, Mark A., *The Economics of Improvement in Intellectual Property Law*, 75 TEX. L. REV. (1997).

Lemley, Mark A. & Lawrence Lessig, *The End of End-to-End: Preserving the Architecture of the Internet in the Broadband Era,* 48 UCLA L. REV. (2001).

Lemley, Mark A. & David McGowan, *Could Java Change Everything? The Competitive Propriety of a Proprietary Standard,* 43 ANTITRUST BULL. (1998).

Lemley, Mark A. & David McGowan, *Legal Implications of Network Economic Effects*, 86 CAL. L. REV. (1998).

Lemley, Mark A. & Lawrence Lessig, *Ex Parte*, IN RE APPLICATION FOR CONSENT TO THE TRANSFER OF CONTROL OF LICENSES MEDIAONE GROUP, INC. TO AT&T CORP. (FCC Dec. 15, 1999) (No. 99-251).

Lemley, Mark A. & Lawrence Lessig, Written *Ex Parte, IN RE* APPLICATION FOR CONSENT TO THE TRANSFER OF CONTROL OF LICENSES MEDIAONE GROUP, INC. TO AT&T CORP. (FCC Dec. 15, 1999) (No. 99-251), *reprinted in* Mark A. Lemley & Lawrence Lessig, *Open Access to Cable Modems*, 22 WHITTIER L. REV. (2000).

Lessig, Lawrence, CODE AND OTHER LAWS OF CYBERSPACE (1999).

Lessig, Lawrence, THE FUTURE OF IDEAS (2001).

Lessig, Lawrence *The Internet under Siege*, FINANCIAL POST, November 1, 2001.

Lessig, Lawrence & Paul Resnick, *Zoning Speech on the Internet: A Legal and Technical Model*, 98 MICH. L. REV. (1999).

Lessig, Lawrence & Tim Wu, *Ex Parte Letter*, CS DOCKET NO. 02-52, Aug. 22, 2003, *available at* http://faculty.virginia.edu/timwu/wu_lessig_fcc.pdf.

Lichtman, Douglas, *Property Rights In Emerging Platform Technologies*, 29 J. LEGAL STUD. (2000).

Licklider, J.C.R. & W. Clark, ON-LINE MAN COMPUTER COMMUNICATION, August 1962.

Lieberman, David, *Media Giants' Net Change Major Companies Establish Strong Foothold Online*, USA TODAY, Dec. 14, 1999, at B3.

Liebowitz, S.J. & Stephen E. Margolis, *Network Externality: An Uncommon Tragedy*, J. ECON. PERSP. (Spring 1994).

Liebowitz, Stan J. & Stephen E. Margolis, WINNERS, LOSERS & MICROSOFT: COMPETITION AND ANTITRUST IN HIGH TECHNOLOGY (2001).

Longworth, Richard C., GLOBAL SQUEEZE (1998).

Maher, Marcus, Comment, *Cable Internet Unbundling: Local Leadership in the Deployment High Speed Access*, 52 FED. COMM. L.J. (1999).

Maislin Indus. v. Primary Steel, 497 U.S. 116, 131 (1990).

Makadok, Richard, *Can First-Mover and Early-Mover Advantages Be Sustained in an Industry with Low Barriers to Entry/Imitation?*, 19 STRATEGIC MGMT. J. (1998).

Mansell, Robin, *Strategies for Maintaining Market Power in the Face of Rapidly Changing Technologies*, 31 J. ECON. ISSUES (1997).

Marcus, J. Scott, The Potential Relevance to the United States of the European Union's Newly Adopted Regulatory Framework for Telecommunications (FCC, OPP Working Paper Series No. 36) (2002).

Mariano, Gwendolyn, *Schools declare file-swapping truce*, CNET NEWS.COM, *at* http://news.com.com/2100-1023-859705.html?tag=rn (Mar. 14, 2002).

Matos, Frank, INFORMATION SERVICE REPORT (1988).

Matutes, Carmen & Pierre Regibeau, *Mix and Match: Product Compatibility Without Network Externalities*, 19 RAND J. OF ECON. (1988).

Matutues, Carmen & Pierre Regibeau, *Compatibility and Bundling of Complementary Goods in a Duopoly*, 40 J. INDUS. ECON. (1992).

McClaskey v. United States Dep't of Energy, 720 F.2d 583 (9th Cir. 1983).

MCI Communications Corp. v. AT&T, 708 F.2d 1081 (7th Cir. 1983).

MCI Telecommunications Corp. v. AT&T, 512 U.S. 218, 231 n.4 (1994).

McKnight, Lee W., *Internet Business Models: Creative Destruction as Usual*, in CREATIVE DESTRUCTION: BUSINESS SURVIVAL STRATEGIES IN THE GLOBAL INTERNET ECONOMY (Lee W. McKnight, Paul M. Vaaler & Raul L. Katz, eds., 2002).

McTaggert, Craig, *A Layered Approach to Internet Legal Analysis* (Dec. 21, 2002) (unpublished article available at http://www.innovationlaw.org/cm/ilg2002/reading/layered1.pdf).

Medin, Milo, Executive Vice President of Excite@Home, Presentation to Regulating on the Technological Edge (Oct. 20, 2000).

Memorial, Inc. v. Harris, 655 F.2d 905, 910-11 n.14 (9th Cir. 1980).

Merges, Robert P. & Richard R. Nelson, *On the Complex Economics of Patent Scope*, 90 COLUM. L. REV. (1990).

Merges, Robert P., *Rent Control in the Patent District: Observations on the Grady-Alexander Thesis*, 78 VA. L. REV. (1992).

Merrill Lynch, AOL TIME WARNER, February 23, 2000.

Minnesota Public Utilities Commission, IN RE COMPLAINT OF THE MINNESOTA DEPARTMENT OF COMMERCE AGAINST VONAGE HOLDING CORP. REGARDING LACK OF AUTHORITY TO OPERATE IN MINNESOTA, Docket No. P-6214/C-03-108, 2003 (Sept. 11, 2003).

Mockapetris, Paul, DOMAIN NAMES - CONCEPTS AND FACILITIES (USC/Information Sciences Institute, November 1983) (available at http://www.faqs.org/rfcs/rfc882.html).

Mokyr, Joel, *Innovation in an Historical Perspective: Tales of Technology and Evolution*, in TECHNOLOGICAL INNOVATION AND ECONOMIC PERFORMANCE (Benn Steil, David G. Victor & Richard R. Nelson, eds., 2002).

Moore, Stephen & Julian L. Simon, THE GREATEST CENTURY THAT EVER WAS: 25 MIRACULOUS U.S. TRENDS OF THE PAST 100 YEARS, (1999), *available at* http://www.cato.org/pubs/pas/pa364.pdf.

Moorthy, K. Sridhar, *Market Segmentation, Self Selection, and Product Lines Design*, 3 MKTG. SCI. (1985).

Morgan Stanley Dean Witter, *The Digital Decade,* April 6, 1999.

Morris, Charles R. & Charles H. Ferguson, *How Architecture Wins Technology Wars*, HARV. BUS. REV. (Mar.-Apr. 1993).

Mowery, David C. & Timothy Simcoe, *The Internet*, in TECHNOLOGICAL INNOVATION AND ECONOMIC PERFORMANCE (Benn Steil, David G. Victor, & Richard R. Nelson, 2002).

Myanmar Internet Use Increasing, But Still Censored, VIGILANT TV, October 25, 2002, available at http://vigilant.tv/article/2383.

Nakahata, John T., *Regulating Information Platforms: The Challenge of Rewriting Communications Regulation From the Bottom Up,* 1 J. ON TELECOMM. & HIGH TECH. L. (2002).

National Association of Regulatory Utility Commissioners v. FCC, 525 F.2d 630, 644 (D.C. Cir. 1976).

National Association of Regulated Utilities Commissioners v. FCC, 533 F.2d 601,608 (1976).

National Association of State Utility Consumer Advocates, *Joint Comments of NASUCA, et al.*, IN THE MATTER OF REVIEW OF REGULATORY REQUIREMENTS FOR INCUMBENT LEC BROADBAND TELECOMMUNICATIONS SERVICES, Federal Communications Commission, CC Docket No. 01-337, March 1, 2002.

National Cable & Telecomm. Ass'n v. Gulf Power Co., 534 U.S. 327, 122 S.Ct. 782, 798 (2002)

National Cable & Telecommunications Association Ex Parte Letter, Feb. 21, 2003.

National Cable & Telecommunications Association Ex Parte Letter, Dec. 10, 2003.

National Research Council, REALIZING THE INFORMATION FUTURE, (1994).

Naughton, John, A BRIEF HISTORY OF THE FUTURE: FROM RADIO DAYS TO INTERNET YEARS IN A LIFETIME (1999).

NCTA, *Cable Believes in Open Connectivity for the Internet, at* http:// www.ncta.com/legislative/legAffairs.cfm?legRegID=20.

NCTA, *Ex Parte Letter*, CS DOCKET NO. 02-52, Sept. 8, 2003.

Nelson, Richard, UNDERSTANDING TECHNICAL CHANGE AS AN EVOLUTIONARY PROCESS (1987).

Nelson, Richard and Sidney Winter, AN EVOLUTIONARY THEORY OF ECONOMIC CHANGE 14 (1982)

New Edge, *Comments of the New Edge,* IN THE MATTER OF REVIEW OF REGULATORY REQUIREMENTS FOR INCUMBENT LEC BROADBAND TELECOMMUNICATIONS SERVICES, Federal Communications Commission, CC Docket No. 01-337, March 1, 2002.

New Hampshire ISP Association, *Comments of the New Hampshire ISP Association*, IN THE MATTER OF APPROPRIATE FRAMEWORK FOR BROADBAND ACCESS TO THE INTERNET OVER WIRELINE FACILITIES, UNIVERSAL SERVICE OBLIGATIONS OF BROADBAND PROVIDERS, COMPUTER III REMAND PROCEEDINGS: BELL OPERATING COMPANY PROVISION OF ENHANCED SERVICES; 1998 BIENNIAL REGULATORY REVIEW – REVIEW OF COMPUTER II AND ONA SAFEGUARDS AND REQUIREMENTS, Federal Communications Commission, CC Docket NO. 02-33, 95-20, 98-10, May 3, 2002.

Newman, Stagg, *Broadband Access Platforms for the Mass Market,* paper presented at TELECOMMUNICATIONS POLICY RESEARCH CONFERENCE, *2003.*

New Mexico Information Professionals Association of America, *Comments of the New Mexico Information Professionals Association of America,* IN THE MATTER OF REVIEW OF REGULATORY REQUIREMENTS FOR INCUMBENT LEC BROADBAND TELECOMMUNICATIONS SERVICES, Federal Communications Commission, CC Docket No. 01-337, March 1, 2002.

Newton, Harry, NEWTON'S TELECOM DICTIONARY (14th ed. 1998).

New York State Department of Public Service, *Comments of the New York State Department of Public Service,* IN THE MATTER OF REVIEW OF REGULATORY REQUIREMENTS FOR INCUMBENT LEC BROADBAND

TELECOMMUNICATIONS SERVICES, Federal Communications Commission, CC Docket No. 01-337, March 1, 2002.

Noll, Roger G. & Bruce M. Owen, *The Anticompetitive Uses of Regulation: United States v. AT&T*, in THE ANTITRUST REVOLUTION (John E. Kwoka, Jr. & Lawrence J. White, eds., 1989).

Non-Accounting Safeguards Order, 11 F.C.C.R. at 21969-71.

NorthNet, Inc., An Open Access Business Model For Cable Systems: Promoting Competition & Preserving Internet Innovation On A Shared, Broadband Communications Network, Ex Parte, *Application of America Online Inc. & Time Warner, Inc. for Transfers of Control*, F.C.C., CS-Docket No. 0030, October 16, 2000.

O'Donnell, Shawn, Broadband Architectures, ISP Business Plans, and Open Access (Sept. 25, 2000).

Odlyzko, Andrew, PRICING AND ARCHITECTURE OF THE INTERNET: HISTORICAL PERSPECTIVES FROM TELECOMMUNICATIONS AND TRANSPORTATION (2003).

Omnibus Budget Reconciliation Act of 1993 § 6002(c)(2)(B) & (d)(3)(B), Pub. L. No.103-66, 107 Stat. 312, 396-97 (1993)

Onramp, *Response of Onramp,* TEN QUESTIONS TO BEGIN THE COMMITTEE'S INQUIRY INTO STATE BROADBAND POLICY, Committee on State Affairs, April 3, 2002.

Ordover, Lansuz A. & Robert D. Willig, *Access and Bundling in High Technology Markets*, in COMPETITION, INNOVATION AND THE MICROSOFT MONOPOLY: ANTITRUST AND THE DIGITAL MARKETPLACE (Jeffrey A. Eisenach & Thomas M. Lenard, eds., 1999).

Owen, Bruce, THE INTERNET CHALLENGE TO TELEVISION (1999).

Owen, Bruce and Gregory Rosston, *Local Broadband Access: Primum Non Nocere or Primum Processi? A Property Rights Approach*, STANFORD LAW AND ECONOMICS OLIN WORKING PAPER No. 263, 21-23 (2003). Available at http://ssrn.com/abstract=431620.

Packeteer, *at* http://www.packeteer.com/products/packetshaper.com (last visited Mar. 13, 2003).

Pa. PUC Approved AT&T Tariffs for Local Exchange Service, COMM. DAILY, Dec. 17, 1999.

Paglin, Max D. (ed.), THE COMMUNICATIONS ACT: A LEGISLATIVE HISTORY OF THE MAJOR AMENDMENTS, 1934-1996, (1999).

Panama Begins Blocking IP Ports, Linux and Main, November 3, 2002, available at http://www.linuxandmain.com.

Panama Decrees Block to Kill VoIP Service, Slashdot, November 3, 2002, available at http://yro.slashdot.org/yro/02/04/14/0252201.shmtl?tid=95.

Paine Webber, AOL TIME WARNER: AMONG THE WORLD'S MOST VALUABLE BRANDS, March 1, 2000.

PDK Labs v. Reno, 134 F. Supp.2d 24, 35 (D.D.C. 2001).

Pearse, Justin, *UK shrugs off American broadband troubles,* ZDNET NEWS.COM, *at* http://news.zdnet.co.uk/story/0,,t269-s2077792,00.html (Mar. 20, 2000).

Perlman, Brett, Commissioner, Public Utility Commission of Texas, Letter to The Honorable Kevin Martin, Commissioner, Federal Communications Commission (January 28, 2003), available at http://www.puc.state.tx.us/about/commissioners/perlman/news/news_bb.cfm?comname=2.

Perry, Martin K., *Vertical Integration: Determinants and Effects,* in HANDBOOK OF INDUSTRIAL ORGANIZATION (Richard Schmalensee & Robert D. Willig, eds., 1989).

Petition to Deny Consumers Union, et al., *Joint Application of AT&T Corporation and Tele-Communications Inc. For Approval of Transfer of Control of Commission Licenses and Authorizations, Federal Communications Commission,* CS Docket No. 98-178, October 28, 1998.

Picker, Randal, ENTRY, ACCESS AND FACILITIES-BASED COMPETITION (working paper 2004).

Ploskina, Brian and Dana Coffield, "Regional Bells Ringing Up Higher DSL Rates," *Interactive Week,* February 18, 2001.

Posner, Richard, ANTITRUST LAW (2d ed. 2001).

Posner, Richard, THE ECONOMIC STRUCTURE OF INTELLECTUAL PROPERTY LAW (forthcoming).

Powell, Michael K., OPENING REMARKS AT THE FCC VOICE OVER INTERNET PROTOCOL FORUM (Dec. 1, 2003), available at www.fcc.gov.

Powell, Michael, *Preserving Internet Freedom: Guiding Principles for the Industry*, the DIGITAL BROADBAND MIGRATION: TOWARD A REGULATORY REGIME FOR THE INTERNET AGE, Univ. of Col. School of Law, February 8, 2004.

Powell, Michael K., REMARKS ON VOICE OVER IP AT MEETING OF THE TECHNOLOGY ADVISORY COUNCIL (Oct. 20, 2003), available at www.fcc.gov.

Practically Networked Earthweb, VPN Comcast Letter, *at* http:// www.practicallynetworked.com/news/comcast.htm. (last visited Mar. 10, 2003).

Pruitt, Scott, *ISPs Missing the Broadband Boom,* PC WORLD, November 14, 2003.

Public Service Commission of Missouri, *Comments of the Public Service Commission of the State of Missouri,* IN THE MATTER OF REVIEW OF REGULATORY REQUIREMENTS FOR INCUMBENT LEC BROADBAND TELECOMMUNICATIONS SERVICES, Federal Communications Commission, CC Docket No. 01-337, March 1, 2002.

Pulver, Jeff, *VON Pioneers: Robert Pepper of the FCC*, VON MAGAZINE, Nov.-Dec. 2003.

Rachlinski, Jeffrey J., *The New Law and Psychology: A Reply to Critics, Skeptics, and Cautious Supporters*, 85 CORNELL L. REV. (2000).

Radcliff, Deborah , *Verisign's 'SiteFinder' Finds Privacy Hullabaloo,* SECURITY FOCUS, September 19, 2003.

Reed, David P., et al., *Commentaries on "Active Networking and End-to-End Arguments,"* 12 IEEE NETWORK, *available at* http:// ieeexplore.ieee.org/iel4/65/15117/00690972.pdf (May–June 1998).

Reed, David, *Presentation to Regulating on the Technological Edge*, BERKELEY CENTER FOR RESEARCH ON TELECOMMUNICATIONS POLICY (Oct. 20, 2000).

Regulatory Auth. For Telecomms. & Posts, *Technical Telecoms Regulation*, *at* http://www.regtp.de/en/ (last modified Mar. 9, 2001).

Ridder, Christopher K., AT&T Corp. v. City of Portland, 15 BERKELEY TECH. L.J. (2000).

Rifkin, Jeremy, THE AGE OF ACCESS: THE NEW CULTURE OF HYPERCAPITALISM, WHERE ALL OF LIFE IS A PAID-FOR EXPERIENCE (2000).

RoadRunner Blocking kaZaA, ZEROPAID.COM, *at* http://www.zeropaid.com/news/articles/auto/07142002a (July 13, 2002).

RoadRunner Blocking Use of Kazaa, Slashdot, July 13, 2002, available at http://yro.slashdot.org/yro/02/07/14/0237258.shmtl?tid=153.

Roberts, L. & T. Merrill, *Toward a Cooperative Network of Time-Shared Computers*, paper presented at the Fall AFIPS Conference, Oct. 1966.

Robinson, Glen O., On Refusing to Deal with Rivals, 87 CORNELL L. REV. (2002).

Roger, Werner, *Structure Changes and New Economy in the EU and the US,* in THE NEW ECONOMY AND ECONOMIC GROWTH IN EUROPE AND THE US (David B. Audretsch & Paul J.J. Welfens, eds., 2002)

Royal Foods Co. v. RJR Holdings Inc., 252 F.3d 1102, 1107 n.6 (9th Cir. 2001).

Rubinfeld, Daniel L., *Antitrust Enforcement in Dynamic Network Industries,* 43 ANTITRUST BULL. (1998).

Rubinfeld, Daniel L. & Hal J. Singer, *Vertical Foreclosure in High Technology Industries: A Case Study of the AOL Time Warner Merger*, 16 BERKELEY TECH. L.J. (2001).

Rubinfeld, Daniel L. & Hal. J. Singer, *Open Access to Broadband Networks: A Case Study of the AOL/Time Warner Merger*, 16 BERKELEY TECH. L.J. 631 (2001).

Rubinfeld, Daniel L. & John Hoven, *Innovation and Antitrust Enforcement*, in DYNAMIC COMPETITION AND PUBLIC POLICY: TECHNOLOGY, INNOVATION, AND ANTITRUST ISSUES (Jerry Ellig, ed., 2001).

Ruby Ranch Cooperative Association, *Comments of Ruby Ranch Cooperative Association*, IN THE MATTER OF APPROPRIATE FRAMEWORK FOR BROADBAND ACCESS TO THE INTERNET OVER WIRELINE FACILITIES, UNIVERSAL SERVICE OBLIGATIONS OF BROADBAND PROVIDERS, COMPUTER III REMAND PROCEEDINGS: BELL OPERATING COMPANY PROVISION OF ENHANCED SERVICES; 1998 BIENNIAL REGULATORY REVIEW – REVIEW OF COMPUTER II AND ONA SAFEGUARDS AND REQUIREMENTS, Federal Communications Commission, CC Docket NO. 02-33, 95-20, 98-10, May 3, 2002.

Sachs, Robert, Remarks to NARUC/NECA Summit on Broadband Deployment II (Apr. 28, 2003) (available at http://www.ncta.com/ pdf_files/RJS_NARUC_04-28-03.pdf).

Salop, Steven C. & R. Craig Romaine, *Preserving Monopoly: Economic Analysis, Legal Standards, and Microsoft*, GEO. MASON L. REV. (1999).

Salop, Steven C., *Using Leverage to Preserve Monopoly*, in COMPETITION, INNOVATION AND THE MICROSOFT MONOPOLY: ANTITRUST AND THE DIGITAL MARKETPLACE (Jeffrey A. Eisenach & Thomas M. Lenard, eds., 1999).

Saltzer, J.H., et al., *End-to-End Arguments in System Design*, 2 ACM TRANSACTIONS COMPUTER SYS. (1984), *available at* http:// web.mit.edu/Saltzer/www/ publications/endtoend/endtoend.pdf (last visited Oct. 9, 2003).

Saltzer, Jerome H., et al., *End to End Arguments in System Design*, in INNOVATIONS IN INTERNETWORKING (Craig Partridge, ed., 1988) (available at http://web.mit.edu/saltzer/www/publications/ endtoend/endtoend.pdf).

Sampler, Jeffrey L., *Redefining Industry Structure for the Information Age*, ENGINEERING MGMT. REV. (Summer 1999).

Saxenian, Annalee, *The Origins and Dynamics of Production Networks in Silicon Valley*, in UNDERSTANDING SILICON VALLEY (Martin Kenney, ed., 2000).

SBC Communications Inc., *Comments*, IN RE APPLICATIONS OF AM. ONLINE, INC. & TIME WARNER INC. FOR TRANSFERS OF CONTROL (FCC Apr.

26, 2000) (No. 00-30), *available at* http://gullfoss2.fcc.gov/prod/ecfs/retrieve.cgi?native_or_pdf=pdf&id_document=6011257512.

SBC Communications, Inc., Comments, WC Docket No. 03-211, October 27, 2003.

Scherer, F. Michael & David Ross, INDUSTRIAL MARKET STRUCTURE AND ECONOMIC PERFORMANCE (1990).

Schilling, Melissa A., *Technological Lockout: An Integrative Model of the Economic and Strategic Factors Driving Technology Success and Failure*, 23 ACAD. MGMT. REV. (1998).

Schmalensee, Richard, *Gaussian Demand and Commodity Bundling*, 57 J. BUS. (1984).

Schumpeter, Joseph A., CAPITALISM, SOCIALISM, AND DEMOCRACY (1st ed. 1942).

Schumpeter, Joseph A. THEORY OF ECONOMIC DEVELOPMENT (1912).

Schwartz, Evan I., *People Are Supposed to Pay for This Stuff?*, WIRED, July 1995, available at http://www.wired.com/wired/archive/3.07/cable.html.

Seely, Brown John & Paul Duguid, *Mysteries of the Region: Knowledge Dynamics in Silicon Valley*, in THE SILICON VALLEY EDGE: A HABITAT FOR INNOVATION AND ENTREPRENEURSHIP (Chong-Moon Lee, William F. Miller, Marguerite Gong Hancock & Henry S. Rowen, eds., 2000).

Seven Cable Modem Manufacturers Seek DOCSIS Certification, CABLELABS, *at* http://www.cablelabs.com/news/newsletter/SPECS/specnewsaug/news/pgs/story2.html (last visited Mar. 13, 2003).

Senate Conference Report No.104-230 (1996).

Shah, Ashish, Douglas Sicker & Dale Hatfield, *Thinking About Openness in the Telecommunications Policy Context,* paper presented at the TELECOMMUNICATIONS POLICY RESEARCH CONFERENCE (2003).

Shapiro, Carl, *Exclusivity in Network Industries*, 7 GEO. MASON L. REV. (1999).

Shapiro, Andrew L., THE CONTROL REVOLUTION: HOW THE INTERNET IS PUTTING INDIVIDUALS IN CHARGE AND CHANGING THE WORLD WE KNOW (1999).

Shapiro, Carl & Hal R. Varian, INFORMATION RULES: A STRATEGIC GUIDE TO THE NETWORK ECONOMY (1999).

Shelanski, Howard A., *Competition and Deployment of New Technology in U.S. Telecommunications*, 2000 U. CHI. LEGAL F.

Shelanski, Howard A., *The Speed Gap: Broadband Infrastructure and Electronic Commerce*, 14 BERKELEY TECH. L.J. (1999).

Shepherd, William G., THE ECONOMICS OF INDUSTRIAL ORGANIZATION (3d ed., 1990).

Sheremata, Willow A., *Barriers to Innovation: A Monopoly, Network Externalities, and the Speed of* Innovation, 42 ANTITRUST BULL. (1997).

Sheremata, Willow A., *"New" Issues in Competition Policy Raised by Information Technology Industries*, 43 ANTITRUST BULL. (1998).

Shih, Daniel, Comment, *Open Access or Forced Access: Should the FCC Impose Open Access on Cable-Based Internet Service Providers?*, 52 ADMIN. L. REV. (2000).

Shooshan, Harry M., III, et al., *MaCable.com: Closed v. Open Models for the Broadband Internet*, at http://www.spri.com/pdf/reports/opennet/macable.pdf (Oct. 15, 1999).

Sicker, Douglas C. and Joshua L. Mindel, *Refinements of a Layered Model for Telecommunications Policy*, 1 J. ON TELECOMM. & HIGH TECH. L. (2002).

Sicker, Douglas C., *Applying a Layered Policy Model to IP Based Voice Services,* IEEE COMPUTER SOCIETY, PROCEEDINGS OF THE 36TH HAWAII INTERNATIONAL CONFERENCE ON SYSTEMS SCIENCES (HICSS '03) (2002).

Sicker, Douglas, *Further Defining a Layered Model for Telecommunications Policy*, paper presented at the TELECOMMUNICATIONS POLICY RESEARCH CONFERENCE (2002).

Silliman, Craig, LETTER TO JOHN J. BURFETE, JR., CHIEF DEPUTY ATTORNEY GENERAL, OFFICE OF THE ATTORNEY GENERAL OF PENNSYLVANIA

(September 23, 2002).

Simpson, Ida Harper, *Historical Patterns of Workplace Organization: From Mechanical to Electronic Control and Beyond*, CURRENT SOC. 47 (Apr. 1999).

Solum, Lawrence B. & Minn Chung, *The Layers Principle: Internet Architecture and the Law* Social Science Research Network (2003), available at: http://ssrn.com/abstract=416263.

Spangler, Todd, *Crossing the Broadband Divide*, PC MAGAZINE, February 12, 2002.

Spangler, Todd, *Initiatives Underscore DSL Future. (UUNET Technologies, Cisco Systems' Digital Subscriber Line Strategies) (Company Business and Marketing)*, INTERNET WORLD, March 16, 1998, available at http://www.findarticles.com/cf_dls/m0DXS/n10_v4/21049642/p1/article.jhtml.

Speta, James B., *A Common Carrier Approach to Internet Interconnection*, FED. COMM. L.J., 54 (2002).

Septa, James B., A *Vision of Openness by Government Fiat*, 96 Nw. L. REV. 1553, 1565-1566 (2001);

Speta, James B., *Handicapping the Race for the Last Mile?: A Critique of Open Access Rules for Broadband Platforms*, 17 YALE J. ON REG. (2000).

Speta, James B., *The Vertical Dimension of Cable Open Access,* 71 U. COLO. L. REV. 975. (2000).

Speta, James B. Written *Ex Parte*, *In RE* APPLICATION FOR CONSENT TO THE TRANSFER OF CONTROL OF LICENSES MEDIAONE GROUP, INC. TO AT&T CORP. (FCC Dec. 15, 1999) (No. 99-251), *available at* http://www.law.nwu.edu/faculty/fulltime/speta/papers/fcccomments.pdf

Spragins, John D. et al., TELECOMMUNICATIONS PROTOCOLS AND DESIGN (1991).

Sprint FastConnect DSL, *Frequently Asked Questions*, *available at* http://csb.sprint.com/home/local/dslhelp/faq.html#gen16 (2003).

Sprint FastConnect DSL, *Questions & Answers*, *available at* http://csb.sprint.com/servlet/Faq/faq_category?category=DSLGenQuestions (2003).

Stevens, Richard W., TCP/IP ILLUSTRATED, VOLUME 1: THE PROTOCOLS (1994).

Stone, Geoffrey, et al., CONSTITUTIONAL LAW (2001).

Sunstein, Cass, ed., BEHAVIORAL LAW AND ECONOMICS (2000).

Tanenbaum, Andrew S., COMPUTER NETWORKS (4th ed. 2002).

Taylor, John B., ECONOMICS (1998).

Teece, David J., MANAGING INTELLECTUAL CAPITAL (2000).

Techweb News, *Broadband Boom,* INFORMATION WEEK, May 12, 2004.

Telecommunications Act of 1996, Pub. L. No. 104-104, 110 Stat. 56 (codified at 47 U.S.C. §§ 151–614 (Supp. II 1997)).

Telser, Lester, *A Theory of Monopoly of Complementary Goods*, 52 J. BUS. (1979).

Texas CLEC Coalition, *Response of Texas CLEC Coalition,* TEN QUESTIONS TO BEGIN THE COMMITTEE'S INQUIRY INTO STATE BROADBAND POLICY, Committee on State Affairs, April 3, 2002.

Texas Internet Service Providers Association, *Reply Comments of the Texas Internet Service Providers Association,* FURTHER NOTICE OF PROPOSED RULEMAKING IN THE MATTER OF THE COMPUTER III REMAND PROCEEDINGS: BELL OPERATING COMPANY PROVISION OF ENHANCED SERVICES; 1998 BIENNIAL REGULATORY REVIEW – REVIEW OF COMPUTER II AND ONA SAFEGUARDS AND REQUIREMENTS, Federal Communications Commission, CC Docket NO. 95-20, 98-10, April 30, 2000.

Texas Office of Consumer Counsel & Consumer Federation of America, *Comments, In the Matter of Inquiry Concerning High-Speed Access to the Internet Over Cable and Other Facilities; Declaratory Ruling; Appropriate Regulatory Treatment for Broadband Access to the Internet Over Cable Facilities*, Federal Communications Commission, GN Dockets Nos. 00-185, CS Dockets No. 02-52, March 15, 2002.

Texas Office of Public Utility Counsel, Consumer Federation of America & Consumers Union, *Comments*, IN THE MATTER OF INQUIRY CONCERNING HIGH SPEED ACCESS TO THE INTERNET OVER CABLE AND

OTHER FACILITIES, Federal Communications Commission, GN Docket No. 96-262, December 12, 1999, January 12, 2000.

The BroadNet Alliance, THE IMPORTANCE OF A BROAD NET: THE SIGNIFICANT ROLE OF ONLINE SERVICE PROVIDERS IN THE DEVELOPMENT AND SUCCESS OF THE INFORMATION AGE, CC Docket No. 02-33 (July 1, 2002), available at www.broadnetalliance.org).

The Internet in the Mideast and North Africa: Free Expression and Censorship, Tunisia, Human Rights Watch, June 1998, available at http://www.hrw.org/advocacy/internet/mena/tunisia.htm.

The White House, ADMINISTRATION WHITE PAPER ON COMMUNICATIONS ACT REFORM, (1994).

Thierer, Adam, ARE 'DUMB PIPE' MANDATES SMART PUBLIC POLICY? VERTICAL INTEGRATION, 'NET NEUTRALITY,' AND THE NETWORK LAYERS MODEL (2004).

Thierer, Adam D., *Net Neutrality" Digital Discrimination or Regulatory Gamesmanship in Cyberspace?* CATO POLICY ANALYSIS Jan. 12, 2004.

Thum, Marcel, *Network Externalities, Technological Progress, and the Competition of Market Contract,* 12 INT. J. INDUS. ORG. (1994).

Time Warner Inc., 123 F.T.C. 171 (1997).

Time Warner, *Cable Modem Service Subscription Agreement* § 5(a), *available at* http://help.twcable.com/html/twc_sub_agreement.html (last visited Oct. 8, 2003).

Tunisia Stifles Web Publication, USC Annenberg, ONLINE JOURNALISM REVIEW, November 7, 2002, available at http://www.ojr.org/ojr/world_reports/1036538983.php.

Turner Broadcasting System, Inc. v. FCC , 520 U.S. 180 (1997).

Turner Broadcasting System, Inc. v. FCC, 512 U.S. 622 (1994).

Twomey, Paul, President & CEO, ICANN, LETTER TO RUSSELL LEWIS, EXECUTIVE VICE PRESIDENT & GENERAL MANAGER, VERISIGN NAMING AND DIRECTORY SERVICES (Oct. 2003).

U.N. Statistics Department by the International Standards Organization, ISO 3166. (available at http://www.iso.ch/iso/en/prods-services/iso3166ma/).

United States v. AT&T, 552 F. Supp. 131 at 179. (D.D.C. 1982), *aff'd sub. nom.* Maryland v. United States, 460 U.S. 1001 (1983).

United States v. Calamaro, 354 U.S. 351, 359 (1957).

United States v. Monsanto, 491 U.S. 600 (1989).

U.S. v. Southwestern Cable Co., 392 U.S. 157 (1968).

U.S. Department of Justice and Federal Trade Commission, HORIZONTAL MERGER GUIDELINES, 57 Fed. Reg. 41,552 (1992, as revised in 1997).

U.S. Department of Justice, Amended Complaint, U.S. v. AT&T Corp., 2000 WL 1752108 (D.C. Cir. 2000) (No. 1:00CV01176), *available at* http://www.usdoj.gov/atr/ cases/indx4468.htm.

U.S. Federal Networking Council, October 24, 1995 Resolution.

United States Civil Serv. Comm'n v. National Ass'n of Letter Carriers, 413 U.S. 548 (1973).

United States v. AT&T, 552 F. Supp. 131 (D.D.C. 1982), *aff'd sub nom.* Maryland v. United States, 460 U.S. 1001 (1983).

United States v. Microsoft Corp., 147 F.3d 935, 950 (D.C. Cir. 1998).

United States v. Microsoft, 253 F.3d 34, 103 (D.C. Cir. 2001) (*per curiam*).

U.S. LEC Corp. *Comments of U.S. LEC Corp.*, IN THE MATTER OF APPROPRIATE FRAMEWORK FOR BROADBAND ACCESS TO THE INTERNET OVER WIRELINE FACILITIES, UNIVERSAL SERVICE OBLIGATIONS OF BROADBAND PROVIDERS, COMPUTER III REMAND PROCEEDINGS: BELL OPERATING COMPANY PROVISION OF ENHANCED SERVICES; 1998 BIENNIAL REGULATORY REVIEW – REVIEW OF COMPUTER II AND ONA SAFEGUARDS AND REQUIREMENTS, Federal Communications Commission, CC Docket NO. 02-33, 95-20, 98-10, May 3, 2002.

Use of the Carterfone Device in Message Toll Tel. Serv., 31 F.C.C.2d 420 (1968).

Varian, Hal, MARKETS FOR PUBLIC GOODS (January 2003).

Vaughn-Nichols, Steven J., *DSL Spells Trouble for Many ISPs*, SMART RESELLER, February 24, 1999.

VeriSign SiteFinder Update, Yahoo! Financial News, Press Release (Oct. 3, 2003), available at http://biz.yahoo.com/prnews/031003/sff057_1.html.

Verizon Online Internet Access, *Terms of Service, available at* http://www.verizon.net/policies/internetaa.asp (2003).

Verizon Online's Terms of Service, at http://www.verizon.net/ policies/internetaa.asp.

Verizon, *Comments*, WC Docket No. 03-211, October 27, 2003.

Vincent v. Apfel, 191 F.3d 1143, 1148 (9th Cir. 1999).

Vonage Holdings Corp. v. Minn. Pub. Utils. Comm'n, 2003 WL 225676345, (2003).

Watts, Duncan, SIX DEGREES: THE SCIENCE OF A CONNECTED AGE (2003).

Weinberg, Jonathan, *The Internet and "Telecommunications Services," Universal Service Mechanisms, Access Charges, and Other Flotsam of the Regulatory System,* 16 YALE J. ON REG.

Weiser, Phil, *Competing Paradigms in Telecommunications Regulation*, 71 U. COLO. L. REV. (2000).

Weiser, Philip J., *Law and Information Platforms,* 1 J. ON TELECOMM. & HIGH TECH. L. 1, 12 (2002).

Weiser, Phil, *Networks Unplugged: Toward a Model of Compatibility Regulation Between Communications Platforms* (paper presented at *Telecommunications Policy Research Conference*, Oct. 27, 2001), *at* http://www.arxiv.org/html/cs/0109070 (last visited Jan. 24, 2003).

Weiser, Phil, *Paradigm Changes in Telecommunications Regulation,* 71 U. COLO. L. REV. 819 (2000).

Weisman, Michael J., *The Regulation of a Layered Regulatory Approach to E-Mail, Internet Radio and IP Telephony* (March 2002) (unpublished essay submitted to Professor Toshiko Takanaka, University of Washington School of Law), available at http://

w w w . l a w . w a s h i n g t o n . e d u / C a s r i p / c l a s s e s /
Layeredregulationpaper.pdf .

Werbach, Kevin, *A Layered Model for Internet Policy*, 1 COLO. J.
TELECOMM. & HIGH TECH. L. (2002).

Whiteley, Jason, AT&T Corp. v. City of Portland: *Classifying "Internet
Over Cable" in the "Open Access" Fight*, 2000 BYU L. REV.

Whitman, Marina N., NEW WORLD, NEW RULES (1999).

Wildstrom, Stephen *At Last, You Can Ditch The Phone Company VOIP
Lets You Make Clear, Fast Calls Over The Net, Using A Plain
Phone*, BUSINESS WEEK, May 17, 2004.

Willig, Robert D., William H. Lehr, John P. Bigelow & Stephen B. Levinson,
Stimulating Investment and the Telecommunications Act of 1996,
October 11, 2002, submitted as *ex parte* filing by AT&T IN REVIEW
OF THE SECTION 251 UNBUNDLING OBLIGATIONS OF INCUMBENT LOCAL
EXCHANGE CARRIERS, CC Docket Nos. 01-338, 96-98, 98-147,
October 11, 2002.

Witt, Ulrich, *"Lock-in" vs. "Critical Masses"– Industrial Change Under
Network Externalities*, 15 INT'L J. INDUS. ORG. (1997).

Woeckener, Berd, *The Competition of User Networks: Ergodicity, Lock-
ins, and Metastability*, 41 J. ECON. BEHAVIOR & ORG. (2000).

Woroch, Glenn A., Competition's Effect on Investment in Digital
Infrastructure (1999) (unpublished manuscript, on file with the
authors).

Woroch, Glenn A., et al., *Exclusionary Behavior in the Market for
Operating System Software: The Case of Microsoft*, in OPENING
NETWORKS TO COMPETITION: THE REGULATION AND PRICING OF ACCESS
(David Gabel & David F. Weiman, eds., 1998).

Woroch, Glenn A., Open Access Rules and the Broadband Race, 2002 L.
REV. MICH. ST. U. DET. C.L. (2002).

Woroch, Glenn, *Economic Impacts of Open Access Rules on The Race To
Deploy Broadband Infrastructure* (working paper 2001, on file with
authors).

Wu, Tim & Lawrence Lessig, *Ex Parte Submission in* CS DOCKET *No. 02-52,* August 22, 2003.

Wu, Timothy, *Application-Centered Internet Analysis,* 85 VA. L. REV. (1999).

Wu, Timothy, Associate Professor, University of Virginia Law School, and Lawrence Lessig, Professor, Stanford Law School, Letter to Marlene H. Dortch, Secretary, Federal Communications Commission, CS Docket No. 02-52 (Aug. 22, 2003).

Wu, Timothy, *Network Neutrality & Broadband Discrimination*, 2 COL. J. TELECOMM. & HIGH TECH. L. 5 (2003).

Yahoo! Inc. v. La Ligue Contre Le Racisme et L'Antisemitisme, 145 F. Supp. 2d 1168 (N.D. Cal. 2001) (No. 00-21275 JF).

Yahoo! Risks Abusing Rights in China, Human Rights News, August 9, 2002, available at http://www.hrw.org/press/2002/08/yahoo080902.htm.

Yoffie, David B., *CHESS and Competing in the Age of Digital Convergence,* in COMPETING IN THE AGE OF DIGITAL CONVERGENCE (David B. Yoffie, ed., 1997).

Yoo, Christoper, *Would Broadband Network Neutrality Help or Hurt Competition?: Understanding the Complex Economics of End-to-End,* SILICON FLATIRONS CONFERENCE, 2004, forthcoming in J. TELECOM. & HIGH TECH.

Ziman, John, *Evolutionary Models for Technological Change*, in TECHNOLOGICAL INNOVATION AS AN EVOLUTIONARY PROCESS (John Ziman, ed., 2000).